BODIES AND CRIMES

A Pathologist Speaks

BODIES
AND
CRIMES

A Pathologist Speaks

Dr F. D. M. Hocking

The Book Guild Ltd.

Sussex, England

The Book Guild Ltd.,
25 High Street,
Lewes, Sussex

First published 1992
Reprinted 1992
Third Reprint 1993
© Dr F. D. M. Hocking 1992

Set in Baskerville
Typesetting by R & H Typesetting
Horley, Surrey

Printed in Great Britain by
Antony Rowe Ltd.,
Chippenham, Wiltshire

A catalogue record for this book is
available from the British Library

ISBN 0 86332 753 2

CONTENTS

LIST OF ILLUSTRATIONS

INTRODUCTION

by

Colin Wilson

I have known a number of pathologists, including Francis Camps and Keith Simpson; of these, Denis Hocking is by far the most amiable — in its true sense of arousing affection — and the most amusing. These are qualities that the reader will sense from the opening pages of this book, and they make it the best autobiography of a pathologist that I have ever read.

The book is also a picture of a Cornwall that no longer exists, and which I remember with some nostalgia. I came to live here in 1957, when I was 25; I was fleeing from London, and the publicity surrounding my book *The Outsider,* and the movement journalists christened 'The Angry Young Men'. After London, Cornwall seemed unutterably peaceful. The whole county was like one small village community. Life moved at a slow, deliberate pace. If you walked into the corner shop to buy a bottle of milk, you might have to wait five minutes while the proprietor finished a rambling conversation with one of his customers — but no one seemed to object. In the pubs — with their low ceilings and great wooden settles — there were rows of pewter mugs behind the bar, each the property of a particular customer; I had my own at a pub called the General Wolfe, in St. Austell. There was little crime — except in summer, when the tourists arrived — and no one bothered to lock their cars or their back doors. The police were friendly, and if you parked in a no parking area, were likely to come into the pub to ask you to move it rather than stick a ticket on your windscreen. One friend of mine *did* manage to get himself charged for being drunk in charge, but that was because he insisted on trying to drive when he was manifestly glassy-eyed and incapable. And even so, the local bobby tried hard to persuade him to surrender his keys and take a taxi home before reluctantly charging him.

It was to this peaceful haven that Dr. Hocking moved in 1934 — fleeing from the teeming and impersonal metropolis. I met him about a quarter of a century later, just after I had made the same sensible decision. It was, I think, in the back room of the General Wolfe, where a group of us — local businessmen, farmers and professional men — used to have a diners' club which met fortnightly. One of the regulars was an ex-Superintendent of Police named Bill Mallett, and he sometimes brought in Ken Julian, who was then Superintendent of Police in Bodmin. It was Ken Julian, I seem to remember, who introduced me to Denis Hocking. Denis was a genial-looking man with a pink complexion and white hair. I was fascinated to learn that he was county pathologist, for I was writing a novel called *Ritual in the Dark* about what would now be called a serial killer, and wanted all the technical information I could get. I had talked extensively to Francis Camps in London — particularly about the Christie case — so was prepared for gruesome details. But listening to Denis Hocking was an unexpectedly different experience. He looked so innocent and good-humoured, and he talked with such enthusiasm, that he might have been a farmer describing some fine cattle that he had just purchased, or a family doctor describing healthy twins he had delivered into the world. So the subject matter of his discourse — women found buried under the garage floor, or corpses in the last stage of dissolution — sounded twice as bizarre. The reader will know exactly what I mean before he has read a dozen pages of this book.

Denis was asked to one of the fortnightly dinners as guest of honour and, inevitably, asked to carve the suckling pig that was the main dish . . .

Some years later, when my daughter was a teenager, and expressed a wish to see a post mortem — teenagers love to convince themselves that they have a stomach for anything — I contacted Denis, who immediately invited us along for

8

the following afternoon. It was at the mortuary in Par, close to the railway line. It proved to be rather small and rather cold. The corpse was that of an old man, and I can no longer recall why a PM was thought necessary. But I can remember Denis making the incisions in the chest and peeling back the skin, then sawing out a section of the ribs, and opening up one of the lungs. I seem to remember that it was full of brown tarry nicotine, and black smudges that looked as if coal dust had been absorbed into the skin. My daughter wanted to know if these were due to smoking. Denis said no, they were simply the normal pollution that accumulates over a lifetime. Babies have beautifully pink lungs, but all adults — even those that live by the sea — breathe in enough smoke and dust to make the lungs look like a coal miner's. I noticed again that sickly smell of exposed intestines that was familiar to me from my own days of working as a morgue attendant in my early twenties. We were glad to get out of the place — not because of the corpse, but because it was so cold. Some of the early pages of this book bring back that experience with uncomfortable clarity.

In 1974, a Cornish publisher, Michael Williams, asked me to contribute to a book called *Murder in the West Country*, and I decided that a good starting point would be to go and see Denis Hocking. With his usual amiability, he invited me to come over and spend the afternoon at his house in Carlyon Bay. I left with a great deal of his excellent hock inside me (he told me he kept it under the roof space, and the high summer temperatures seemed to do it no harm), and with my head so filled with amazing anecdotes that I was thinking seriously of writing a history of murder and suicide in Cornwall. Other projects intervened, but some of his stories found their way into my introduction to *Murder in the West Country*. There was the case of the Chacewater smallholders — a man and a woman who were found battered to death in 1933; a coroner's jury reached the remarkable conclusion that they had quarrelled and killed each other. There was the strange story of the religious maniac who knocked on the door of a cottage at Colan, near Newquay, and asked the lady who opened the door whether she was a wicked woman. The lady, presumably a pious chapelgoer, answered 'Yes', whereupon the man battered her to death, then went into the next cottage and killed an old lady and a child. He was found to be insane. There was the tale of the cripple who used to slide head-first down the banisters, and who died when his head collided with the large wooden knob at the bottom. There was the man who tried to kill his mother-in-law by forcing her head down the toilet and pulling the chain — the attempt was unsuccessful — and the story of the old lady who committed suicide by sawing off her head . . .

And one of the strangest cases of all concerned an old man near Bude, who told his cronies that one of these days he would commit suicide from a certain tree. He was not unhappy; in fact, he admitted that he had thoroughly enjoyed his life; but he felt that he was getting old, and that a time would come when there would be no further point in living. One day he vanished from his usual haunts. His cronies had no doubt about what had happened, and hurried to the tree. The old man was nowhere to be seen. then one of them looked over the hedge, into a lane; their friend was lying on the ground with a rope in his hand and a broken neck. The inquest revealed that he had been trying to tie the rope around a branch when he had tripped and fallen through the hedge, breaking his neck. Which raises the interesting question: was it suicide or accident? Then there was the case of the baby-sitter of Bude, and the case of the violent lesbian, and the case of the old man who drowned himself in three inches of water with the aid of a millstone.

Most of these cases will be found at greater length in the present volume. So will a case that has always fascinated me — that of Miles Giffard, the Cornish youth who murdered both his parents and threw them over a cliff in a wheelbarrow. Miles had been sentenced to death in 1953, the year before I first visited Cornwall, and when I came to live here, there were still many locals who had known Miles well and who knew every detail of the case. Miles's father, Charlie Giffard — the clerk of the St. Austell court — was generally disliked; one man who heard that he had been murdered remarked: 'About time too'. Miles, on the other hand, was greatly liked. A local solicitor, Philip Stephens, who had been present at the trial, was convinced that the jury should have acquitted him on grounds of insanity.

Since Denis Hocking had examined the bodies — and had been a friend of both victims — I asked his views on the case. He agreed that many of Miles's problems could be attributed to the sadistic nanny who used to lock him in a dark cupboard. Yet on the whole, he seemed to agree that justice had been done. It was Denis who gave me the address of P.C. Max Mutton, who had been summoned to the scene of the crime by the maidservant; I drove over to see him near Doublebois. He made the refreshing comment that his first feeling on entering the house was bafflement that anyone who lived in such a comfortable place should want to commit murder.

A visit to the scene of the crime reinforced my conviction that Miles knew what he was doing; the path along which he had to wheel the bodies was long and difficult. But it led to a spot where the rising tide broke against the cliffs, and where it would be a reasonable assumption that bodies would be washed out to sea.

Yet I still found it hard to understand why he should decide to kill his parents, in the fairly certain knowledge that he would be caught.

It was Denis Hocking who handed me the vital clue. He remarked of Charlie Giffard: 'He was the sort of man who hated to admit he was in the wrong.' And suddenly I saw the solution. Giffard was one of these people that the writer Van Vogt called 'Right Men' or 'Violent Men' — I have devoted a whole chapter to them in my *Criminal History of Mankind*. An obsessive craving for self-esteem makes them family tyrants; they *have* to think of themselves as infallible. No one is allowed to contradict them for fear of violence. In their own home, they are little tin gods.

Miles's problem, I believe, was not his nanny, but his father. He detested Charlie Giffard with the manic intensity that the oppressed feel for a tyrant. That is why, when he felt trapped and totally frustrated, something in him revolted and he decided that nothing mattered but to do away with the tyrant. Unfortunately, his mother returned home soon afterwards, and he felt obliged to kill her too.

Was he, then, guilty of murder in the first degree? On the

whole, I think so. Yet the death sentence nevertheless seems inappropriate; if the defence had made its main line of argument the impossible character of the dead man, Giffard would almost certainly have received life imprisonment. This is a matter on which I leave you to make up your own mind after reading Denis Hocking's account.

Before concluding this introduction, I should at least describe briefly the most celebrated of Cornish murder cases, which occurred four years before Dr. Hocking came to Cornwall, and to which he devotes only a tantalising mention. Mrs Sarah Ann Hearn lived with her sister, Miss Everard, at Lewannic, near Launceton. In 1930, Miss Everard died of a stomach complaint, accompanied by painful vomiting. A neighbouring farmer, William Thomas, took pity on Mrs Hearn, and often invited her to the farm. On October 18, 1930, Mrs Hearn, together with Thomas and his wife, went for an afternoon outing to Bude, and had tea in a cafe, at which Mrs Hearn produced her own salmon sandwiches. Mrs Thomas became ill on the way home. Mrs Hearn moved in to nurse her. But Mrs Thomas died. And a post mortem revealed traces of arsenic. Mrs Hearn left a note protesting her innocence and fled. Her sister's body was then exhumed, and also contained traces of arsenic. Mrs Hearn was arrested in January 1931 — working as a housekeeper for a Torquay architect — and tried for murder. Yet because of the weakness of the evidence against her, and her apparent lack of motive, she was acquitted. The case has remained the most celebrated poison mystery of the West country, and has intrigued many crime writers. If Dr. Hocking had performed the autopsies, I suspect he would have pointed out that, since the soil in that area contains tin (which contains arsenic), it would have been unsafe to convict Mrs Hearn of murder.

The surprising thing about this book is that, in spite of the grimness of its subject, it is so good-tempered and so amusing. This is because Denis Hocking is more amused by the foibles of human nature than shocked by its sinfulness. In my introduction to *Murder in the West Country* I find an anecdote that has all the hallmarks of his sense of humour. A celebrated London advocate came to Cornwall to defend a farm labourer accused of unlawful intercourse with a calf;

to his surprise, the Cornish jury acquitted his obviously guilty client. After the case, the advocate was offered a lift by the foreman of the jury, and asked why they had acquitted his client. 'Well,' said the old farmer, 'we reckoned he didn't do the calf no harm.'

It is this attitude of amused tolerance that makes this — as inappropriate as it sounds — the most delightful book on forensic pathology that I have ever read.

PROLOGUE

A small procession forms outside the Parish Church. It consists of HM Judge of Assize, his Sheriff, his Chaplain (my very dear friend, Canon Harmer) and the Chief Constable, flanked by a police guard carrying white staves. Occasionally the Judge carries a posy of flowers to ward off the plague. He is greeted with a fanfare of trumpets.

The little procession winds its way to the Assize Hall, where the Commission of Assize is read out, the full-bottomed-wigged Judge standing and bowing when his name is read out.

The Clerk of Assize intones:

'Elizabeth the Second, by the Grace of God of the United Kingdom of Great Britain and Northern Ireland, and of our Realms and territories, Queen, Head of the Commonwealth, Defender of the Faith.

'To our Chancellor of Great Britain, Our Lieutenants and Sheriffs of Counties, Our Lord Chief Justice of England, Our Judges for the time being of Our Supreme Court of Judicature, Our Circuit Judges and all other persons to whom these Presents shall come, GREETING. WHEREAS We, being most closely concerned to ensure that justice is done to all Our Subjects, have appointed as Judges of Our Supreme Court of Judicature and Our Circuit Judges, persons in whom We have especial trust and confidence, Requiring them to try all persons committed for trial in Our said Courts and all causes and matters depending therein, Doing what to justice doth appertain according to the laws and usage of this Realm.

'KNOW YE that it is Our Will and pleasure that Our

concern for the doing of justice in Our Courts should be declared to all persons having business therein, AND THEREFORE WE COMMAND you to ensure that these Our Letters Patent be read at such sittings of Our Courts as Our Chancellor of Great Britain for the time being may direct.

'IN WITNESS WHEREOF We have caused these Our Letters to be made Patent. Witness Ourself at Westminster the ____ day of _____ in the _____ year of Our Reign.

'And whereas the Honourable Sir _____, Knight, being one of the Judges of Her Majesty's High Court of Justice, and _____ one of Her Majesty's Circuit Judges present at this Court to hear and determine the causes of all persons committed to this Court for trial or sentence and all other causes and matters depending in this Court, now let all persons who have been so committed as aforesaid and all other persons having business in this Court attend now or in the time for justice to be done accordingly.'

A rather hapless and self-conscious constable, HM Coroner's Officer, stands in the doorway of premises where an Inquest is to be held, and shouts:

'Oyez! Oyez! Oyez!

'All manner of persons who have anything to do before Our Sovereign Lady the Queen's Coroner for this County, draw nigh and give your attendance, and if anyone can say how, when and where _____ came to his/her death, let him come forward and he shall be heard.'

Nobody ever came forward, all the witnesses already being in the Court.

Besides, his audience generally consisted of an increasing crowd of street urchins thoroughly enjoying a free entertainment.

And then:

'I swear by Almighty God that the evidence that I shall give shall be the truth, the whole truth, and nothing but the truth.'

Thus began many hundreds of days of enjoyment in our Courts.

My relations with the many Barristers and Solicitors with whom I have come into contact over the following pages (and many, many others) have always been of the most cordial and pleasurable. I have greatly enjoyed their company. We have had great times together, with great mutual respect and camaraderie, and it still goes on.

Only twice have I been shouted at and gone at by Counsel. The first by 'Khaki' Roberts QC, who (along with Mr Justice Hilberry) did not like my appearance on the behalf of James Camb in the 'Porthole' murder case. I made a rather facetious reply to one of his questions. He went for me like a ton of bricks and told me that this was no place to be funny in, and other remarks that I have fortunately forgotten. Fortunately it did not disturb me, or at most only momentarily. We were the best of friends, both before and afterwards.

The other occasion was during the trial of Menheniott for the Isles of Scilly murder. At the outset, Mr Owen Thomas QC attacked my claim to be the Cornwall County Pathologist — which I was. He went for me tooth and nail, not only on that but also on other matters, and I must admit that on that occasion I was a bit harrassed.

Subsequently, we both met on other occasions in a most friendly way. Of course they had their jobs to do.

I have had a lifetime of wonderfully happy association.

Dedication to
Goeland Poppy Basset

Our late, universally beloved Basset Hound, without whose intervention these pages would never have been written. Instead, there would have been a notable double Inquest held by my friend Mr E. Gill, HM Coroner for Mid Cornwall on the corpses of my wife and myself.

It all started when the new gasman cometh to convert us to natural North Sea gas. Amongst other appliances that had to be changed were two Bunsen burners in my upstairs laboratory. I brought them down and showed them to the gasmen for their approval for conversion, and they duly authorised replacements. When I went to reconnect them, I noticed that the indiarubber tubing had perished danger- ously — it had been in use for some forty years! I replaced it by a length of also rather ancient (wartime) hard 'plastic' tubing. I used the burner the same afternoon, and after finishing, turned off the gas supply by a tap at the foot of the burner, leaving the main tap in the wall still on — quite a usual practice.

During the following night, I awoke to a strange smell. I turned over and said to my wife, 'Woman, you have been eating garlic.' This she hotly denied, and after some rather acrimonious conversation we turned our backs on each other and went to sleep again. How long afterwards we have no idea, but we were awakened by Poppy Basset trampling all over us; all eighty-six pounds of her. This did really wake us up, and I then said, 'Woman, you have left the gas stove on.' This again was hotly denied, but not feeling too well, we got up and investigated. The taps of the stove were all turned off, but the house was full of gas. We

17

opened up all the doors and windows, and then went to investigate further. What did we find? — that the hard plastic tubing of my bunsen burner had fallen off the gas tap, and gas with a high percentage of carbon monoxide in it was pouring into the room. It could not have been long before we were fatally gassed.

That evening my wife was giving a buffet party. Nearly everyone who arrived said, 'Oh! doesn't your house smell of gas!' We could have crowned them.

But it would have made a lively Inquest.

PREFACE

Sometime about 1920, I bought a ream of 'Pioneer Fine' foolscap paper, and said to myself, 'One day, I will write a book.' It has taken me over sixty years to fulfill this promise.

That great Victorian critic and philosopher, John Ruskin, once wrote (or said) that every sensible man should feel under an obligation to leave to his descendants some account of his experience of life. This is what I have tried to do in the following pages.

My professional activities have by no means been confined to the investigation of murder, fortunately. In fact, a very large number of murders are of little or no interest. They made the headlines in the newspapers in older days mainly because of the implication that somebody was going to be hanged, and it was this that whetted the public appetite. I have dealt only with those murders that occurred 'down here' (mainly in Cornwall) that have had an element of interest in them apart from the fact of just killing. In fact, many of my other cases have been far more interesting than many murders. They are all a cross-section of cases where medical and scientific investigations have been of use to the Police Authority (and others) in helping to solve crimes of great disparity. Some may not be of outstanding interest, but they are part of the record.

All the facts recorded in these pages are correct, and have been taken from notes and reports made at the time and still in my possession. For some of the background in a few instances I have had to rely on my memory, which might be a little at fault, but generally it can be accepted that the record is completely correct.

Most of the cases refer to my earlier days, when a pathologist was expected to know everything about his particular science.

Pathology then (and now) consisted of four main branches. One, haematology, the study of blood diseases. Two, biochemistry, dealing with diseases associated with alterations in the chemical make-up of the body, such as diabetes. Three, bacteriology, dealing with the infectious diseases. Four, morbid anatomy and histology, the visual and microscopical changes in the body tissues brought about by various diseases. A very small branch of this discipline is forensic pathology, dealing with unusual and unnatural causes of death and mainly concerned with violent death and the sorting out of the problem; accident, suicide or murder. This is expanded to cover all cases in which a doctor is unable to issue a certificate of death.

Now this is all changed. It is quite impossible for any one doctor to assimilate all the advances that are continually being made in the science of medicine and pathology. The four branches have split apart, and each is now a speciality, and even these are now becoming subdivided. This has its advantages in both medical treatment and in the scientific investigation of crime, but it does limit one's outlook, and I think makes life less interesting.

Up to the time of the amalgamation of the police forces of Devon and Cornwall, I was indeed Pooh Bah in Cornwall, even extending my activities into the realms of handwriting identification — which is essentially only an exercise in mensuration and geometry. In these days of necessary over-specialisation, nobody in the future will be able to have so varied an experience as I have had. I have been fortunate. Nowadays there is no truer statement than the one that a specialist is one who knows more and more about less and less. But I must not cavil and decry modern methods of investigation. This great technical advance has made for far greater efficiency and far less likelihood that mistakes are made. More agreement is likely amongst specialists, less wrangling in the Courts and much time and money is saved. But I think there is much less fun; something of what I think as the exciting quality of life has been lost, and life will be that much duller.

This is not an autobiography. Heaven forbid. It is intended more to be a record of experiences that are part of local forensic history at a time of transition from days when medical and scientific evidence was in its infancy, to the present time when very exact scientific tools used by super-experts are available with a degree of accuracy unheard of fifty years ago. This degree of accuracy is now such that mistakes are almost unheard of — but there is always a human element to be considered; mistakes still do occur, but fortunately they can be challenged in the Courts.

Of course I have made mistakes. I can think of a few now. But I do not think on reflection that any of these ever led to a miscarriage of Justice.

I

In the Beginning

As a brief introductory background, I was born in Bristol of a Cornish parson, and Yorkshire mother. The wheel has turned, and I have come to live within a couple of miles of my father's birthplace, The Churchyard, St Austell, where his father had been the Wesleyan Minister. My sister and I often puzzled over why our poor grandmother was allowed to give birth in the churchyard, apparently without help and exposed to the public gaze, until many years later when we discovered that The Churchyard was an address!

Apparently I was such a weakling that at first I was carried about on a pillow in case I broke up. Probably many people must have subsequently wished that I had. Anyway, this was fortunate for me because the doctor decreed that my only chance of survival was to move to the country. So, by blessed good fortune, when I was only three months old, we moved to the Cotswold hamlet of France Lynct, a 'suburb' of Chalford in the Golden Valley. The hamlet had been founded by French Huguenots after the massacre on St Bartholomew's Day, 1572. I still have as a cherished possession one of the candlesticks that they brought over with them. I loved the Cotswolds and the peaceful countryside. Later, circumstances dictated that we move to London. I hated it, and determined that I would get away from it as soon as possible. It took me thirty-five years.

As a comment on changing values over the years, our old

Manse at Chalford is now on the market for £290,000, and the old Church has been converted into five flats, each £190,000!

My professional training started at the City & Guilds of London College, Finsbury, since closed, studying technical chemistry and allied sciences. This was under two great masters, Prof. Meldola, and Prof. Sir Gilbert Thomas Morgan. Prof. Meldola was canonised by the Royal Institute of Chemistry, which founded the greatly prized Meldola Medal in his memory. I did not get it.

A further year studying pure science introduced me to the fascination of organic chemistry and its connection with vital processes. The turning point came one afternoon in January 1921, when, with nothing else to do, I went to the library of the Chemical Society in Burlington House, and browsed along the shelves. There I found an early edition of Taylor's *Principles and Practice of Medical Jurisprudence*. Turning over the pages, I came to a paragraph describing the inability of a certain man to have satisfactory sexual intercourse unless his partner was wearing elastic-sided boots. I read on, and was hooked. This was the life for me, but it necessitated taking a medical degree, on which I embarked the following autumn, qualifying in June 1925 — you could become fully qualified in four years (after 'First MB') in those days and let loose on the Public! On qualifying, I naturally married my two professions and became a scientific medical man, otherwise a pathologist. I became at once an Assistant Director of the Clinical Research Association, at 4/6d. an hour and six months later was appointed Biochemist and Assistant Pathologist to the Westminster Hospital, at the then princely salary of £550 per annum, with private practice allowed. With all this wealth, and following in the steps of all other Teaching Hospital Consultants, I took consulting rooms, first at No. 35 Welbeck Street, and later at 140 Harley Street. I never made enough consulting money to pay for the rent, which, even in those days, was £80 per annum.

I was not a success in this appointment. The social round inseparable from such a position did not appeal to me, and, more important, I have not got a research brain, and this is essential in such a position. I did invent a cure for cancer

(International Conference on Cancer, London 1928), but none of the patients referred to me survived any longer than they would have done without my intervention, nor do I think that anybody's life was shortened by it. I was also involved in a piece of work on the cause and cure of disseminated (multiple) sclerosis, but this was also a flop; I still, however, have some reservations about it. It had been sponsored by our Consultant physician, the late Sir James Purves-Stewart, a very famous neurologist, and no fool. There were obvious flaws in the research, but also much that was good. However, nothing is now thought about it. Pity. Some may be suffering because of this neglect.

These were the days when every Consultant, and every other member of the hospital staff was properly dressed.

On Wednesdays we had what were called consultations. These were for cases of particular difficulty, when the whole Medical and Surgical Staff of the Hospital gathered together in the out-patient department, aired their views and tried to sort the matter out.

I well remember one particular case. A young woman presented herself with a small, rather questionable, tumour in her breast. Asked how long she had had it, she replied that she did not know. Her boyfriend had found it a few nights' ago when they were at the pictures. On these occasions, we all arrived dressed in morning dress and top hats. I still have mine, now alas never used on such occasions. It is let out at the back a little, and is donned for formal occasions still. Nowadays, some doctors seem to think that they can dress anyhow, even worse than many hospital porters. I have seen even professors going about, and broadcasting, tieless and jacketless. What an example to set, reflective of today's generally sloppy attitude to many issues. I still believe that one's appearance goes a long way to reassuring an anxious patient. A sloppy appearance suggests a sloppy mind, and when one is ill one requires an appearance that gives an air of reassurance. What reassurance can be given by a doctor, 'unconventionally dressed', whose first words are, 'What's the matter with you? I can only give you five minutes.' Most of all, an ill person wants reassuring that he is not going to die, and an impressive appearance is essential in these circumstances. Of course, there are countless, and an increasing number, of remedies and surgical operations now available to save more lives than could possibly be contemplated in my time, but it is comfort and reassurance that most patients also require. This is not conveyed by a sloppy appearance. Perhaps the pillbox has replaced the old GP who sent out a bottle of (?useless) medicine, beautifully wrapped and labelled 'One tablespoonful to be taken every four hours', placed on the mantelpiece in the sick room, under constant visual reminder of the presence of the imposing doctor who has reassured you that you are going to get well. You believed it, and you got well.

I have nothing against the modern pill. In fact, I subscribe to the fact that they are indeed marvellous and have made possible cures unthought of in my early days. But I do wish that they were prescribed with more thought.

Unfortunately, the general public, and many doctors, seem to be obsessed with pills. They are so easy to dish out compared with the old bottles of medicine, and many people seem almost to live on them. It appears that many of the present kind of patient simply demands pills for any real or imaginary ailment, and will even shop around for the doctor who will prescribe the most. In this respect, herewith a cautionary tale. Some few years ago I was asked to do a post-mortem examination on the body of a lady who had died under no suspicious circumstances, but whose death certificate could not be signed up because it was a long time since she had seen her doctor. When I examined her liver I found it more like pâté de fois gras than anything else. It was yellow-brown in colour and could have passed for a couple of pounds of butter. My Coroner's Officer informed me that she had been taking rather a lot of pills — in fact ten different kinds, three times a day. She must have rattled. I sent for her doctor and showed him the result, and asked, 'Why?' I was told that she had a minor illness for which a particular pill had been prescribed. Looking up any adverse effects of this pill, he decided to give an antidote, and so on and so on until ten pills had been prescribed. I showed him the result. Years after when I again met him, he was a rabid advocate of minimum prescribing of drugs.

In spite of my lack of social and professional success,

those years at 'Westminster' brought me two inestimable experiences, my friendships with two outstanding personalities. One was the late Mr Ingleby Oddie, HM Coroner for Central London, who took me under his wing and initiated me into the mysteries of forensic pathology and criminal practice. One of my treasures is an autographed copy of his book of memory, *Inquest*. In his time he dealt with most of the notorious cases that were then intriguing London. I worked for him at the old Horseferry mortuary, on enhanced LCC fees for services rendered. Two guineas for a post-mortem examination, three for a PM with following Inquest. The odd shillings invariably went to HM Coroner's Officer. These miserly fees were not increased until after the last war! At the Horseferry mortuary I often met the doyen of Forensic Science, Sir Bernard Spilsbury. He took me under his wing and gave me invaluable advice, and did all he could to encourage me.

I might add one small feather to my otherwise unadorned cap; no student that I taught ever failed his pathology examinations.

Pathologists in those days were employed at a salary by the hospital Governors. We were therefore paid servants, hirelings and so utterly inferior socially compared with the magnificent body of physicians and surgeons who gave their services voluntarily. They relied wholly on being called in consultation by their numerous former students after the latter had graduated and gone out into general practice. Medicine is one of the oldest of the professions, surgery a little less. Even then, the surgeon was often looked down upon by the physician as the surgeon worked with his hands, as a kind of carpenter, under the supervision of the presiding physician who worked with his brains. The pathologist was almost the latest addition to the profession. There was practically no private practice, certainly not enough to live on, and so, as he was indeed indispensible, he had to be paid — with loss of social stature. The position was not put right until the coming in of the National Health Service in 1948, when all specialists were treated as equal. Now, the wheel having turned full circle, the pathologist is becoming the leader of the medical orchestra.

Being such inferior beings, we were often situated in the

most undesirable locations in the hospitals, even in the bowels in some cases, near the boilers, store or cleaning rooms; anywhere where inferior beings could not be seen. However, when I went to 'Westminster' they did build me a first-class laboratory on the roof above the well-equipped laboratory presided over by my Chief, the late Dr Braxton Hicks. Incidentally, when my laboratory was being built, the architect had forgotten to put in a stairway to it, a lapse overcome by the provision of a very difficult spiral stairway.

Increasing dissatisfaction with my lot in London made me look around, and my eyes turned in the direction of Cornwall, my native land. A glance at the Medical Directory showed me that there was no pathologist there, the nearest being Dr Wordley at Plymouth and Dr Robb at Exeter. The next pathologists were in Bristol! When I finally retired, there were over a hundred pathologists between Penzance and Bristol. This is some indication of the growing importance of pathology in the new medical era. But I do sometimes wonder, are we not rather overdoing it, and is all this really necessary?

In those early days specimens for pathological investigation had to be sent by post to one or other of the commercially operated pathological institutions, very often arriving in an unsuitable condition for accurate analysis. Chief amongst these institutions was the Clinical Research Association, a branch of Guy's Hospital pathological department. For some years I was an assistant director of this establishment, and spent some of my happiest times in London there. The other very successful postal service was run by Virol. Both of these and many others have now disappeared, but in those early days they did an invaluable service to general practitioners and the smaller hospitals. However, a major drawback to this kind of service was that it took about a week to get an answer to a problem. Incidentally, whilst I was at the Clinical Research Association, I must have examined many specimens coming from Cornwall. One in particular I remember — a doctor who had prescribed a dose of phosphorus one hundred times too strong. The organs fairly glowed in the dark.

There being no specialist pathologist in Cornwall I

decided that there ought to be one, and that the one should be me. It was my great opportunity. I therefore wrote to the medical staff of the Royal Cornwall Infirmary (all five of them), asking them what they thought about the idea. They were delighted, but sadly added that I should not be able to make a living, and they could not afford to subsidise me. However, these were the days of great rivalry between the Royal Cornwall Infirmary, Truro, and the Miners' and Womens' Hospital, Redruth. Great was the competition, rivalling that between neighbouring towns in Cornwall — Redruth v Camborne, Falmouth v Penryn, Penzance v Newlyn and so on. Truro had orthopaedic and eye specialist departments. Redruth had a maternity and gynaecological block, and also a radiological department. The latter was presided over by Dr Rivers, who also ran a very efficient, but entirely local pathological service and no post-mortem service.

The temptation to get one up on Redruth was too great to be ignored. Shortly after my disappointment, I received a letter from the Management Committee offering me the £100 a year that they were already spending on sending specimens to the Virol laboratory, and also another £100 a year that they had persuaded the County Council to give me to do routine analyses (mainly milk samples) that they required.

I gladly accepted. I had arrived. I had attained my ambition — a little empire of my own, deep in the countryside, by the sea (I lived then in Perranporth) and in my own county. I came with a guarantee of £200 per annum. I never looked back. Good riddance, London.

The rivalry between the two hospitals at Truro and Redruth continued after my appointment, and was not finally settled until the two hospitals were amalgamated in 1965 to form the new hospital at Treliske.

After my appointment, Redruth countered by appointing a specialist gynaecologist and obstetrician. Truro then set up an ENT department. Both hospitals then appointed consultant radiologists, followed by specialist anaesthetists and Consulting Physicians, Dr C. T. Andrews at Truro, and Dr L.W. Hale at Camborne. There the quarrel stopped, there being no likely other specialities to be appointed.

On 2 August, 1935, Major Hare, the then Chief Constable of Cornwall, appointed me as Consultant to help the police with specialist scientific problems, and assist in the detection of crime. I have vastly enjoyed the association. On 26 February, 1941, the Cornwall County Council appointed me part-time County Pathologist. Both appointments I kept until my retirement.

2

Early Days

Of course a boy was required to do the washing up and general chores, as well as to be trained in the practice of pathological investigations — a very well worthwhile career. I suggested that he should be paid £1 a week. The Governors threw up their hands in horror; no boy leaving school had then ever been paid more than 7/6 a week — and this was for a seven day week. I finally got them up to 10/- a week in view of his responsibilities. There was also a promise of an increase of 2/6 a week every year up to a maximum wage of £4 a week. Douglas James, my first 'boy', gave me many years of very faithful service at this ridiculous rate of pay, but I am glad to add at a rather accelerated rate of increase in later years. Soon, more assistance was required, and a second boy, Brian Mansell, was employed, this time starting at 5/- a week, increased after a year by 2/6 weekly to a maximum of £3. He too gave me many years of faithful service (again later at a much increased rate of payment), finally marrying an evacuee from London who had come to work for me in the early days of the war. They ultimately settled down in Canada where they made a great success of their lives, earning a salary many times that which I had when I retired from the Hospital Service in 1964.

Sailing on the River Fal and surf-riding at Perranporth soon began to make inroads into my time, and further assistance was required to cover this and also the great increase in work that had occurred. Jointly with the Hospital Governors, I appointed a retired Naval Chief Petty Officer, Mr E. E. Kent, who was a fully trained laboratory technician. This was a great step forward, and relieved me of a great many chores. We were now a fully equipped and adequately qualified pathological staff, able to do practically every kind of test that at that time was available to the medical profession.

Between us, we paid Mr Kent £3 a week in addition to his Naval pension of £120 per annum. Mr Kent remained with me until his retirement in 1962. An old seaman, he told me that he had spent twenty-two years in the Navy, mainly dodging work. The well-tried methods apparently were for officers to walk about with a sheaf of papers under an arm, and for ratings to walk about with a bucket. Whether or not he dodged work in the Navy I do not know (I suspect he did), but I do know that he and all my staff worked from 9 a.m. until the day's work had been done; during the war, this was often until the late evening, but nobody ever complained. There was no overtime pay, and no complaint about working unsocial hours. Everything was done willingly and cheerfully. Present workers please note, and reflect. I can add that we were all supremely happy and contented, helping each other out whenever there might be pressure of work in another department. There was no such thing as 'that is not my job'. I would like here and now to pay my tribute to all the members of my staff for their unselfish, willing and uncomplaining help, co-operation and support during those days, and particularly during the days of the war.

Mr Kent used to bicycle to work. With great daring, in his latter years with me, he propelled himself to work more easily on a moped. One of my more outspoken lady technicians, Mrs Jean Bray, who was very fond of the old man, told him that one day he would fall off the bloody thing, and break his neck. This is precisely what he did on 5 December, 1967, to my very great sorrow.

My first laboratory was formed by partitioning off the end of the main corridor. It measured 10 ft. by 7 ft. There were two benches, one along the long wall, and the other at right-angles, under a window. It had shelves to the ceiling, filled with our apparatus. When a particular test had to be done, this was taken down and put back afterwards. There was no question of having a row of apparatus immediately available for use. I also had the use of an unheated outhouse used as an animal and sterilising room. Still, we survived, and enjoyed it.

This was the set-up in which all the hospital, general practitioner, County Council and police work was done until we moved into palatial premises in the new wing of the enlarged hospital just before the outbreak of the 1939-45 war.

It was then that I appointed my first secretary-typist, Brenda, from Miss Hoar's Young Ladies' Secretarial College.

Until the takeover of the hospital service by the National Health Service in 1948, I ran that department for a cost to the hospital of approximately £400 a year. Now there are six pathologists and some seventy technicians in our place, at a cost of goodness only knows how much. Mind you, they do a much better job!

When I began, the CID in Cornwall, instituted in 1935, consisted of three people, Det. Inspector Morcumb, Det. Con. Julian (later Chief Superintendent, CID) and Constable Burge, who left shortly after my arrival; no connection, I understand. The amount of work they did with limited resources is now almost unbelievable, and their success phenomenal. Then they were not fettered by the enormous number of do's and don'ts now incorporated by law into police procedure, mainly at the instigation of do-gooders, all designed apparently to frustrate the police in the execution of their duty, which is to protect you and me. Now the CID in the County number dozens, and they have all the resources of modern science and its incredible advances at their disposal. This is necessary now. Most criminals in my days were simple fellows, easily detected. Now they are sophisticated and much more difficult to catch so that detection devices have to march in line.

Morcumb and Julian put their heads together and said, 'Let's have a look at this chap and see if he is likely to be any good,' — they told me later on. We fell for each other at once, and worked hand in glove harmoniously for many years, until one after the other they retired before me.

Our first essay together was a burglary at Bugle railway station. The burglar, either through fright or dysentery, left visible traces of his presence underneath the window which he had forced. Unfortunately for him, he stepped in the mess prior to entering the premises, and left considerable traces wherever he walked. Very shortly after leaving, he was picked up by the police, and his boots and samples from outside the window and inside the station were sent to me for examination. They were all identical, and without going into details, all showed a rather abnormal peculiarity that undoubtedly connected all the specimens together as having come from one source. He was tried at Penzance Quarter Sessions, and was very abusive to me when convicted. He had never heard of such evidence being given, and thought it most unfair.

The first case of murder in Cornwall that I helped to investigate occurred in April 1937. This was the first murder in Cornwall since the case of Mrs Hearn, who was accused in 1930 of poisoning a Mrs Thomas, the wife of a farmer at Lewannick — a notorious case.

Mine concerned a man, Davis by name. He lived in the Camborne area, and had trouble with his wife, who he accused of being lazy. In 1935 he left her, going up to Coventry where he was tracked down and brought back to Cornwall under warrant for maintenance. He decided to live with her again, and they went to Hayle. About this time a girl, Monica Rowe, came into the picture, being a relative of Mrs Davis. Things went very well until Mrs Davis was taken ill and removed to Penzance Hospital. Davis and the girl took themselves to Tuckingmill, to a house with a large garage attached. They became 'friendly', a thing Mrs Davis objected to after her return from hospital. After that, things did not run smoothly.

Both Mrs Davis and the girl disappeared towards the end of April 1937.

Searching the premises, we found that the garage pit had been filled with earth and stones, so we began digging. I was given the job, with Superintendent Hosking, Police Sgt Rogers and Dr Blackwood looking on and not helping a bit.

After removing the first six inches of the earth and stones,

I came across two bodies, Mrs Davis and Monica Rowe, lying side by side and covered with a dark grey blanket. Stones were packed all around the bodies, filling all the hollows between them, and then earth piled on top.

Mrs Davis was clothed in a vest and nightdress, and covered with a white sheet, coat and pillow, all bloodstained. The head was wrapped first in a dress, then a pullover which was secured around the neck with a stocking, and around the head with another stocking. Both stockings were pulled tight and knotted. Outside all this, a lady's jumper was wrapped around the head, the sleeves being tied with one knot around the neck. Both wrists were tied with a strip of blanket, and there was a length of rope around the legs. The reason for this became apparent when it was considered that she weighed 15 stone 9 lbs., and Davis was a slight man; he could not possibly have carried her and even dragging the body from the bedroom to the garage would have presented a daunting feat. Supt Hosking thought that the body had been dragged on an eiderdown (also found in the pit) by the rope around the legs.

The body of the girl was curled up and lying on the left side of the body of the woman. She was clothed in a vest, brassiere (called bust bodice by Sgt Rogers) dress and dressing gown, and was covered with a coat. The head was wrapped in the skirt of the dressing gown, which was secured around the neck with a stocking pulled tightly and knotted. Outside this again, a skirt was wrapped round the head and kept in place by another stocking tied around the top and knotted. When all this was removed it was found that the girl had a gag in her mouth, and that her jaw was kept shut with a leather strap tied underneath it and over the top of the head. She was a slightly-built girl, weighing only 6 st. 13 lbs., and would have been easy to carry.

Underneath all this lot in the garage pit there were an eiderdown, bedspread, woollen cardigan, woollen jumper, two pairs of knickers, a skirt, an apron, a piece of webbing and a belt.

They had both been dead for some five to seven days, corresponding to the time when they had last been seen.

Both had bruises in the scalps, and there were fractures of the skull bones. Actual damage to the brain and bleeding inside the skull were not marked, and were wholly insufficient in themselves to account for death, but the injuries would have caused unconsciousness. Examination of the rest of the bodies, particularly the lungs, showed that there was a large element of suffocation in the cause of the death, and in both cases I gave the cause of death as suffocation following blows on the head of sufficient severity to cause unconsciousness.

Superintendent Hosking put the findings together in a resume that was followed by the Prosecution at the trial of Davis.

His summary suggested that, after the return to Tuckingmill, matrimonial relations because increasingly difficult on account of the girl. On the morning of the murder, Davis came home from work (he was on night shift) and went into the girl's bedroom. She was partly dressed — as we found. Mrs Davis, being suspicious, came into the girl's bedroom in her nightdress, and a quarrel broke out. Davis hit his wife on the head and she fell down, for all intents and purposes, dead. The girl naturally became frightened, and would not listen to Davis' plea that he should put his wife away and that they could go on living together. She obviously refused, and probably started screaming. Hence the gag, and the realisation that he would be informed upon sealed her fate. She was also struck on the head, possibly initially to keep her quiet. Faced now with two unconscious women, either of whom on recovering consciousness would have informed against him, he decided to save his skin by finishing them off by suffocation by tying their clothing tightly around their heads. To make sure that they could not inform against him, he decided to make them disappear by burying them in the garage pit. The garage is still there in Tuckingmill.

Although there was blood about the clothing, he made a thorough job of cleaning up the respective bedrooms. The Jury accepted Supt Hosking's account. Davis hanged.

In 1938 I agreed to open a venereal disease clinic (which I afterwards regretted), which I did with the help of sister Keeling, who was also doing a part-time job in the laboratory as secretary and part-time technician. Like all the others, she gave me invaluable service, ultimately leaving to become Assistant Matron at Charing Cross Hospital. During the war, Dr O'Donnell's daughter, Kathleen, then a medical student, also came to work for me. She again became my general and post-mortem assistant, leaving after the war to go back to University, but this time as a graduate in science. After graduation, she came back to my laboratory doing invaluable work, and then did the best thing in our lives — she married me, and has been my assistant in all ways ever since.

I must say that I found the clinic a bit of a bore, but it had its highlights and a certain amount of fun and comic relief. Many and varied were the stories told as to how the sufferers contracted their disease — never, or hardly ever, the obvious one. The old lavatory seat excuse is now so worn that it would be dangerous to sit on it for fear of collapse.

One young man did tell me a plausible reason for a most unusual finding — a primary syphilitic sore in the middle of his back. It appeared that he had gone to a rather wild party during which a game was played involving the ladies riding (literally) bare-backed around the room astride the gentlemen on all fours. They were not only bare-backed, they were altogether bare.

Wednesday was clinic day.

On Wednesday 31 July, 1940, Mrs Julia Carnanton was found dead with very severe head injuries, and also injuries to her arms and neck. She was slumped by the fireplace in her dining room. Her worst injury was a slash across the front of her neck which had almost beheaded her. It had been a truly maniacal attack. The reason was never discovered, but it occurred at a time of considerable stress amongst a section of the population of Truro. This section had just moved away from a very sordid slum area, where houses were cheek by jowl, to a new housing estate (Trelander) with gardens. It should have been a delightful change, but rumour had it differently. Prior to the time of removal it had been almost customary, and very easy and convenient, for husbands and wives to borrow or exchange each other without being seen. Now, in their new, open estate, it meant climbing fences in full view of everybody.

However that may have been, Superintendent Burroughs,

Insp. Morcumb and Police Sgt Julian were in charge, and came to see me. They appeared at one of the laboratory windows and asked for me, and were interviewed by Miss O'Donnell. Instead of stating their business, they just said that they wanted to see me. The reply was blunt and to the point — 'Round the corner and the first door on the left.' The Wednesday afternoon clinic was devoted to the female of the species. They arrived to find themselves amongst this down-and-out female crowd awaiting my attention. The superintendent was in full uniform, the others in plain clothes. Can you imagine the conversation? 'Look who's here!' 'Have they got it as well?' 'Where they get it from? — anybody here?' and so on. They were not amused. The Superintendent was a pillar of the Methodist Church. I don't think he ever forgave me, but the others treated it as a great joke.

In my early days, facilities for post-mortem examinations were more often than not extremely primitive, and in many ways utterly disgusting. They were bad enough for me, but distressing to a degree for relatives having to go to such places to identify their dead. Generally there was no heating, not even means to heat water. In any case, I was told, 'Whoever heard of keeping a corpse warm?' The pathologist's feelings obviously did not come into the picture. I have worked in extreme discomfort in winter time, even having to try and do a post-mortem examination on a corpse frozen so stiff that it could not be cut. In some places there was not even lighting; I have done a post-mortem examination by the light of a policeman's torch. Corpses have been laid out on stone slabs, covered with a sheet of tarpaulin or indiarubber; the last indiarubber covering was removed from the Launceston mortuary only in about 1980.

The worst of all post-mortem rooms was the original one at Saltash. It was at the angle of a high walled street, the walls forming two sides of the room. It was covered by a sloping, rusty piece of corrugated iron. Inside, it measured three feet by six, a low bench of cemented stones along the long wall being my operating table. A long man could not be accommodated without bending the knees up, and to get at a head was almost impossible. There was no lighting, and the only water supply was a cold water tap outside. I performed there only once! Equally, the old mortuary on the quay at Penzance was almost as dreadful. There were many places almost as bad: Padstow, St Agnes, Perranporth and Camborne, to mention only a few. However, with a little judicious, and sometimes injudicious, prodding things gradually improved, and at the time of my retirement I had no grumbles and indeed worked in some palatially constructed mortuaries.

Fate took a merciful hand in two cases. The old mortuary at St Just consisted of two barren basement rooms underneath the Council Chamber. One had an enormous fireplace in it. There was no heating, rough walls, a built-up stone slab and a cold-water tap. The floor separating it from the Council Chamber was of ill-fitting elm board. We could often hear what was going on in the Council Chamber, but, until one notable evening, obviously the councillors did not know what was going on below them. One very hot summer's day there arrived in the mortuary a body that had been in the sea for a long time. Not a nice sight, and not a nice smell. When we arrived, we heard voices above, and learned that the Council was in full session. Now, I thought, was our opportunity. I made rather more than the usual number of incisions in the body. The meeting above collapsed after only a very short session, and the next thing I knew was a new, palatial mortuary on the outskirts of the town.

A similar incident resulted in the closure of the Torpoint mortuary. This was situated underneath the public hall, and again separated from it by defective flooring. On this occasion a body had been recovered after several weeks from the River Tamar; when we arrived, we were greeted with strains of valiant music floating from above. They did not practice for very long, and we were rewarded by being removed to new premises at Saltash.

Probably the most curiously sited post-mortem room was the original one at Helston. To reach it, one walked through the abattoir, between rows of hanging carcasses before being confronted with the corpse on which a post-mortem examination had been ordered.

The most unlikely place in which I did a post-mortem

examination was in a guard's van in sidings at Par, in 1938. Edwin Edgar Starke had died in Penzance; his death certificate had been duly completed and accepted, and he was on his way to London for burial. Soon after the train left Penzance, it was reported to the Coroner that he had been taken ill with severe gastro-enteritis a day or so before his death. The funeral was stopped, the train was stopped at Par, and the guard's van detached and replaced by another one for the journey to London. The post-mortem examination showed that there was no doubt about the gastro-enteritis, so the necessary bits were taken for later analysis. This showed the presence of antimony and tin. Antimony is almost as poisonous as arsenic, and the symptoms are similar. It is used along with, or as a substitute for, tin in cheap enamel or holloware; it can be dissolved from these vessels by acids, even such mildly acid as citrus fruit. Enquiries showed that not only the deceased but other members of the family had been taken ill on the same day with similar symptoms of poisoning, although, fortunately in their cases, not fatal. We found that they had all consumed lemon juice stored in an enamel crock. Later examination of the enamel showed that it contained a high percentage of antimony.

In somewhat similar vein, a barman working in a pub (also in Penzance) nearly lost his life, this time as a wrong-doer. Every morning he pinched a pint of beer, drawing the first pint of the day. This was normally thrown away because, unknown to him, the pipe from the barrel was made of pewter, a mixture of lead and tin. Beer, being slightly acid, dissolves some of the metal, and for this reason the conscientious bar owner discards the first pint that has stood overnight in contact with the metal. The barman became increasingly ill, and it was found that he was suffering from lead poisoning; just retribution and entirely his own fault.

For some years we were baffled by outbreaks of severe illness amongst visitors to St Ives, and particularly visitors to one particular hotel. Culinary arrangements were impeccable, the kitchens spotless and food controls beyond reproach. Further investigations showed that all the affected visitors were suffering from acute lead poisoning, traced to old lead plumbing that was being disolved by the very soft water of that district. I can now assure all visitors to St Ives generally, and not only to this specific hotel, that this danger has now been rectified.

3

The Police

My relations with the police have always been of extreme friendliness. I suppose I have really always been a policeman at heart. I have an enormous regard for them; we have worked together amicably for over sixty years, and I owe them a debt of gratitude for providing me professionally with everything that has been my absorbing interest during this long time. They have really made my life for me. I could not count the numbers of times they have taken us into their homes at all hours of the day and night, and always refreshed us with countless cups of tea, coffee and often something more warming. Generally the tea or coffee was suitably 'laced' to fit the occasion. Only once did we suffer grevious disappointment. We had gone on a bitterly cold night, at about 2 a.m. to the Par mortuary. At that time this edifice consisted of a stone slab on two pillars, surrounded by four walls and a gas light that would not work. There was no heating, but water was available. The Coroner's Officer spent most of his time standing on the table continuously relighting the spluttering gas light. Things improved after I inadvertently pulled the table with a very heavy body on it over one day and completely smashed the slate slab; it was replaced by a fine porcelain one, still in use. The occasion was the finding of a newly-born baby floating on a sort of raft amongst the reeds in Par Mere. Unlike Moses in somewhat similar circumstances, this baby was dead, and had died (as subsequent examination showed) from cold and exposure, and inattention at birth — as indeed did so many babies at about that time, the result of wartime associations quickly made and quickly forgotten. We never traced the mother. After the examination was over and we were visibly shivering, we were asked if we would like to go back to the Police Station for something to warm us up before returning to Perranporth where we lived then. Knowing police habits and hospitality, we said, 'Would we not!' Arrived at the station, a kettle was produced and put on the hob. Splendid, we thought, hot punch! Not a bit of it. A bottle of Camp coffee and some milk were produced, and we had to be content with that. For once even my wife's conversation failed.

My nicest policeman's story is that of a young constable and his wife, stationed at that time at Wadebridge. In the natural course of events, a son and heir was born. When he was about a year old, father came home one day and suggested that it might be a good thing if junior began as soon as possible to learn to live with animals, and what about a puppy? Mother thought otherwise, and the idea was turned down. However, the matter was avidly pursued, and at last the penny dropped; there was a stray puppy at the Police Station, and PC would love to have him. Wifey then agreed to go and have a look at the puppy. Next day she was seen wheeling son and heir towards the Police Station. Shortly afterwards she was seen coming back home with son and heir under her arm, and two puppies in the perambulator.

I remember many other occasions. A Mr and Mrs Woodcock, an elderly couple living at Hayle, had become increasingly hateful to each other. Both were chronic alcoholics. One morning, Mr Woodcock decided on the ultimate way to solve his problem, so he slit his wife's neck from ear to ear whilst she was sitting up in bed. She was found in this position some four hours afterwards, and of course the hue and cry went out for her husband. He was spotted in the town, ran back to his home, where he was chased to the bottom of his garden, where he proceeded to slit his throat with the same razor that he had used on his wife — thus saving a lot of Police and High Court time.

When I had finished the post-mortem examinations, the

constable acting as Coroner's Officer said to me, 'There is a lot of brandy in that house. Do you think he could have drugged some and given it to his wife before slitting her throat? Should it not be analysed? The penny dropped, and I agreed. Within a half-hour he returned, his bicycle festooned with bottles of Bisquet de Bouche, only one of which had been opened. We decided to test this one by the well-known taste test; it seemed all right, and no further action was taken apart from dividing up the spoils. I should add that I did subsequently analyse the already opened bottle for any other specific poison; to our relief, none was found.

After examining the house, just as we were going out, I absent-mindedly opened a drawer in an old-fashioned coat stand in the hall. It was stuffed full of pound notes. This started things off; we found hundreds of pounds hidden away in drawers all over the house, particularly in the drawers of a sideboard. There were hundreds, if not thousands. I suggested that I might have some for forensic examination, like the brandy, but this suggestion did not find favour in the eyes of the Senior Police Officer. Pity. Anyway, the brandy served for laboratory entertainment for a long time.

I had a rather similar stroke of luck some little time afterwards.

An elderly lady was found dead in her home in Bodmin. There were no suspicious circumstances, but as she had not been seen by her doctor for a long time, a post-mortem was necessary. The result of this examination was that death was due to natural causes — as far as could be seen. But HM Coroner's Officer said to me, 'You know, Doc, that she made quantities of home-made wine from basic sources. There are dozens of bottles of the stuff in the house. Do you think that she might inadvertently have picked up some poisonous plants?' I did not think so, but the penny dropped. We collected many bottles of beautiful home-made wine. Chemical examination of such a large cache seemed out of the question, so we decided between us to do the much simpler taste and consumption test, which we found very enjoyable. Neither of us came to any harm.

I am sure the old girl would have approved.

This was not by any means the only house in which we came across vast sums of money.

We were on our way to London by the Cornish Riviera train on 14 January, 1960, when I was waylaid by a 'phone call from Mr Rowland, Asst Chief Constable, saying that two old ladies had been found dead in their home at Gunnislake. I said I was on my way to London, and would do them next day. 'But doctor, this might be a case of double murder; you must come at once,' said Mr Rowland, so off we had to go. We eventually caught the night train to London.

When we got to Gunnislake, we were taken by Supt Glover to an almost indescribable 'dwelling'. It was really converted stables, with an upper floor reached by a ladder.

The place was utterly squalid, vermin-infested (including rats), filthy and apparently poverty-stricken.

Downstairs, the furniture consisted of a broken-down settee, some chairs, mostly broken, a stool, wooden seat and an old mattress. Papers, old newspapers and cardboard boxes littered the place. There was a poverty-stricken larder presided over by a coloured print of the Charge of the Light Brigade.

'Upstairs' there were two broken-down iron bedsteads with verminous mattresses, and an assortment of very scanty and dirty bedclothing. The roof had partly collapsed, and let in rain water.

These premises had been inhabited by two very elderly sisters, Miss Hannah Thomasina Sullivan, aged eighty-five years, and Miss Mary Sullivan, aged ninety-four years. Miss Mary had not been seen for about a fortnight, and Miss Hannah not for several days, so the premises were broken into, and both were found dead on the floor of the downstairs room, Miss Mary behind the door, and Miss Hannah by the fireplace. Both women were completely, but scantily, clothed; the clothing had not been disturbed in any way.

Miss Mary had been dead for about a fortnight. Her body had been thrown behind the door, and furniture piled over her. Was this a crude mode of burial, done by a crazed sister? On top of the pile there was a wooden stool. The seat was cracked, and in the crack there was a white hair, similar to that of Miss Mary's head. There was a fairly severe bruise on the left side of the forehead above the hair line, but the skin had not been broken and there had been no bleeding. There was also bruising around the left eye and over the left cheek. No bones had been broken, and no damage had been done to the brain, which was not even bruised. It was just shrunken and atrophied through old age. The weight of the blow would normally be quite insufficient to cause death, but it could have caused unconsciousness. In the prevailing cold, such unconsciousness could easily have terminated in death from exposure. Or did these old things have a quarrel, with Miss Hannah hitting her sister over the head with the stool? Any blow struck by her would not likely to be very heavy. Having knocked her sister unconscious, she might have thought that she was dead, and forthwith 'buried' her underneath the furniture, where she died of cold and exposure. I could not completely exclude this, but did not think it likely. However, no purpose would have been served by my giving any opinion other than that Miss Mary died from cold and exposure after being rendered unconscious following a blow on the head consistent with a fall. She might even have had a 'heart attack' that caused her to fall. This had all happened about a fortnight before Miss Hannah was found. She did not survive her sister for very long. She was found slumped on the floor before the fireplace, with her head in the ashes. The fire had not been lit, as there were no signs of burning. Possibly it had not been lit for a very long time, as no reserves of fuel were found anywhere. Miss Hannah was unkempt, dirty, but fully, although scantily, dressed, the clothing undisturbed. A thin blanket had been pulled over the body. There were no injuries at all to be seen, and none were found during the post-mortem examination of the body. The stomach was empty, and the condition of the body generally suggested starvation over a long period. In my opinion, death was due to general senile degeneration accelerated by cold and exposure.

Was there any need for this pathetic state of affairs — and why weren't there any do-gooders about? Probably they were too busy looking after juvenile delinquents. However, as I said, this was not the end of the story. 'Upstairs' was up a rickety ladder into a loft that contained two broken-down single bedsteads. The roof leaked; there was no furniture; there were no proper mattresses, and the bed coverings were worn, utterly inadequate old blankets. The place was rat-infested and covered with their, and mouse leavings. Rummaging around, we came across boxes crammed full of pound notes, and deeds of property in Ireland. From documents it appeared that the old ladies were related to Irish aristocracy, but I do not recall that this line was followed up.

The end of this story is that as we were leaving the Police Station in Callington to catch the night train to London, we saw the Station Sergeant literally surrounded by piles of pound notes, diligently counting them. My memory may be a little at fault, but by the time we left, the count had reached the thousands. There was therefore no reason for the utterly poverty-stricken conditions that these two old ladies had been living under. The Station Sergeant did not respond to my veiled suggestion that a few of the notes might be useful in London, but he did send us away with suitably warmed tummies.

One almost naturally associates a house in respectable Killigrew Street, Falmouth, opposite the park, with opulence. How deceived can one be? In spite of such respectability, strange things can go on. Such was the case in one of these terraced houses in 1952. I am, for obvious reasons, witholding the number.

One morning, in very cold winter time, the sole occupant of one of the houses was found, fully dressed in her nightgown, spreadeagled across the yard at the back of her house. She had fallen, injured her head sufficiently to cause unconsciousness, and had died of cold and exposure. There seemed to be no reason whatever to suspect foul play.

Inside, the house was incredible. There was a basement kitchen, very damp. Huge fungi, such as are seen on the boles of rotting timber in neglected forests, festooned the door jambs. There was a large table in the middle of the room, piled as high as possible, and on the point of collapse with food remnants of all and everything. Curiously, considering the dampness of the room, these had not decomposed, nor were they smelling. Similar remnants of food and their containers littered the rest of the room. The bedroom

46

was incredible. There was a four poster bed there. It was completely festooned with cobwebs which filled the space between the top and the ceiling, and ran in cascades down the sides. Similar cobwebs covered the rest of the furniture. It was an exact replica of the bedroom of Miss Haversham's home as portrayed in Dickens's *Great Expectations*. In another room there was a high-piled cone of human hair some four feet high; obviously the lady never threw anything away. Also on the wall there was a certificate to the effect that she had been an LRAM. The bath was used for storage purposes.

I have never seen so many fleas. One abiding memory is of seeing Police Sgt Toms just as we were leaving. I think that out of every hole of every button of his waistcoat there twinkled a flea. When I got home, I took off my outer clothing and went into the hottest possible bath with everything else on. This had no effect other than making them jump about more lively, and bite more viciously; they were obviously hungry. Even the addition of Dettol had no obvious effect, and I finished up by plastering both sides of a cake of soap with them. My wife (who was not my wife then) had a very important dinner party that night, and had no time to take the precautions that I had been able to do. She scratched herself continuously through the whole of the evening, and nearly lost a very important employment engagement.

Still dealing with my relations with the police, I have had only one real quarrel with them, and one rather serious disagreement over a matter of possible or probable murder.

The quarrel was over a case of grievous bodily harm. A gypsy and another man had had a serious argument, leading to a fight during which the other man received severe face injuries. He said, and this was the Prosecution's case, that he had been knocked down by the gypsy and had then been repeatedly kicked in the face. The Defence was that the injured man had made a swipe at the gypsy, lost his balance and fallen flat on his face on to very obviously rough and stony ground. The gypsy's solicitor approached the late Sir William Kelsey Fry, then one of the leading forensic dental surgeons in London, for his opinion on these injuries. Sir William replied that they could have been caused either way, by kicking, or falling onto rough, stony ground. Asked my opinion quite independently, I gave the same reply. As Sir William would have been a very expensive witness to call by the Defence, the task fell to me as being a much cheaper one — in those days! I gave my opinion accordingly, and the Defendant was acquitted. A memorable feature of the case was that the whole of the public gallery in the Court was crowded with gypsies, and there was a massive overflow outside. The proceedings went off in an utter and complete silence that could be felt. After the verdict, the crowd just melted away in similar complete silence. I was met outside the Court by the head gypsy. He produced a huge bunch of five pounds notes, peeled off more than I had asked for and departed in complete silence. No bill, no receipt. A day or so afterwards, I was summoned to meet the Assistant Chief Constable, Mr (Reggie) Rowland. He fairly took strips off me for opposing the police. We had a first-class row, during which I maintained that I did not belong to any side. I never have done so, and have appeared as often as not on behalf of the Defence as on behalf of the police. This is one of the beauties of this job. One makes up one's opinion and sticks to it. No one is 'bought' by either side. Opinion is impartial and based on fact and experience. It is no good 'making something up' to please either the police or the Defendant. Wise Judge and Counsel will soon find you out, and then you can have a perfectly dreadful time, and serve you right.

After this, 'Reggie' and I became very fast friends up to the time of his death.

The only other time that I had such a dressing down was by my old headmaster after I had written 'Glad to hear it' on a card hung outside his room bearing the legend 'Engaged'. Again we became fast friends for life, up to the time of his death at the age of ninety-two years.

I had a rather similar case of facial injury some years afterwards in Weymouth, affecting a young man who was not so lucky with his jury. He had been involved in a fracas at a dance hall, and a number of very decent, and apparently very honest and likeable youngsters came forward to testify that they had seen him kicked in the face whilst lying on the floor, by a man who subsequently became the Defendant. There is no doubt that some sort of melée took place and that there was quite a lot of blood about, some of it undoubtedly from the face of the injured man. I was asked to look at the clothing of the Defendant and express an opinion as to whether spots and smears of undoubted blood on his trousers could have been made by kicking the bloodstained head of a man lying on the ground. The distribution of the spots did not suggest this, but that they had got there in the course of a general melée during which spots of blood were being flung about. The Defendant admitted taking part in this disturbance, but stoutly denied any kicking. I made up a dummy head from a core of wood covered with cotton wool and outside a layer of tough paper to simulate a scalp, and wool to simulate hair. This was soaked in blood and kicked about wearing paper 'trousers'. The pattern of blood spots obtained in this way was altogether different from the pattern on the trousers of the accused man, and I went to Bournemouth Crown Court convinced of his innocence and to say just that. As the case developed however, I began to have my doubts because of the undoubted sincerity of many witnesses' versions of the events. I gave my evidence, but not with the conviction with which I had started. The Defendant was convicted, and I came away with the feeling that on some occasions forensic science, like the law, is an ass.

However, my faith was restored some two or three years afterwards when I again attended the Crown Court at Bournemouth and was told 'off the cuff' that some of the evidence given by the Prosecution witnesses regarding the kicking had subsequently been found to be, shall we say, rather coloured.

But to go back with my other brush with authority. It was not exactly a brush, but the Police just did not believe a word of what I said, and took no further action.

On 13 December, 1953, a farmer, Norman Wills by name, aged thirty-nine years, was found face downwards in a stream on his farm. The stream at this point ran out of a culvert some two feet square; the bottom was very rough and stony. He was found with his head pushed deeply into this culvert, up to his shoulders. Water covered his face.

It was a curious family. Norman Wills was one of a family of five brothers farming a 220-acre farm near Liskeard. The family had been dominated by the mother, and the dead man had been persuaded by her to contract a marriage a few years before his death. There seemed to have been no objection to the arrangement, and the marriage turned out well.

The mode of death of many members of the family appeared to be firmly established as suicide. The father had committed suicide; one brother hanged himself, another brother shot his daughter and then himself, and a cousin also committed suicide. Soon after the present event, another brother shot himself through the head with a .22 rifle.

The day before his death, Norman Wills had been fined by the Magistrates for not having his books in order. This upset him quite a lot, but there does not appear to have been a family row about it.

On the morning of his death, he got up as usual at about 7 a.m., fed the chickens, and then disappeared. A brother living in the same house and another brother living nearby went to look for him, being joined later by two forestry men, who ultimately found him in the stream. Only one track of footmarks led to the site, and the natural conclusion was that this was just another of the family suicides.

When found, he was outstretched on his front, with his head underneath a culvert through which a fair amount of water was running. The culvert is two feet across at the base, square in shape, and about two feet high. His shoulders were just inside the opening, but the head was definitely inside and the face would have been covered with water. There was no difficulty in removing him. It was done by the two brothers who took him by the arms and shoulders. Both brothers said that he was not caught up in any way, and, most significantly that his neck was not handled by them in any way, at any time.

The post-mortem examination showed no water in the lungs, but this is not unusual when drowning takes place in fresh water. There was, however, bloodstained froth in the air passages. Whilst I was busy about the body, my wife was investigating his neck and suddenly said, 'B-----H---, look at this lot.' 'This lot' was a series of bruises in the muscles of the neck, a fracture of the tip of the hyoid bone in the windpipe, and an associated bruise. The hyoid bone is a small ring-like bone at the top of the larynx (Adam's apple). It has an upward projection at each side, and is more or less tucked under the lower jaw. To break a tip requires upward pressure to the throat, and so a broken tip is almost always associated with manual strangulation. The bruises in the neck muscles suggested fingertip pressure, one on the right side (thumb) and four on the left side. I also found that the tongue was bruised, again a common finding in manual strangulation. The only other finding of significance was water in the stomach. This could have come from the stream, but as the household water was taken from the same source, nothing could be certain as to the origin of the water in the stomach. However, the pool water was muddy, and that in the stomach was not.

All the indications suggested manual strangulation, and I gave this as my opinion. The Police did not believe a word of it, so I sought refuge in my forensic friends. I sent the throat to the late Prof Webster, Home Office Pathologist in the Midlands (Birmingham), one of the most able forensic pathologists of that time. He completely supported my view, much to the disgust of the Police Authority, which ignored it as much as they did me. He did add that I should look a pretty fool if after some years somebody came up with a confession that he had indeed murdered the man.

I also sought the advice of my friend Prof. Polson, Professor of Forensic Pathology at Leeds University. He was greatly intrigued — so much so that he has written an account of it in his textbook on Forensic Medicine. He confessed himself baffled, as we all were, emphasising that there were aspects of the case which favoured both suicide and murder. On the whole, his inclination was towards the suicide aspect.

At the beginning of this account, I mentioned that there was only one track of footmarks leading from the house to the culvert, but on the opposite side of the stream there were many tracks of footmarks, so that the dead man could easily have been met by an assailant.

In the end, the Coroner's jury brought in a verdict of wilful murder against some person or persons unknown, and that was the end of it apart from a rather curious remark by HM Coroner that this must have been the perfect murder! The perfect murder, of course, has never been discovered.

It is a pity that at that time the importance of diatoms in the bone marrow in cases like this (about which there is more further on) was not appreciated.

Some years afterwards I related this case at a meeting of the British Academy of Forensic Sciences; they agreed that I had no option but to voice my opinion that this was a case of strangulation.

On the other hand, there was no evidence whatever that Norman Wills had an enemy in the world.

Whilst we were still arguing, Prof. Webster returned the specimen to me. It never arrived. I often wonder what the Post Office authorities thought when perhaps they opened an undelivered parcel. However, nothing more was heard about it.

Obviously, during my career I have been involved in many cases of fights. There are always opposing accounts given by onlookers, accounts seemingly to be genuinely held. When an event occurs in a public house at about closing time, such memories are likely to be somewhat clouded, and judgment, visual impressions and memory confused.

One night in September 1945, Alfred James Pellow, the Superintendent of the local power station at Hayle, was regaling himself and friends in the saloon bar of the White Hart Hotel in Hayle. He was described as being merry, but by no means drunk. At closing time he was reluctant to leave and put his two arms across the doorway, saying, 'Oh, you can't throw me out even if you want to.' Then, as so often happens, the story varied as to what happened. Some said there was a fight and that Pellow fell down. Others said that the landlord applied a 'Half Nelson' grip on him — that is standing behind the man, putting the arms underneath the armpits and then closing the hands behind the neck — then running the man out. The landlord agreed that he did this, but said that he used no force whatever. However, Pellow suddenly collapsed and was found to be dead. On post-mortem examination he was found to have a fracture of his neck. The landlord was convinced that no undue force had been used.

Re-enacting the event on the premises, it was at once apparent what had happened. Almost on the spot where Pellow fell there was a step downwards. Putting a 'Half Nelson' on a policeman, I ran him along the same passage. When he came to the step, he suddenly dropped and my hands tightened on his neck, pushing his head forwards. Fortunately I was expecting this, and my grip was very loose, otherwise I might have been up for manslaughter.

There have been a number of occasions on which I have been asked for my advice and help in circumstances not at all connected with criminal matters.

One of these occurred early in July of 1945, when the Police received many complaints of Matelot seamen coming off ships at Falmouth and finding their way to Truro for a night out, with change of company. Often this occupied them until after the last bus had departed for Falmouth, so they took to spending the night in covered lorries parked on Lemon Quay. Although toilets were provided at the bottom of Lemon Street, adjacent to the Quay, this was too far for HM Matelot to walk, and the result became a nuisance and scandal. Could I suggest anything? I could, and gave the police a bottle of ammonium sulphide and a syringe with which to spray it into the sleeping makeshift tent. For those unacquainted with chemical terms, ammonium sulphide is about the most evil-smelling liquid in existence, the stench from a long unattended midden being similar in character, but sweet in comparison. A condition of my assistance was that I should receive a report on what happened. This duly arrived, written on 6 July, 1945, in the following terms:

Dr Hocking v. Personnel of HM Navy

Reference the above, we respectfully report on the series of occurrences as far as we are able. Unfortunately HM Matelots fell to using language of a foreign country so that we are not in a position to repeat verbatim the whole of the conversations.

Some of the words and their meanings were, however, familiar so that we came to the conclusion that, prior to joining the Navy, the attacked persons had considerable experience with sewers, lavatories and arseholes. Not ordinary ones, either.

The programme was as follows:

1.30 a.m	Dr Hocking's side crept to the enemy's camp. Found enemy (six Matelots) sleeping soundly.
1.31 a.m.	Dr Hocking's side poured all available strength into opening attack.
1.31 ½	All windows, doors, etc. flung open by enemy.
1.31 ¾	Enemy speaking in foreign tongue except when referring to sewers, lavatories and arseholes. (These few words Dr Hocking's side seemed to understand.)
1.32	One of enemy violently sick.
1.33	Three Matelots seen travelling hurriedly through car park.
1.34	One Matelot seen travelling in Boscawen Street at steady gallop.
1.35	Sixth member of enemy seen climbing into another empty lorry, all powers of resistance broken.
1.36	Police expressed regret at unusual happenings and wished Matelots 'Good night'.
	Police amazed at happenings.

Signed, R. M. Smeath & J. C. Deacon.

Things returned to their usual quiet after this, but some fortnight afterwards the nuisance returned — and so did we.

This time the report went:

At 2.15 a.m., 25.7.45, Dr Hocking's side approached enemy from downwind. Rear entrance to enemy found partly open. Dr Hocking's side (one Special Constable and one Lousy Police Sergeant) entered and opened the attack, closing door on making hasty retreat.

2.30½	Two of enemy violently sick.
2.30¾	One of enemy surrendered but violently sick.
2.31 a.m.	Enemy No. 2 surrendered with request that S. Constable cut his throat.
2.31½	Gawd 'elp us. Special Constable violently sick.
2.31½	Remainder of enemy sick, but between release of old beer and stale food, enquire of each other, 'Whose shit?'
2.32	Remainder of enemy leave camp and surrender. All enemy now sick. Enemy No. 2 demanding Special Constable cut his throat. S. unable to oblige as he too had difficulty finding top dentures on sidewalk.
2.35 a.m.	Lousy P. Sergeant arrives and expresses sympathy. Enemy No. 2 still wants his throat cut. Enemy collect their full strength and hasten to Falmouth via Lemon Street. Stating far better to walk to Falmouth than be bloody well gassed in Truro.
	LPS agrees with them, and promises enquiries will be made. These came to nothing, but the word had gone out, and there were no more incidents.

Shortly afterwards, an officious young Police Officer suggested that I should be 'done' for administering a noxious thing to a person or persons unknown. He was, of course, quite right, but I heard nothing more about it.

In what I call 'my good old days', juvenile delinquency was dealt with summarily by the local 'copper' — a strict talking-to for minor offences, a clip round the ear for those more serious, followed by a couple from father when he got home. Now even father is not allowed to lay a hand on the little horror. Oh! no! Now they have to be 'put in care', psychoanalysed and have all sorts of probation reports made on them, and then brought before Authority and probably again 'put in care' where they learn even more bad habits from other inmates. All this could be saved by a clip around the ear. I remember one young constable whom I asked why he had joined the Police Force — a regular habit of mine. He told me that Police Sgt Timmins (then at Hayle) had caught him out in a minor misdemeanour and had given him a ticking-off and the necessarily accompanying clip round the ear. The young policeman told me that then, at once, he decided to join the Police Force.

A short while ago, a Chief Constable had the guts to suggest a return to this form of juvenile correction. I do not know what happened to him, but a few days afterwards, a promising young Police Officer was dismissed for doing just that. What a waste in every sense of the word.

Many years ago I had a great friend in the Police Force, Constable and then Police Sgt Goldsworthy.

He used to dispense juvenile justice in just the way the Chief Constable advocated.

At one time there was trouble at a public house on the Cornish side of the River Tamar, up from Plymouth. I think it was at Cargreen, but am not quite sure. It became a habit for yobs from Plymouth to sail up the river and cause a disturbance. PC Goldsworthy was sent for. He met them one evening coming up the steps from their boat on to the quay. Now, the quay was very roughly paved, and as the first yob arrived on the top step, Goldsworthy slipped; unfortunately he collided with the yob and sent him spreadeagled into the river. Recovering his balance and slipping the other way, he collided with the second yob just emerging at the top of the steps, and he too went into the drink. By the time the two had been rescued by their pals from a very muddy river, their enthusiasm had waned. They never returned. What would have happened now?

Mr Goldsworthy, as would be expected, had a great sense of humour.

Before the days of blood and breath tests for alcoholic intoxication, generally in connection with motoring offenses, came into general use, samples of urine were sent to me for

56

this kind of investigation.

One day I received from PC Goldsworthy a small cardboard box containing a sample of urine. The box was labelled on the outside:

Surprise Peas
Small size (2 servings)
48 Packs.

I hope they still make them — I mean policemen like Goldsworthy, Timmins, Alfie Jenkin, George Brown, Arthur Pill, Ken Julian, Arscott, Deakin, 'Bunny' Hare, Mr Matthews and a host of others who have been my close and indeed dear friends over so many years. I believe they do — I have met a few recently.

What a pity that their little empires, ruled over so justly by summary Justice, with everybody happy and accepting the position, are no longer allowed to exist, replaced by dogooders with devastating results.

Our 'Happy Family' was finally broken up by the amalgamation of the various police forces in Devon and Cornwall in 1967 to form the Devon and Cornwall Constabulary. Nobody wanted it, excepting Higher Authority, but I have to concede that it was inevitable in view of the strides of so-called modern progress. But so much of local camaraderie was lost. I have said so often that I am grateful that I had my time when I did.

Here and now, I would like to pay my tribute to the police for all my years of happy association with them, years that are quite unforgettable.

Of course the police were not all saints or always above the law.

I recall a senior police officer who used to give marvellous cocktail parties. Whilst the male guests were thoroughly enjoying themselves, their wives stood around the walls of the room like wallflowers at a charity ball, necessarily with their backs to the wall.

On numerous occasions the friendly police have been put in a quandary. In those far-off days, when the police had friendly relations with almost everybody, there dwelt in St Austell a dear old doctor, beloved of everybody. Unfortunately, he was rather addicted to the bottle. Traffic was very light in those days, and he was not really much of a menace, and most drivers who knew him were able to avoid him. However, he had been warned time and again about his habits, although no action was taken. On one famous occasion he was seen trying to drive up the steps of St Austell Church. As this was witnessed by a number of people, the police decided that on this occasion something must be done, and so he was charged. It was in the days long before blood and breath tests were thought about, and diagnosis of being 'under the influence' was based on walking a straight line and repeating such tongue-twisters as 'The Leith Police dismisseth us'. I could never do it myself, but fortunately was never asked to. Very obviously, the dear doctor failed lamentably. What could we do? A conference of 'locals' (including myself) decided to inspect the scene. Walking along the approach to the steps, we found a slight depression in the road. We came to the conclusion that the doctor had driven over this, lost his steering, and the car, out of control, drove towards the church steps. On encountering them, the doctor was thrown upwards, banging his head on the roof, and suffered concussion, the symptoms of which are very similar to alcohol intoxication. He was, of course, admitted to hospital, where he received appropriate concussion treatment, in effect nothing, and he made a rapid recovery. The police and everybody else were delighted, and no charge was made. I am glad to add that there was never again any similar incident.

This was in wartime, when traffic was at a minimum. A rather similar incident happened to a young police officer who was a great friend of mine. He and another officer supplied my wife (who was then Miss O'Donnell) and me with reasonable quantities of gin and whisky during those lean years.

This particular officer was driving near Malpas along a road bordering the Truro river. Halfway along he landed in the river, fortunately at low tide so that he was engulfed only in mud. His excuse was that he had 'seen a pussycat' and swerved to avoid it. Again, our examination was consistent with him having hit his head when the car took the plunge, and in consequence suffered mild concussion.

For many years afterwards he suffered from 'I thought I saw a pussycat', but he was one of the most good-natured persons I have ever known, and accepted the joke.

I can confirm the paucity of traffic on the roads at that time. On one occasion I drove in daytime from Cornwall to Windsor, cutting all corners (except blind ones) to see how much mileage I could save. It was a total of three miles, saving six (old) pence.

One other ploy we had in those far-off days was that it was practically impossible to find a doctor who would turn out in less than three hours to certify a drunk. Symptoms of drunkenness are much more evident whilst alcohol is mounting in the body, and after reaching a peak, the symptoms subside and might become negligible. After three hours, almost everybody could perform our limited tests. The police knew all about this, but never raised a finger in protest. It saved them a lot of trouble, and was also a salutary lesson to the offender.

As would be expected, on many occasions I have been asked my opinion on strange happenings.

One of the strangest was related to me by Mr Mathews, sometime Chief Constable of Cornwall. As a young policeman in London, he was walking along a road one evening when he saw what he thought was a sausage on the pavement. Being a tidy man, he picked it up, and found that it was a recently severed penis. He immediately took it back to the police station, and asked if anyone had recently called to claim a missing one. Nobody had. Enquiries at all the local hospitals yielded no information, and nothing more was heard about it. Mr Matthews asked me my opinion, particularly in regard to the possibility that the owner had bled to death. I could only reply that I thought it was either an act of voluntary mutilation, revenge, or surplus to requirements.

4

Bones

I am always having bones brought to me. Most come from the North Cornwall sandy beaches, particularly from the Perranporth area. Many are from seals, cattle or sheep that have fallen over the cliffs, but some are of human origin. They come up singly, in groups, and occasionally in quite sizeable portions of a skeleton. Most of those of human origin have been buried in the sands for a hundred years or more. They are the remains of sailors (and others) washed ashore from wrecked sailing vessels. The habit of the times was to bury the unfortunates in the sand dunes, above high tide mark, where they have remained until disturbed by enterprising visiting children digging in the sand.

On 26 October, 1938, some human remains were recovered from the beach at Perranporth. They had been first seen some five days before by one of the villagers, and duly inspected daily by others as they gradually moved up the three mile-long beach towards Ligger Point. By this time, somebody thought that perhaps the police should be informed; this was done, and the remains were brought to me.

They consisted of a human left arm and hand, scapula (wing bone) and adjacent skin, underlying fat and connective tissue, and some of the muscles of the shoulder girdle, with a long strip of skin going down to the level of the thigh. It had been separated from the rest of the body by a sharp cutting instrument, all the tissues having been cleanly divided. It had been in the water for some three months.

Mounted on a tailor's dummy which I had carried up Infirmary Hill, much to the amusement of passers-by, it could be seen that the remains were those of a rather portly middle-aged person. There were no arthritic changes in the joint, and the small size of the markings of the muscle insertions on the bones strongly suggested that the remains were those of a woman. The hand was small, very well-kept, and not the hand of a manual worker. There were no signs that any rings had been worn. The skin had disappeared from the fingertips, but the underlying ridges were examined and identified by Supt Cherrill, Scotland Yard's fingerprint expert. The fingers were slim, tapering, with small filbert-shaped nails having the appearance of having been well manicured.

There was no bruising along the lines of the cuts, but a bruise measuring three inches by one inch was found in the middle of the back.

The finding of these remains set off a search along the coast and headlands for any other bits that might have been associated with this body. The beaches and surrounding cliffs were searched by enthusiastic locals, who brought me a mass of articles. These were mainly bones of seals, cattle, sheep and smaller animals that had come to an untimely death. These piled up on my lawn, covering an area more than a yard in circumference and a foot or more deep. Only recently (7 March, 1985) I was told by the present resident of my old home at Perranporth that they were still occasionally digging up bones! Also were found masses of discarded clothing, mainly womens' underwear, that had been stuffed into rabbit holes. The other articles might have been of some importance in identifying the remains, but as things turned out there was found to be no connection. Amongst the bones recovered there were some of human origin — a right and left lower leg bone (tibia), a right thigh bone (femur), a right heel bone and some small bones of an ankle. Measurement of these showed that they could have come from the same body, part of which had already been recovered, and they were comparable in size and features with those already seen.

Calculation of the height of the person, from the length of the bones available, gave it as five feet two and a half inches. This also applied to the separate bones recovered. These remains therefore all came from the same person, a woman, short in stature, rather tubby, probably unmarried, aged between twenty-five and fifty years and not accustomed to manual work. She had been sliced in halves by a sharp cutting instrument at the time of her death.

Who was she, and what had happened to her? Nobody local answering this description had been reported to be missing. An enquiry at Scotland Yard revealed that at that time they had records of about two thousand missing women, and the tentative description given of these remains would have fitted at least two hundred of them.

This was the age of a number of murders the victims of which had been dismembered. The age of the killing of Emily Kaye on the Crumbles at Eastbourne, and the London and Brighton trunk murders. Was this another one?

Scotland Yard was therefore called in, and Chief Det. Inspector Hatherill and Det. Sgt Spooner arrived, complete with Sir Bernard Spilsbury to investigate. Sir Bernard (fortunately) completely agreed with me and my findings.

Who was she, and how had she been sliced up in this way?

Turning to the records of women missing from two to three months before the discovery of these remains, the police recalled an incident that had occurred off the Casquet Rocks off the Channel Islands. Here, at about the right time, a woman answering the description of the remains had been lost, apparently overboard. Now, it might be thought silly to suppose that anything floating about the Channel Islands would come up onto the beach at Perranporth two or three months afterwards. But only the previous year, a small French coaster laden with rum and wine went down off these Islands. Three months later, practically the whole of her cargo came up on the beach at Perranporth. This was a God-sent opportunity for the locals. We all went down with anything and everything that would hold liquid, and beat the Excise man to it. Unfortunately, the sea had got into every barrel. The wine was undrinkable, but the rum was not too bad. Anyway, here was a precedent. A visit to Southampton to inspect a transatlantic liner in dry dock showed that a ship's propellor can be worn to a knife edge, and this was just the kind of instrument that could have sliced up our body.

Mr Cherrill had the fingerprints, and these were taken to the home of the lost woman in the north of England. Our description of the remains tallied almost exactly as to height, build, weight and age, and to the fact that she had never done rough work with her hands. Unfortunately, the relatives refused to have anything to do in the way of helping to identify the remains, and even went to the length of going through the home and removing any possible remaining fingerprints. Perhaps the fact that her insurance policy had a suicide clause in it influenced their behaviour.

Some will remember the case of Commander Crabb. He disappeared during the visit of a Russian warship to Spithead. He was a frogman who, either officially or unofficially, was investigating the undersides of this ship. His fate was completely unknown, whether he had met his death by accident or design. And, of course, it was important to find out, if possible. A month or so after his disappearance, the body of a man was washed up on the beach at Portreath. Having in mind the case of the bones on Perranporth beach, it was not impossible that this corpse might have been that of Commander Crabb. In general appearance they were similar. Unfortunately, decomposition had destroyed the features, and all the teeth had fallen out. Teeth and their stoppings are almost as characteristic of an individual as are fingerprints, and countless bodies, otherwise unrecognisable, have been identified by their dental charts. These charts have been employed on very many occasions to identify persons who have drowned whilst bathing, and have been washed up weeks or months afterwards on the coasts.

There was no clue to the identification of the Portreath body. There were no injuries; no sign of his having been stabbed or shot. No bruises were seen. His lungs were full of water, and the supposition could have been that he had simply drowned. To make quite certain of this, however, as water can enter the body after death, it was decided to examine the bone marrow. This may sound odd, but is of cardinal importance in such cases. If water is inhaled during life, in with the water go countless single-celled organisms. Some of these have an indestructable silica coating, much like a crab or lobster. If they get into the lungs whilst a person is drowning, ultimately some of the fine blood vessels rupture, and the water and organisms (diatoms) enter the circulation. The little organisms are stopped in the finer capillary vessels in other parts of the body; if they are found there after death, it is almost certain that they have been inhaled during life, and that death is due to drowning. Amongst other places to look for them, and probably the best, is the marrow of a long bone, the favourite being the thigh bone. I therefore proceeded to take out the left thigh bone in this case. To my complete astonishment, I found that it had been fractured, and the ends had joined together not end to end but side to side, overlapping some three to four inches. Measuring the two legs, they were found to be the same length. Something very peculiar had therefore occurred. Taking out the thigh bone on the right side for comparison, it appeared to be perfectly normal until it was sawn in halves longitudinally. Then two large screws appeared. What had happened of course was that this man had broken his left leg; it had not been set properly, but the ends had united side to side instead of end to end with a three inch overlap, shortening the limb by that amount and making walking very difficult. He had obviously been operated upon subsequently and his right leg shortened by an equivalent amount. Well, anyway, this was not Commander Crabb, but who was he? Nobody answering this description was missing locally. The police as usual went to immense trouble, and indeed it took them several months to solve the problem, but they finally came up with the answer. During the latter stages of the late war a plane had been shot down over Germany, and one of the occupants on landing had fractured his left thigh. In the confusion of the time, proper treatment was not available and he had to be carried for some weeks on a stretcher without medical attention. During this time his broken bones united, but side to side instead of end to end, leading to his deformity. On returning to his home in Wolverhampton after repatriation, he was taken into the local hospital, where he was operated upon and his right thigh bone shortened to the equivalent length of his damaged left thigh.

The X-rays taken at that time were still in existence, and on comparison with the bones taken from the body, the match was found to be complete. A very nice piece of indefatigable police work. It transpired that he had committed suicide.

On several occasions I have examined caches of bones found walled up in old country houses.

The *Sunday Express* of 23 November, 1958, published an account of bones having been found walled up at Trevethoe House, Lelant, St Ives, the home up to four years previously of Col. Tyringham.

Two workmen formerly employed by the Colonel and now working for the new owners, became engaged in pulling down the walls of a small room on the ground floor adjoining the main entrance hall. This room had been constructed as a strong-room and the walls were over two feet thick, the inner part being of stone with brick outside. As the workmen got almost to ground level, where the wall was of solid stone construction and probably older than the upper part, one of them noticed a few bones in the old earth and mortar in the centre of the wall. More bones were subsequently excavated. According to local legend, Trevethoe House is said to have been haunted in the past by the ghost of a lady dressed in white. In view of these findings, Mr Noall, Curator of the local Museum, informed the editor of the *St Ives Times and Echo*, and the report subsequently appeared in the *Sunday Express*. After all this, rather belatedly, the matter was reported to the Police and Coroner, and the bones were sent to me for examination. My report was as follows:

'This is a miscellaneous collection of bones, none of which is of human type. There are large and small ribs, probably from a cow, and either pig or sheep. A number of vertebrae are present, again of pig or sheep size, and there are also short limb bones that might have come from either animal. A few small limb bones, probably the remains of a fowl are also present. Several of these bones have sharp cuts across them, made either by a heavy knife or possibly a chopper; there are also marks, especially on two of the vertebrae, suggestive of sawing. The most likely origin of these bones is from kitchen waste; they are probably of from one to two hundred years old. There is nothing to connect them with any woman in white.'

As far as I know, the ghost has not been seen since.

On 3 January, 1951, there was a cliff fall on the St Mawes side of Carrick Roads. This revealed the partial skeleton of an adult person who had been buried some two feet down at the cliff edge. There was no sign of any depression or grave above the body, and the whole cliff top was covered over by grass, gorse, fern and scrub trees that had obviously been there for a very long time.

Examination of the bones showed that the head, spine and most of the right side were intact, the left side having disappeared with the rubble of the cliff fall. From the nature of the bones it could be deduced that they were those of a male person, muscular and some six feet two inches tall. The age was from thirty to fifty years. I estimated that they had been there for at least fifty years, and more likely about a hundred. It was impossible to determine the exact cause of death, but there was a significant fracture of the skull some four inches in length on the left side, running upward to the top of the head from just in front of the left ear; the bone above the left ear was slightly depressed. In front of the fracture, and running upwards from the inner angle of the eye for a distance of some three inches, there was a series of sharp cuts. The whole was suggestive of a knife attack on the man. An interesting find was made amongst the remains, namely a domed button, a small bone button, and a nondescript button. These were sent to Mr Parkes, the Director of the Forensic Laboratory at Bristol, who reported:

'On 3 January, 1951, I accompanied Dr Hocking, Detective Superintendent Julian and other officers to the foreshore of Carrick Roads, further up the roads from St Mawes Castle. At this point the cliff is some eight or more feet high, and above the indigenous rock is a deposit of schist pebbles and yellow clay with some ten to fourteen inches of topsoil above. From some two to three feet from the top of the cliff coastal erosion had exposed a skeleton and removed the major portion of the left side. On exposing the cliff face, it was seen that the body was lying in a pit or grave slightly longer than the body, and the filling in was similar to the surface soil and not the yellow clay on which the body rested. My examination of the portion of the femur removed by me indicated a complete absence of organic matter and is entirely consistent with the skeleton being of considerable antiquity, and I am in complete agreement with Dr Hocking that it is certainly not less than fifty years old.

'On careful cleaning of the domed button, which was found approximately on the right chest below where the right wrist was positioned, it was found to bear a number 59 in Spencerian Italic on a ribbed background surrounded by a double ring suggestive of a buttoned belt bearing the inscription of 2nd Nottingham Regiment. As far as my information goes, the 59th Regiment of Foot, the Nottingham Regiment, was raised between 1870 and 1880 as a result of the Cardwell reforms. If this button, which from its location would appear to be part of the clothing of the buried man and not carried as a souvenir in his pocket or otherwise, was indeed contemporary with the skeleton, the burial must have taken place at least seventy years ago. This is amply supported by the thickness and age of the ivy and hawthorn roots growing through the soil above the body.

'Nothing relevant was discovered from the examination of the other two buttons, although the bone button is of an archaic pattern, and might well be dated after prolonged research if thought necessary.

'In view of the positive nature of the evidence obtained, the other material was not examined in detail.

'Signed: E. F. Parkes, MSc, FRIC, director.'

More bones were exposed when a new grave was being dug in the West Looe burial ground in September 1970. The gravedigger unearthed an oblong plywood box buried some two feet under the ground by the west wall. When opened, the box was found to contain the skeleton of a new-born infant doubled up on itself. Radiological examination suggested a normal full-term birth. It was difficult to determine with any great degree of accuracy how long ago death had occurred, but I fixed it at about twenty years, and this was confirmed by the state of the vegetation above the burial place.

All the soft parts had disappeared, but in the skull there were two almost circular holes, one inch by three-quarters of an inch in size. The injuries were consistent with blows by a weapon such as a pointed hammer.

But this did not seem altogether to have been an unwanted infant, killed at birth or shortly afterwards and disposed of unceremoniously. Instead it was enclosed in a craftsman's made box, beautifully made, and buried in an out-of-the-way part of a consecrated churchyard.

The other possibility was that this had been a large infant, and the birth a difficult one. Although rarely (if ever) done in these days, at that time one method of perhaps saving the mother's life was to perforate the child's skull and reduce its size to render possible its passage through the mother's bony pelvis — the operation of craniotomy.

Since the 1926 Births and Deaths Registration Act, all stillbirths have had to be registered. Any operation carried out on the infant before it has been completely expelled from the mother does not have to be recorded. The normal procedure is that the attending doctor satisfies himself that the baby being born is already dead before he performs puncture of the head, but this would not necessarily apply if the mother's life were in great danger. In any case, the operation would have been performed before the infant had wholly issued from the mother and before it had had a separate existence.

Disposal of the body of a stillborn infant presents no difficulty. It has to be disposed of in a graveyard, but there is no need for the services of a clergyman or sexton. In fact it is a common procedure for an undertaker to dispose of such remains in his own way, without official sanction in any graveyard.

Enquiries amongst local undertakers and doctors failed to show anything hopeful.

I was not altogether happy, but as so much time had elapsed it was thought unlikely that any further enquiries would result in worthwhile findings. There was no positive indication indeed that the infant had been born locally.

A small skeleton, suggestive of that of a child aged five to six years old, was one day found on the beach at Millandreath. All the flesh had gone, but the bones, rather unusually, had almost all hung together. They were shown to be those of a monkey that had escaped from the local monkey sanctuary.

Many murderers try to conceal the bodies of their victims; I have already dealt with some of these.

Another was a man, Davey, of Millbrook; he calculated well, but was unlucky. He too was convicted on the evidence of bones.

About the middle of September 1971, some children playing on an old rubbish dump at Millbrook were seen to be fencing with makeshift swords; these turned out to be the thigh bones of a human being. Immediate investigation revealed an almost complete skeleton near the bottom of the dump, just above the high water line. The bones were rather scattered about, but this was thought to be due to the habits of scavenging animals and the depredations of the local children, who obviously made the most of them. Little or no flesh remained on the bones, and it was considered that they had been there for about a year — an accurate estimate as it turned out. From their size, configuration and subsequent X-ray examination it was suggested that these were the remains of a male person of some twenty-five to thirty years of age.

My wife and I had taken our faithful Basset Hound with us. She was let out later on for obvious purposes. The local press reported that we had been observed with our tracker dog looking for other remains.

How had this body got on to this rubbish dump?

At first it was thought that the body had been brought up on a high tide and caught inside a barrier of wire netting that surrounded the dump. Examination of the bone marrow put drowning out of court as no diatoms were found.

There were extensive injuries to the head (fractures). These could have been done by a fall down a cliff, causing death by head injury, and not by drowning. They could equally have been caused by rubbish having been tipped over the body after it had landed at the foot of the dump.

Almost the complete skeleton was subsequently recovered, and after my preliminary examination the bones were taken to the Plymouth Hospital, cleaned and beautifully mounted by my friend and colleague Dr A.C. Hunt, now Home Office Pathologist in the South-West. This revealed something of supreme significance, namely fractures at the sides of the eighth to the eleventh ribs on the left side. This at first seemed to confirm a suggestion of mine that the man had been the victim of a hit and run motor accident, the body afterwards being thrown over the dump to conceal the evidence. Most of the clothing that the man had been wearing was still present in a heap at the site, and examination of it suggested a much more sinister cause of death. A fairly well-preserved woollen pullover enclosed the upper part of the body, and examination of this showed a ragged hole in it corresponding to the position of the fractured ribs. Moreover, when the edges of this hole were examined by a hand lens, the ends of the broken fibres appeared to be melted. What could do this but the near discharge of a shotgun? This immediately put Det. Sgt Carter on his mettle, and he went after it like a ferret. He himself undertook the X-ray examination of the bones, and was rewarded by the finding of a shot in the right scapula (wing bone of the shoulder girdle). The hunt was now on. With indefatiguable patience he sifted all the earth around the patch where the body had been found, and was fully recompensed for his labours by the finding of some thirty or more shot. This could not have been a suicide; the angle and distance from which the shot had been fired completely ruled this out; the only conclusion that could be arrived at was that the man had been murdered — or accidentally shot under such peculiar circumstances that his body had to be concealed.

Police enquiries soon solved the problem. Adjacent to the rubbish dump there lived one Davey. There was an association between him and a Mr Robin Wadman, who had disappeared about a year previously. The remains had meanwhile been identified as those of Wadman from tooth records and the clothing. During a quarrel, Wadman had been shot — and the weapon hidden under floorboards, from under which the police recovered it. A body on hand had to be disposed of or risk immediate discovery. The town rubbish dump was within a few hundred yards of the house; what more easy way to dispose of a body than to bury it there and get it covered over by loads and loads of rubbish? Unfortunately for Davey, the Council at almost that exact time decided to stop tipping at that particular site, so that the body remained comparatively lightly covered, until disturbed by scavenging animals and enterprising children.

I am often told what a nasty profession I have adopted, and some people even wonder that I have any friends. Ugh! Cutting up bodies — worse than a slaughterman. Many have queried the value of the work and ask why it is necessary.

The answer is simple. It can be asserted that almost all the advances in medicine have come from a correlation of symptoms of disease observed and the findings at post-mortem examination, should the patient die. How otherwise can we learn? Even recently, it was calculated that only about 30% of death certificates are correct, 30% were totally wrong, and the remainder wrong in essential parts. This applies not only to General Practitioners' opinions as to the cause of death, but also to hospital Consultants. Only by correlating symptoms to post-mortem findings can we learn. The whole of modern medical advancement has been based on this correlation. Clinical symptoms and morbid changes in the organs can be pieced together, sometimes only after microscopical examination of sections of tissues. Many new diseases have been unearthed in this way. Adverse effects of drugs can be detected, and the drug modified or abandoned. The reasons for some surgical catastrophes can be pinpointed, and steps taken to prevent a recurrence. And, of course, there is the eternal worry, was death due to natural causes, accident or murder? Only a post-mortem will sort out this difficulty. Murder is generally obvious, especially when there has been violence, but there are many subtle ways in which an unwanted person can be eliminated, and these can only be discovered by an autopsy.

Sometimes there are different interpretations of the post-mortem findings by two or more pathologists, and both interpretations have to be presented to the Court. It is in this battle of the wits that the proceedings in the Court are so fascinating. A pathologist (or any other scientist) appearing in Court must be wholly and completely satisfied with his interpretation of the findings, and be prepared to stand over them in the face of severe cross-examination. If a pathologist appears for the Crown, the Defendant and his legal advisers have the inalienable right to consult a pathologist of equal professional standing to give his opinion on the findings. Generally, the pathologist called by the Defendant will make his own post-mortem examination and draw his own conclusions. The pathologists called by the two sides usually agree. Occasionally they do not, and then the fun begins. I have always enjoyed the thrust and parry of examination and cross-examination by Counsel. No pathologist is ever 'bought' by either side. Not once in the whole of my career have the Police asked me to 'stretch a point' in their favour. Only one solicitor had the temerity to do so, and I made short shrift of him. Their opinions are absolutely independent. Unless one believes thoroughly in his own independent opinion and is prepared to fight for it, it is disastrous to go into the witness box and invite inevitable castigation by extremely knowledgeable and able Counsel in cross-examination. It is the fascinating task of the Jury, guided invariably by a very learned Judge, to sort the matter out and come to a verdict on the probability of the facts as presented to them, and tested by the most rigorous cross-examination.

Nobody in his senses contends that he is always right. We do our most conscientious best with the material available and our experience. Most Juries accept this and act accordingly. When there is a dispute between expert witnesses, the Jury accepts the opinion of the one whose conclusions, in their view, more accurately fit into the other evidence in the case, taking everything into consideration.

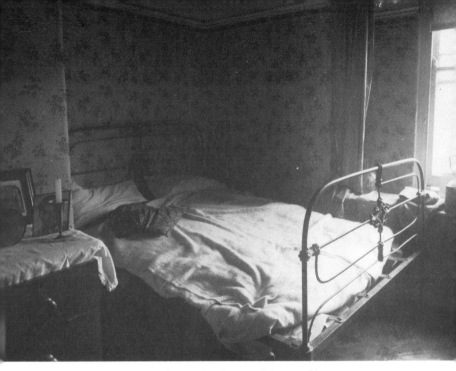

Bedroom in the Davis case (chapter 2)
police photo

The Davis case — the pit in the
garage where the bodies were found (chapter 2)
police photo

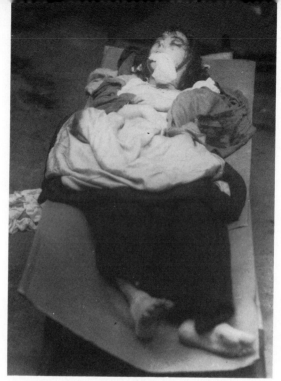

The Davis case — the dead girl Monica Rowe (chapter 2)
police photo

The Norman Wills's case — the stream where the body
was found (chapter 3)
police photo

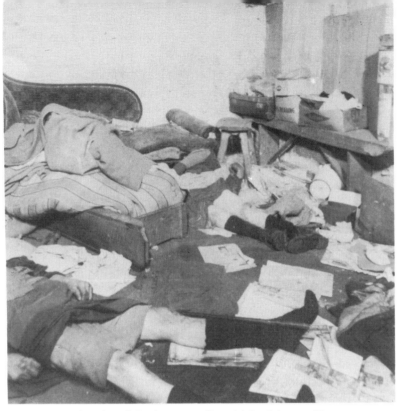

Interior of the house at Gunnislake (chapter 3)
police photo

The Wadman case — photograph taken from refuse tip showing
the shed used by the accused (chapter 4)
police photo

Robin Wadman murdered in 1970 (chapter 4)
police photo

The Wadman case — photograph taken from the top of
tip showing location of remains (chapter 4)
police photo

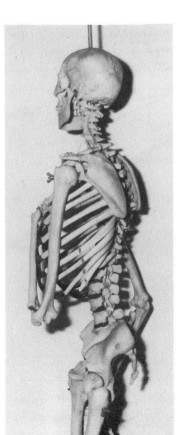

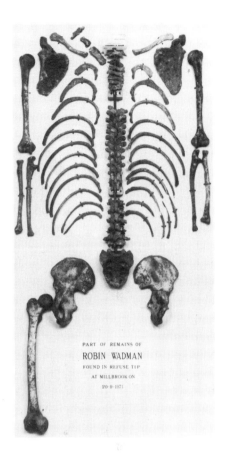

PART OF REMAINS OF
ROBIN WADMAN
FOUND IN REFUSE TIP
AT MILLBROOK ON
20-9-1971

The Wadman case
— the bones (chapter 4)
police photo

The Wadman case
— plastic skeleton showing marked
area on ribs (chapter 4)
police photo

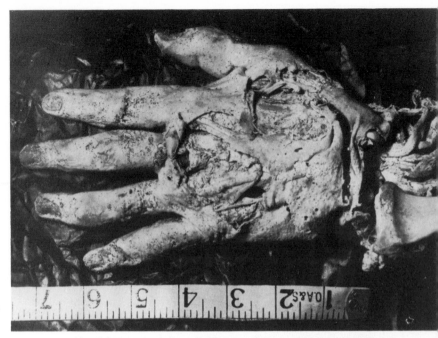

Hand from remains washed up at Perranporth (chapter 4)
police photo

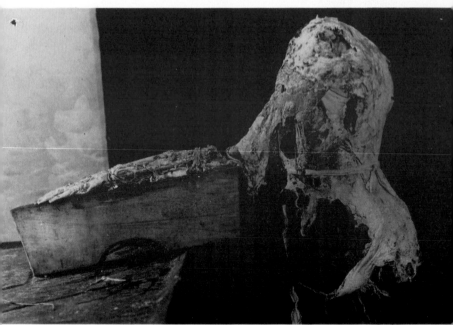

Remains washed up at Perranporth (chapter 4)
police photo

The body behind the tobacconist's shop counter (chapter 10)
police photo

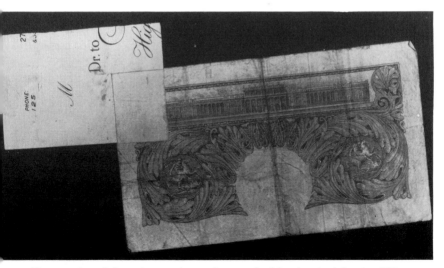

The murder of the tobacconist — the repaired banknote (chapter 10)
police photo

The body of Charles Giffard (chapter 14)
police photo

The body of Mrs Sandeman (chapter 15)
police photo

5

My Most Interesting Murder

What I have always regarded as my most interesting murder concerned the disappearance of the actress Gay Gibson from the *SS Durban Castle* on the night of 10 October, 1947, on her passage from Cape Town to Southampton. It was intriguing because we had no body and so could let our imaginations run riot — a favourite pastime of mine. Dr Donald Teare of St George's Hospital, London, thought that she had been strangled. Prof. Webster and I thought that she had died from natural causes, possibly associated with sexual excitement.

This case has been recorded elsewhere as 'The Porthole Murder' in *Facets of Crime,* published by Bossiney Books along with ten other stories. It is reproduced here by kind permission of the proprietor of Bossiney Books, Mr Michael Williams. Incidentally, the cover of his publication, depicting the victim as she would have appeared after having been thrown to the sharks is well worth the price of £1.50.

To whet your appetites, not all the evidence obtained by the Defence from South Africa was allowed to be given at the trial. We were limited to three witnesses from that country, but we had significant affidavits from a number of others. As their testimony, however, tended to attack the morals of the dead girl, it was thought that the Judge would probably disallow it. From his conduct of the trial, I felt certain that he would most certainly have done so. The significance of this unrecorded evidence was that the girl had been in the habit of indulging in unusual sexual exercises, and there was a possibility that she had lost her life during one of these adventures.

This is from memory; unfortunately the original documents have disappeared after being sent to Prof. Webster.

Amongst her sexual perversions, it was stated that 'she sucks a cock'.

☆   ☆   ☆

The Porthole Murder

F. D. M. HOCKING

Only one person knows exactly what took place in cabin No. 126 in the Union Castle liner *Durban Castle* on the night of 17th-18th October 1947.

This is James Camb, a one-time Promenade Deck Steward who was tried for the murder of the occupant of that cabin, Miss Eileen Isabella Ronnie Gibson, at Winchester Assizes between 18th March and 22nd March 1948.

The case is cited by Mr Justice Humphreys as 'yet another instance of convincing proof of the guilt of an accused person being afforded by circumstantial evidence'. Yet, to the minds of many lawyers, and even more medical experts, there was equally compelling proof of the Defendant's innocence. A great many of the known facts were not in dispute, and readily admitted by the Defendant. There is no doubt that the girl died in her cabin that night; it is how she met her death that is so intriguing.

Eileen Isabella Ronnie Gibson, quiet and friendly in manner, was just over twenty-one years of age when she boarded the *Durban Castle* on 10th October at Cape Town, bound for Southampton. The ship was practically empty, there being only fifty-seven first class passengers, most of them elderly, and apparently most of them rather bored. Gay Gibson's two main companions, with whom she usually dined, were an elderly Mr Hopwood and Wing-Commander Bray.

Her background suggested a desire for much more lively companionship. She did most of her war service in a touring company of Service personnel, having a taste for the theatre, although probably not brilliant. She was described as having been a beautiful girl, slim built with dark hair and large, dark, almond-shaped eyes. An outstanding feature was her white skin, likened by her theatrical producer to alabaster. She had the grace and poise of a good, professional actress.

She left the Forces on compassionate grounds, and when medically examined on her discharge, was graded AW1, but it was also noted that she had a chronic ear infection and she was marked as 'non-tropical'. After her release from the Forces, she toured South Africa with a repertory company, playing a leading part with considerable success. It was whilst engaged in this way that she met, amongst others of the cast, three people who were to give evidence of the greatest significance on behalf of the Defendant at his trial.

Through no fault of the repertory company, the play in which she was taking the leading lady's part, Clifford Odet's famous play *Golden Boy* came to an abrupt end in Johannesburg, but the producer made plans to take it to Pretoria. But Gay Gibson suddenly threw in her part and announced her decision to return to England by the next available boat, which in fact she did.

Life on board with only elderly companionship must have been dull for her, and it is therefore no surprise to find her, even when only two days out from the Cape, having chatty conversation with the young and good-looking Promenade Deck Steward, James Camb. He was rather thick set, with bright eyes and a good complexion. Confident in manner, he looked attractive and dashing in his white Steward's uniform. But nobody could say that Camb was an exemplary character. Aged thirty, with a wife and daughter of three, he enlivened his life as a first class Deck Steward by having sordid little affairs with unattached female passengers. He even boasted that 'some of them like us better than the passengers. I have been with them several times on other trips.' This was said during an early interview with the police (Detective Sergeant Quinlan) at Southampton; and then he added a most significant phrase

— 'Of course, if I was found out, I would get the sack.'

This was confirmed by the Master of the ship, Captain Patey, who said at the trial that Camb, as a Deck Steward, had no right to visit any cabin, and that if found in one, he would have been logged, his book endorsed, and finally he would have been dismissed. He would find it very difficult to get another job.

Gay Gibson was presented as a young woman of impeccable character. Her mother, quite properly, said that she was one of the finest types of English womanhood, physically, mentally, and morally. One of the South African witnesses, Dr Schoub, the wife of the producer of the play *Golden Boy*, said that she liked her very much: 'she was a nice, charming girl.'

And yet a very different picture developed as a result of inquiries instituted by Camb's solicitor, Mr Geoffrey Wells of Southampton. Camb told him of many personal and intimate details of the girl's past life that he could have got only from the girl herself. Only three or four days out from Cape Town, in conversation with Miss Gibson's Stewardess, Miss Field, he said that Gay Gibson had told him that she was three months pregnant. Asked why she did not marry him, she replied that he was already married, but she was crazy about him. In any event, she suddenly decided to throw up her job and return to England. She had travelled out to South Africa in an emigrant ship. She was returning as a first class passenger, and there was no dispute that her fare was being paid by a Mr Charles Sventonski. In all, Miss Gibson received something like £500 from this man, but it was with the knowledge and approval of her mother, who said that it was a proposition by a wealthy and successful man who was ready to back Gay's career as a business proposition. Although, as far as was known, he had never been in England, he gave Miss Gibson a letter of introduction to the Abbey Theatre, Dublin.

A contraceptive was found in her cabin. One other thing that came out of these apparently intimate conversations was that Miss Gibson told Camb that she had gone to South Africa for her health as she suffered from asthma.

As a result of the information obtained from these conversations, Mr Wells went to South Africa and interviewed members of the cast of the repertory company, run by a Mr Gilbert, in which Miss Gibson had played the leading lady. Three of these were brought over by the Defence to give evidence on behalf of the Defendant. They were Mike Abel, Henry Gilbert, and his wife Dr Schoub.

Mike Abel testified that Miss Gibson had told him that she had come out to South Africa because she had a chest complaint, and mentioned asthma. She often behaved in an hysterical manner, and on one occasion she collapsed, became blue about the lips, and in the corner of her mouth there was white saliva. There were times when she fainted, when she coughed a great deal, and when her breathing was laboured. On occasion, she complained of pains in her tummy and left arm — a sort of shooting pain coming right down into her fingers. These are all possible symptoms of lung and heart disease. Mike Abel went on to say in his evidence that Miss Gibson had told him that she was pregnant, and asked him for £200 to get to England to get a doctor to take care of her; she said she had no faith in South African doctors and wanted to get to England.

Henry Gilbert, also of Johannesburg, testified that he was an actor-manager, and had produced Gay Gibson as 'Lorna' in *Golden Boy*. He often found her distraught and highly strung, tiring easily, sometimes drinking too heavily and becoming highly emotional. He also said that she had come to South Africa for health reasons, as she suffered from asthma. She also said, 'I cannot love like other people' and 'I am not like other girls'.

Dr Ina Schoub, the wife of Henry Gilbert, in her evidence also said that Miss Gibson had told her, too, that she had come to South Africa because of her health, as she suffered from asthma. She tired easily and became short of breath on exertion, but the doctor said she had never seen her in an actual asthmatical attack. Miss Gibson discussed sex rather intimately, said that she had had sexual experience, and later became worried as she thought that she had become pregnant — a thing apparently known to the whole cast.

This was the background to the subsequent tragedy. A young actress of possibly dubious morality, not averse to the attentions of a very presentable and highly-sexed young man who risked his career in order to be with her in her cabin.

The Crown called compelling circumstantial evidence to prove that James Camb strangled Miss Gibson in her cabin on board the *Durban Castle* at about 3 a.m. on the morning of 18th October 1947; afterwards, he threw her body out into the shark-infested sea through the porthole of her cabin, in order to conceal evidence of his crime. It was alleged that he raped, attempted to rape, or attempted to sexually assault the girl; that she resisted and raised the alarm, and in order to preserve his job and prevent her giving evidence against him he killed her — by strangulation.

The Defence admitted that the girl died in her cabin at the material time, and they called equally compelling medical evidence that her death could have been due to natural causes. The Defendant was there at the time of her death, but because he had been disturbed and possibly recognised, he panicked and threw the body of the girl out of the ship hoping that her disappearance would be put down to suicide or accident.

The trial opened on Thursday, 18th March 1948 in the Assize court at Winchester. The court was a temporary one, formed of plywood partitions in the Great Hall of Winchester Castle, and presided over by King Arthur's Round Table.

Going into the witness-box was physically very similar to 'walking the plank' of old, and felt very much like it. One mounted some four or five steps, walked six to eight feet along a narrow rail-guarded walk, and then found oneself perched four or more feet high up in the middle of the court, completely isolated. The Judge was on one's left, the Defendent on the right, the Jury in front, and Counsel seemingly lost around their table on a much lower level.

Counsel for the Crown was that able, and to a guilty prisoner, dangerous KC, the late Mr G. D. (Khaki) Roberts, with Mr H. H. Elam as his junior. The Defence was led by the equally able Mr J. D. Casswell, KC, with Mr T. J. (now Sir Joseph) Molony to assist.

The Judge was the late Mr Justice Hilbery, and in this choice Camb was unfortunate. The Judge's attitude throughout the whole of the trial was clearly against the Defendant, as was his summing-up. So much so, that one of the grounds of the ultimate appeal was that the Judge's summing-up was too unfavourable to the prisoner. But the Lord Chief Justice, Lord Goddard, sitting with Mr Justice Pritchard and Mr Justice Humphreys dismissed this argument, saying, 'Undoubtedly the learned Judge's summing-up was not favourable to the prisoner,' and he went on to quote an earlier judgment given in the Appeal Court to the effect that a Judge is bound to give some assistance to the Jury on questions of fact as well as on questions of law.

In the court, in full view of everybody there was the bed from cabin 126 of the *Durban Castle,* a porthole of the size of the one in the cabin mounted in a wooden frame, and the bell-push in the cabin; this was at the head of the bed, and in a narrow opening beside the bed was a small chest. Other exhibits included plans of the cabin and cabin deck, bedding and pillows from the bunk, and photographs.

On the night that Gay Gibson disappeared, she had dined as usual with her friends Mr Hopwood and Wing-Commander Bray. She danced a little afterwards, and then as it was a very hot night she left her companions to look for her swimsuit to go bathing in the liner's swimming pool. She returned about half an hour afterwards, saying that she could not find it. It was during this half hour that the senior night-watchman saw Miss Gibson and Camb talking together, and he overheard a very significant remark made by Camb, *viz:* 'I say, I have a bone to pick with you, and a big one at that.' This was the first of two remarks of supreme significance in this case. The obvious inference drawn by the Crown was that Camb had indeed a grudge to be paid off. His own explanation was a perfectly rational one. There was no question of these two people being on very friendly terms from almost the beginning of the voyage. As a Deck Steward, Camb was not allowed in the cabin area. Orders had been given by Mr Hopwood that Miss Gibson was to have her tea every afternoon in her cabin. These trays were prepared by Camb and left out for the Stewardess to take down to the cabin. On the 17th, orders were given for a special tea tray to be prepared. This was done, but the tray was never collected. He was angry: hence his remark. Could anything be more rational?

After his remonstrance, Miss Gibson said that she was sorry, and then asked him to leave out a rum for her to collect later in the evening. Pushing his friendliness a little further, probably with obvious intentions, he asked her if she would like him to prepare a supper tray or bring her some lemonade, adding that he had a good mind to bring a drink down and join her. Her reply was, 'Please yourself. It's up to you,' or words to that effect. At 12.45 that night, he noticed that the glass of rum had been taken, and in its place there was Miss Gibson's alarm clock, normally kept on the dressing-table top. That clock appears never to have been seen again.

At about 12.40 a.m., Mr Hopwood escorted Miss Gibson back to her cabin; but it was a very warm night, and some twenty minutes later, the boatswain's mate saw her leaning over the rail at the after end of the Promenade Deck. She must have made an attractive picture on this her last appearance in public around midnight, in her long black evening dress, her feet in silver dancing shoes. The boatswain's mate was in charge of a party cleaning the decks, and asked her to move on, otherwise she would get wet.

This was the last that was ever seen of her by anyone — excepting James Camb.

The subsequent tragedy was heralded in by the ringing of bells. At night-time, the bell-pushes in the cabins are switched through to the night-watchman's galley. At 2.58 a.m. on the 18th, Murray, the senior night-watchman and his assistant Steer, heard the bell ringing above their heads. Following a trail of lights, Steer arrived at cabin No. 126.

The light was on, coming through the fanlight; and — most surprisingly — both red and green lights were showing, indicating that both bell-pushes had been pressed at the same time, as there was only one ringing of the bell. One bell would have called the stewardess, the other the night-watchman.

Something very peculiar had happened, something probably of great urgency, as emphasised by the Crown; but, as always in this curious case, there was an alternative explanation as will be revealed later.

Steer said that it would take him under a minute to reach the cabin from his galley. There was no noise coming from the cabin when he reached it. He knocked on the door and tried it; it was not bolted and he opened it a couple of inches. It was immediately slammed in his face, but not before he had seen the face of James Camb, who said, 'All right.' Returning to his senior, Murray, Steer told him that he had seen Camb in the cabin, and then they both went back. They found the cabin in darkness, with all lights, including the indicator lights, extinguished. Both men then decided to report the matter to the officer on the bridge, but not wanting to get a colleague into trouble, they merely reported the matter. Believing that it was probably another passenger in Miss Gibson's room, the officer said there was nothing he could do about it, and that it was not for him to interfere with the passengers' morals.

Four hours later, at 7.30 a.m. Miss Field, the Stewardess knocked on the door of cabin 126; there was no reply, and she found the door unlocked. This was unusual, as Gay Gibson invariably bolted her door at night. It was also of great significance, because whoever, including Camb, might have been with the girl in her cabin that night was obviously there with her consent, if not by her invitation. Miss Field entered the cabin and found it empty. Thinking that the occupant might have gone to the bathroom, Miss Field was not alarmed. She found the bed a little more disarranged than normal and there were some stains on the pillow and sheets, but she did not take particular notice of these. The bedclothes had been pulled back. The porthole was open, but this would be natural in tropical seas; Miss Gibson's evening dress was hanging in its usual place at the foot of the bunk; her dressing-gown, and black pyjamas were missing. Miss Field tidied up the cabin, and it was only a little later after she had asked the Bedroom Steward if Miss Gibson had had a bath, and was told 'No' that she became alarmed, and reported her missing. Her disappearance was broadcast over the whole ship, but without response. Captain Patey reversed course for over an hour, but realising the futility of any further search in shark-infested waters, he resumed his course at 11.40 a.m. Incidentally, amongst many other wild rumours in this case, there was the report of a shark caught off the West Coast of Africa shortly afterwards, having a woman's painted fingernail in its stomach.

Captain Patey immediately set inquiries afoot. Steer told him that he had seen Camb in Miss Gibson's cabin early that morning, and Camb was sent for. Camb, thinking he had not been recognised, immediately embarked on a series of lies designed to protect his job. He said he was nowhere near any passenger cabin, since retiring at 12.45 a.m. He continued on this course, until his line of defence was broken by the police after arrival of the ship at Southampton. He got himself into serious trouble by this line of conduct, and the first devastating question asked in cross-examination at his trial by Mr Roberts was, 'Would you describe yourself as a truthful man?' He obviously was not, at that time, anyway.

Captain Patey, at the first interview, did not tell Camb he had been recognised in Miss Gibson's cabin. He merely suggested that Camb was suspected of being in the neighbourhood of the cabin at about 3 a.m. Camb's reply was a flat denial. The captain then sent for William Pott, a steward who shared a cabin with Camb. Pott said that contrary to normal practice, Camb turned up that morning wearing Steward's full dress, a long-sleeved jacket, to do the ordinary routine work of cleaning-up. Was there something on his arms that he wanted to conceal?

Captain Patey decided that Camb should be medically examined. By this time Camb's nerves were becoming somewhat frayed, but he agreed to be examined by the ship's doctor, Dr Griffiths.

Dr Griffith's findings were of the utmost importance. He gave evidence at the trial that he found three main groups of injuries on Camb. First, there were some scratches over the back of the right shoulder, quite recent, and similar to those made by a cat's claws. The inference was that they could have been done by a woman's finely-pointed fingernails. Camb explained these away by saying that he had done them himself with a rough towel — a quite reasonable explanation. Secondly, there were some rather old scratches on the left collar bone, obviously of no recent significance except that they did bear out Camb's contention that he had recently been scratching himself rather severely with rough towels. The really important group of injuries was the third, on the front of the right wrist. These injuries were of intriguing interest. There were about twelve of them, some linear, some crescentic, running more of less horizontally across the inside of the right lower arm, commencing some four to five inches above the wrist. Dr Griffiths described these injuries as having been done probably by digging with finger-nails into the flesh. This was an important feature in the evidence, but as usual in this trial, there were divergent opinions as to how they might have been caused. The Crown said by Miss Gibson, who being manually strangulated, had attempted to tear away the hand of her assailant by pulling on his arm, digging her nails into him in the process. The Defendant offered an alternative and completely acceptable explanation as will appear later. These marks, however, had obviously caused Camb to wear his long-sleeved jacket on the morning of Gay Gibson's disappearance.

Camb, now thoroughly rattled, then wrote two notes to his Captain. In the first, he denied again having been anywhere near the girl's cabin on the night, and in the second he gave rather unconvincing explanations as to how he came by his injuries — mainly by scratching himself with his nails or with rough towels.

On the morning of 25th October, the liner steamed into Southampton and at 1.25 a.m. Detective Sergeant Quinlan boarded the ship; at 5.25 a.m., after preliminary inquiries, he interviewed Camb. Camb continued to deny that he had ever been near Miss Gibson's cabin on the fatal night, but after a while, he sensed that the night-watchman Steer had given away to the authorities the fact that he had been recognised in her cabin, and he made the not unexpected remark, whether he was innocent or not: 'That puts me in a tight spot.'

Later the same day, Detective Sergeant Quinlan decided, quite properly, to increase the pressure, saying that he had definitely established that Camb had been in Miss Gibson's cabin at about 3 a.m. on the night of her disappearance. A very worried Camb then confessed that he *had* been down to the cabin that night, asking Miss Gibson if she wanted some lemonade with her rum; she was looking for a swim suit — confirmed by her friend, Mr Hopkins. She asked Camb to leave her rum in its usual place. He still denied having gone later to the cabin. Later Detective Sergeant (Acting Inspector) Gibbons said to him, 'You are being given an opportunity to make any explanation you may care to about this. That explanation, so far, has been a categorical denial that you know anything about the death of Miss Gibson. You may find that such a complete denial will be difficult to explain if later you are called upon to explain it.' Camb replied: 'Does that mean I murdered her and that I shall be charged with murder?' Gibbons said that he could not say whether or not a charge would be preferred. And then there occurred a conversation which set in train all the investigations that became the basis of the evidence for the Defence.

Gibbons said: 'We have to give particular care to any explanation which you may put forward. You may be able to give a reasonable explanation of the cause of her death and her disappearance.' Camb replied: 'You mean that Miss Gibson might have died from some other cause, other than being murdered? She might have had a heart attack, or something?'

How does one interpret such a remark?

One explanation, put forward by the Crown, was that it was a heaven-sent invitation to Camb to adduce a heart attack as the cause of Miss Gibson's death. The other is that it is equally consistent with the mental attitude of a worried man who had racked his brains to find some explanation as to why a woman should suddenly die in his arms, and, in a flash, the explanation comes to him. After only a short while, during which he boasted that he and other members of the crew were often preferred at night-time by female passengers, he elected to make the following statement:

'I have already stated to you that I went to Miss Gibson's cabin at about eleven o'clock, and during the course of conversation with her I made an appointment to meet her that night. I knocked at the door after I had finished work at about one o'clock, but there was no answer. I opened the door of her cabin and found it empty. I then went forward to the well deck, where I sat for about half an hour smoking. I then returned to Miss Gibson's cabin at about two o'clock and found her there. After a short conversation I got into bed with her consent. Intimacy took place. Whilst in the act of sexual intercourse she clutched me, foaming at the mouth. I immediately ceased the act, but she was very still. I felt for her heart beats, but could not find any. She was at that time very still, and I cannot offer any explanation as to how the bells came to be rung, as I most definitely did not touch them myself. Thinking she had fainted, I tried artificial respiration on her. Whilst doing this, the night-watchman knocked at the door and attempted to open it. I shut the door again, saying it was all right. Then I panicked, as I thought he had gone to the bridge to report to the officer of the watch, and I did not want to be found in such a compromising position. After a few minutes I could not find any sign of life. After a struggle with the limp body — by the way, she was still wearing her dressing-gown — I managed to lift her to the porthole and push her through. I am fairly certain that at the time she was dead, but I was terribly frightened. I then went forward and turned in. The time would be about 3.30 a.m.'

After saying that he was glad to have got the matter off his mind, Camb then added: 'What will happen about this? My wife must not know about this. If she does I will do away with myself.' Camb's Counsel, Mr Caswell, believed that this was absolutely true and proved his innocence. He had lied like a trooper up to this point to save his job, but it still did not occur to him that he might face a murder charge.

Camb is then alleged to have said something to a Detective Constable, unconfirmed, which no man in his senses (anticipating that he was about to be charged with murder) would make. The Detective Constable said that when he was alone with Camb, the Steward said to him, 'She struggled. I had my arms around her neck and when I was trying to pull them away she scratched me. I panicked and threw her out of the porthole. It was a hell of a splash when she hit the water. I can't understand why the officer of the watch did not hear something.' This was manifestly ridiculous. The porthole was some twenty-five feet above the water line, there was backlash from the bow wave immediately below, and machinery in the dummy funnel above all would have drowned any sound of splashing, as was confirmed by Captain Patey. The Detective Constable who made the statement had 'left the Force before the trial to better himself, but was still unemployed'.

The Prosecution produced two more important witnesses.

The first was Dr Montgomery, a senior Scientific Officer at the Metropolitan Police Laboratory at Hendon. He had received various exhibits in the case for scientific examination. The only things of any significance that he found were:

On the top sheet, two small blood spots, each about the size of a sixpence. The blood was of Group 'O'. This was not the group of Camb, which was Group 'A'. On the bottom sheet, there were faint blood spots, too small to group. No hair from the accused was found, and nothing of significance was found in scrapings from around the porthole, or elsewhere in the room. It was obvious that no fight had taken place there.

I later examined all the exhibits with important results that will appear later.

The last, and very important witness for the Crown was Dr (now Professor) Donald Teare, then Assistant Pathologist and Lecturer in Forensic Medicine at St George's Hospital, London.

Dr Teare described the signs he would expect to find in a case of death by strangulation, the most important relevant to this case being probable slight haemorrhage from the lungs or upper air passages due to constriction of blood vessels by pressure on the neck, and hence in this case, the possible explanation of the blood on the sheets. The blood might also have come from scratch marks by the victim injuring her throat during attempts to relieve the pressure. Unconsciousness would supervene in a matter of only a few seconds, probably not more than fifteen, and death would be within a minute. Dr Teare refused to express any opinion concerning the scratch and other marks on the body of Camb. He agreed that signs of muddiness in Miss Gibson's finger-nails, noticed by her friend Mr Hopwood, would indicate that the girl was suffering from some circulatory defect, confirmed by pains down the left arm, and that she was possibly suffering from some form of heart disease associated with asthma. On balance, however, he felt that what had been found was more in keeping with death by strangulation than death from a heart attack, although in all conscience what had been found was very little.

Dr Teare concluded the evidence for the Prosecution, and then came the turn of the Defence.

This was outlined at the beginning by Mr Casswell. His main contention was that Miss Gibson was a young woman not at all averse to the attentions of a presentable young man, even to the extent of not opposing his visiting her in the early hours of the morning in her cabin, more or less naked. There was a well-authenticated history of long-standing illness, though not by any means of a serious nature; also very experienced medical evidence that the girl could have died in exactly the way described by the Defendant, and with signs exactly as were found. Camb knew nothing about the significance of Miss Gibson's past medical history. Indeed, it was remarkable that he should have told a story about what happened on the fatal night, so close to what might have been *expected* to happen in the circumstances. Confirmation was surely almost complete.

The first witness for the Defence was the accused himself.

He outlined the increasing friendliness that grew up between himself and Miss Gibson during the early days of the voyage, and confirmed his part in preparing tea and drinks for her, to be taken down to her by the night-watchman. He explained, too, his use of the phrase: 'I have a bone to pick with you.'

He then went on to detail the events of the fateful October night.

After the episode of ordering the rum for the night, he went to the cabin soon after 2 o'clock. The door was not fastened. As, according to Miss Field, Miss Gibson invariably bolted her door after retiring to her cabin, Camb's advent in the early hours of the morning cannot have been a surprise to her. She was wearing nothing underneath a yellow quilted dressing-gown. Camb was emphatic, and could not be moved, that she was not wearing black pyjamas. There were no black pyjamas in the room, and he did not throw them out of the porthole after the girl when he put her through. Much was made in cross-examination of the loss of these pyjamas. The Crown contended, most reasonably, that they were missing because the girl was wearing them and was therefore not inviting intercourse. They were never found. Rumour again had it that they were, in fact, in the cabin of a distinguished male fellow-passenger who is alleged to have said that he would come forward if there was any danger of Camb's being hanged — which there was not, as capital punishment was in abeyance, fortunately, at that time. There is indeed an interval of time, from about 1 a.m. to 2 a.m. completely unaccounted for, but of course the girl could have gone back at once to her cabin after being moved on by the crew swabbing decks.

However that may be, the couple talked, for some time, about the dullness of the dance. Then almost inevitably Cambs climbed on to the bed beside her. Raising no objections, she unzipped her dressing-gown, revealing her nakedness beneath. He then went on to describe exactly what he mentioned in his statement to the police. He added, however, that she had her right hand round his neck with her left hand holding his right arm. When her body stiffened as she was gasping for breath, her right arm was still round his neck, and her left hand holding his forearm, gripped tightly. Of course, a perfectly rational happening, which would account for the nail mark injuries seen in his neck and arm. Verbally he added somewhat to the content of his written statement to the police — and it was of significance. In his own words: 'I immediately got off the bed. She was completely relaxed, as though she was in a dead faint. One eye was just slightly open. Her mouth was a little open too. There was a faint line of bubbles, which I assumed to be froth, just on the edges of the lips. It was a muddy colour and appeared to be slightly blood-flecked. I was rather stunned for the moment. First of all I listened and felt for her heartbeats. I could not find any and I attempted to massage the stomach towards the heart to bring back circulation.' It was at this stage that in all probability Camb pressed his thigh against the bell-pushes, and set off the alarm that was his undoing. He swore that Gay Gibson herself did not ring the bells, nor did he know how they had been rung. Confronted by Steer, he panicked and thought only of destroying any evidence. His whole career was now in jeopardy. He hoped people would presume that she had fallen overboard. It was at this point that Camb had a gruelling cross-examination by Mr Roberts, who quite rightly said that he had wilfully destroyed the only positive evidence. If there were no marks on her body, and other things were found out by a post-mortem examination showing that she was not a healthy girl, then his story would have been proved to be correct, and he would have been completely exonerated. This was a point hammered home by the Judge in his charge to the Jury. It was certainly a very valid point, but one can perhaps visualise the man in his dreadful predicament behaving as he did.

The whole of Camb's cross-examination was a testing experience, but he stood up to it superbly, without being shaken or departing in one detail from his account of the way in which the girl died. So composed was he that the point told rather severely against him in the eventual final speech to the jury by Mr Roberts. Mr Roberts said: 'Camb says he threw her through the porthole in panic. Did he panic? Panic? Do you think he is the sort of man to panic? Did you see any sign of panic at all? Did you see any lack of poise, or composure, or full control of the thinking facilities?' The same point was also pressed home by the Judge.

The main plank in the evidence on behalf of the Defendant was the medical evidence.

Professor Webster, Professor of Forensic Medicine at Birmingham University and a Home Office Pathologist, had been asked by the Director of Public Prosecutions to review the medical evidence and give his opinion as to the possibility of Camb's statement being correct. He did so in characteristic no-nonsense terms, saying that, in his opinion, Camb's statement was perfectly possible. On this account Professor Webster was naturally offered to the Defence. What impressed him most was the detailed description of the way in which Gay Gibson died, by a man without any possible medical knowledge. Professor Webster said: 'The account given by Camb of this girl's death could have occurred.' He instanced three cases in his experience in which death had occurred during sexual intercourse, when there was no question of any violence. In none of them had the dead person shown any previous sign of any disease. Death could occur from the rupture of a small aneurysm in the brain, or from heart disease, the latter either primary or secondary to some other condition, including asthma. (An aneurysm is a thin-walled dilatation of a blood vessel. It is not unusual, and rupture frequently occurs. Such rupture in the brain can cause instant death in many cases, an occurrence which is by no means rare in young people, and more likely to occur under strain or excitement. With regard to heart disease this can, of course, be primary, due to some affection of the heart itself, or secondary. Secondary causes of degeneration of the heart muscle include chronic infection resulting in bacterial poisoning of the tissues, or such conditions as asthma, which throw an increasing strain on the heart to pump blood through increasing resistance in the lungs.)

He thought that in Gay Gibson's case it could have been heart disease associated either with asthma, or her chronically septic ear. Professor Webster's conclusion was that the chances of natural death were equal with those of strangulation. Dr Teare put the chances of strangulation as greater than those of natural death, but admitted to the latter possibility.

I was called in to the case on two grounds. Firstly to help assess the possibility of natural as opposed to violent death; and here I agreed entirely with Professor Webster. I assessed the chances as about equal. Secondly, I had been asked to re-examine the bedding. This revealed something of very great importance which had hitherto been overlooked.

On the top pillow, I found a light smear of blood mixed with cells from the mouth, and digestive ferments found in saliva. This was proof that the blood had come most likely from congestion in the respiratory tract, and not from any external damage that might have been done to the girl. Something of much more importance was evident: on the top sheet, not visible in ordinary light, but showing up quite clearly when examined in ultra-violet light, was a stain, roughly oval in shape, measuring fifteen inches by six inches. It was dried urine.

This finding set off a whole chain of examination and cross-examination questions. In the first place, it provided the Prosecution with a missing link in their evidence. It was almost certain proof that Gay Gibson had died in her cabin, and that she was dead when thrown out of the porthole. This apparently was a great relief to public opinion. Mr Roberts seized on this additional information at once, as confirmation of strangulation. Voiding of urine almost inevitably occurs when a person is strangled, but it occurs equally in many cases of sudden death by natural causes, so that its occurrence is no actual proof of strangulation. Mr Roberts also argued that urine on the top sheet showed that the girl was lying on her back at the time of her death, covered by the sheet. Urine voided by a female lying on her back, of course, goes upwards. This finding, according to Mr Roberts, was also proof that Camb could not have been lying on top of the girl, as he said, at the time of her death. But, unfortunately for Mr Roberts, this finding completely destroyed his previous contention that, at the time of her death, the girl was wearing her black pyjamas. He obviously could not have it both ways. Furthermore the finding of the urine on the top sheet did not mean that the girl was covered by the sheet. If she and Camb were lying on the top of the bed together, and she passed urine this would run down on to the uppermost, i.e. the top sheet, as was found — again confirming Camb's statement. It does not seem reasonable to suppose that these two, having intercourse, would have covered themselves with a sheet.

That, then, was the evidence in the case.

The trial had lasted for four days. The Judge's summing-up lasted about four hours, and the Jury brought in their verdict of Guilty after a retirement of only forty minutes. Mr Casswell complained bitterly about the Judge's summing-up, reminding him of many matters in favour of the Defendant which he had not mentioned, but Mr Justice Hilbery, brushing this aside, said: 'I have not attempted to mention everything, and I am not bound to do so'.

The case naturally went to Appeal. It was dismissed without even calling on the Crown to answer Mr Casswell's arguments.

At the commencement of the trial, the Clerk of Assize read out the indictment: 'James Camb, you stand charged upon the indictment with murder, and the particulars state that, on the 18th of October last year, on the high seas, you did murder Eileen Isabella Ronnie Gibson; to that charge do you plead Guilty or Not Guilty?'

Camb replied: 'Not Guilty.'

After conviction, the Clerk of Assize asked him, as is usual, if he had anything to say before sentence of death was passed upon him. His reply was not unworthy of note: 'My lord, at the opening of this case I was asked to plead Guilty or Not Guilty; I pleaded Not Guilty, and I repeat that statement now.'

Guilty or Not Guilty?

Mr Casswell thoroughly believed in his innocence, as he repeats in his own account of the affair in his book *A Lance for Liberty*. Professor Webster and I thoroughly believed that Camb's account of the happenings on that tragic night was medically possible and reasonable, with at least a fifty-fifty chance of being correct. Dr Teare agreed, but put the chances considerably less in favour of the accused.

Camb's neat appearance and supreme confidence in himself never left him throughout the whole ordeal of his trial, but in many ways he was his own worst enemy. He completely lost any sympathy the Jury might have had for him by his own utter selfishness in putting his job and future before the life of a young girl. He 'concluded that she was dead' but was not certain, and he made no attempt to summon any medical aid for her. He thought only of himself. He denied that he could have inadvertently rung the bells, although it was quite possible, and denied that he had received any injury from the girl which was one of the main planks of his defence.

To Mr Casswell's mind, the Jury convicted him because they could not forgive him for his brutal and callous action.

The case has often been debated by lawyers, pathologists and medico-legal experts. On balance, I would say that generally the legal minds supported the conviction, whilst the medical men supported the opinion of Professor Webster and myself. After all, why kill the goose who is laying the golden eggs?

Mr Justice Humphreys, one of the judges who sat in the Court of Appeal is alleged to have said afterwards: 'That man wasn't given a chance'.

Nobody knows what he meant by that remark.

☆   ☆   ☆

A full account of the trial was published in the series of *Notable British Trials*, edited by Geoffrey Clark, William Hodge & Co.

It even attracted interest in the United States, where a transcript was published under the title *The Girl in the Stateroom* by Charles Boswell, Louis & Louis Thompson.

The most fascinating account, however, has been written by Denis Herbstein in his book *Porthole*, published in June 1991 by Hodder & Stoughton. He not only gives a complete account of the Court proceedings, but also most skilfully analyses all the aspects of the case.

I have suffered remarkably little abuse during my career, in fact really only on one occasion connected with this case of Gay Gibson.

One newspaper reported a short paragraph recording my evidence that this girl might have died from natural causes. The reader wrote 'liar' across the paragraph and sent it to me.

The other incident was an anonymous letter sent to me in the following terms:

'Dear Sir,

'I see by the enclosed press report you said in evidence in the Camb trial that it was perfectly possible for Miss Gibson to die as you say. Well now, you being a pathologist should know that what you said was a lot of damnation rot and many thousands are of the same opinion as myself that you was a Bluddy old waster to give such evidence to try and influence the Jury on the verdict they come to a right conclusion for Camb was nothing more than a blasted rotten blighter; what about the other 3 young women who he tried to strangle the same as he did what did the Judge

93

say about her epitaph.

'What Camb did was to enter Miss G's cabin with the intention of criminally assaulting her and when she objected he seized her around the throat with his hand his own words and thereby strangled her to hide his result and put her out of the porthole but what about the blood on the bottom sheet does this not prove her to have been a virgin as her mother said you ought to know but it appears you know Bugger all about it and so the sooner this dirty rotten Bugger is *hung* the better it will be for the general public and as for you you are too a rotten dirty, Bloody old waster, there was no need for you to have poked your nose on the case at all so once more to Hell with such a rotten old Bugger for you are nothing more I wonder what you would have said if it had been *your* Daughter its a pity it wasn't you rotten old scoundrel and Bugger you once more.'

It was not signed.

6

Some Tragic Poisonings

Apart from obvious natural and violent deaths, many people are found dead from no obvious cause, and without any history of illness. Many have not seen their doctors for weeks, even months or years. Death is unexpected, and the cause must be ascertained to see if it was indeed a natural one. The vast majority turn out to be natural, but there are occasional surprises. One of these is the taking of an overdose of drugs, generally sleeping tablets, either deliberately or accidentally.

The 'middle classes', particularly pensioners, have been particularly hard hit over recent years by increasing taxation and inflation. They had been used to a gracious kind of living. Coming home from work, it was the custom to have what my wife and I call 'pre-medication' to smooth away the cares of the day and give a feeling of wellbeing to inaugurate the evening. It worked marvellously. Spirits at ten shillings a bottle easily provided this. At seven pounds a bottle, and increasing, the old way of life became endangered — in fact we were becoming an endangered species. There was a subtle way out. It became known that the barbiturate sleeping tablets, taken in small doses, have almost exactly the same euphoric action as alcohol. Of course they did not taste so good, but added to a single measure of spirits the latter provided the taste and had the effects of a double measure at half the cost. Until recently there was no difficulty in getting a supply of these drugs, but lately the ability to do so has been drastically curbed. But of course I am now talking about the forties and fifties. All one had to do then was to say, 'Please doctor, I can't sleep' and the pills were handed out *ad lib*. In 1964 there were 16.1 million scripts for barbiturate drugs, and some 8,000 cases of barbiturate poisoning. At the same time, there were 3.75 million prescriptions for 'pep' amphetamine pills.

I have been told that in certain establishments for the elderly the old dears experimented with their tranquillising tablets to find out which suited them best. A kind of bartering took place — 'One of your pink ones for two of my blue, dear.' All very sad and apparently harmless, but potentially lethal as the subsequent investigation into the cause of death revealed. A mixture of alcohol and barbiturate is much more potent than the drugs taken individually. In a doped state it can be forgotten that a 'cocktail' has already been drunk, and a further measure of the lethal mixture is taken.

These overdose deaths are a great worry. Many could be called self-inflicted. But what is easier than to 'lace' a glass of spirits with tasteless barbiturate to get rid of an unwanted person? This theme became the central pin in my dear cousin's (Ann Hocking) novel *Death in the Cup*. When a massive dose of barbiturate is found in the blood, with considerable remains of the drug still in the stomach, it can be confidently assumed that this large amount was voluntarily (suicidally) taken. No murderer could force a large quantity of pills down the throat of a resisting victim without some signs of that resistance being obvious. But I could suggest ways in which a potential poisoner, if he had medical knowledge, could do this without trace. Vide the play by Winston Graham *Circumstantial Evidence*. The largest number of barbiturate tablets that I have ever seen in the stomach of a suicide was in the region of 5,000. This lady arrived at the Queen's Hotel in Penzance, complete with bottle containing this number of barbiturate tablets. The bottle was empty, the stomach full. I hasten to add that the prescription had been given in New Zealand. I have also seen up to 400 aspirin tablets in a stomach. How they manage to swallow them is a mystery.

It is when just a lethal amount of barbiturate is found

that worries begin. However, neither the potential murderer or the suicide is likely to know just how much would be required to kill, and in the vast majority of these cases they make no bones about it and administer or take a definitely lethal dose. Even then, the determined poisoner of an elderly person or child might go about it in easy stages and cause a most worrying situation.

Of the number of people who have taken just about enough sleeping tablets to ensure death there is a group in which the overdose can be considered to have taken inadvertently. The original suggestion was made, I believe, by Sir Bernard Spilsbury, dealing with people found dead in bed with the minimal lethal amount of barbiturate in their blood. There was no background to suggest any intention of taking their lives. These are people who suffered from insomnia for whom, quite rightly, sleeping tablets were prescribed. Having taken a nightly dose, they wake up in a somewhat dazed state, and finding themselves awake, do not realise that they have taken their sleeping pill and proceed to take another and later on perhaps another, until they have taken too many. In these cases, only a minimal lethal dose has been taken. I know that many of my colleagues do not believe this, but I do — and in any case it is a kinder way of dealing with the matter, but only if there is a minimal amount present and there are no suspicious circumstances. Doctors now take particular pains to warn all sleeping tablet patients to be aware of this danger, and to put out only one nightly dose of the drug, and lock the rest away.

It is not so common now, but thirty to forty years ago it was quite common in the wintertime to find elderly people dead in their small homes. Of limited means and a necessity to conserve warmth and cash, they lit their small fires and then plugged up every nook and cranny through which fresh air could enter the room. Result, gradual using up of the limited oxygen in the room leading to faulty incomplete combustion of the fuel in the grate, leading then to the formation of carbon monoxide and final carbon monoxide poisoning. In the aged and debilitated, only 20-30% saturation of their blood is required to cause death, and this can be easily reached in a number of circumstances.

Defective (cracked) stoves and gas heaters are abundant sources of carbon monoxide. Inadequately burning fires, especially if the flues have not been cleaned recently, are a common source. Many years ago in Newlyn we had a series of tragic deaths. It was a very cold winter, and the occupants of small houses often stopped up every available source of air entry to overcome draughts. As a result the oxygen in the room became increasingly used up until there was insufficient to maintain complete combustion in the fire; the result, incomplete combustion with the formation of lethal carbon monoxide. I have seen the same in an almost hermetically sealed room heated by a portable gas burner.

It may sound somewhat funny, but it is far more tragic, that a number of people, mainly elderly and confused or not very bright mentally, have lost their lives through a silly mistake. They have turned on a gas ring adjacent to a kitchen sink, and then applied a lighted match to the water tap. Burned-out matches have been found in the sink, and sometimes soot around the mouth of the tap; meanwhile lethal gas poured out of the gas tap. Fortunately, with non-poisonous North Sea gas which contains no carbon monoxide, this sort of tragic death will not be seen again.

Two instances of carbon monoxide poisoning that might have had tragic consequences occurred in primary schools at Portreath and St Columb Major about twenty years ago. Teachers and children all complained of feeling drowsy and sick, and some fainted. Investigation showed that the classrooms were heated by old-fashioned cast-iron coke-burning stoves, some cracked, and all when very hot leaking large quantities of carbon monoxide into the air. The classrooms of my old school were similarly heated — but we survived!

I am relating this sad case of death by fire as a cautionary tale. How often have we been told that when a fire is suspected to keep all doors and windows, and anywhere through which air might enter, tightly closed? To do otherwise, and open up, is inviting an explosive flare-up.

This occurred on a rather ancient yacht moored off Tresco in the Isles of Scilly, during the early hours of the morning one April day in 1973. On board were a young couple who had visited friends on the island and returned to the yacht for the night. It was a rather cold night, so that the rather primitive coal-burning stove, placed right against a wooden bulkhead, was stoked up. Unfortunately the young couple did not know that the stove was cracked at the back; we found it after it was all over. During the night, the young man woke up 'feeling funny', and smelling something funny. Without waking the girl (a perfectly natural thing to do) he got up, opened the cabin door, and went out. Immediately, the cabin burst into flames. The girl cried out, but it was impossible to reach her. The young man tried to put out the fire with extinguishers, but was unsuccessful; he himself suffered extensive burns. It was not until the fire brigade arrived that the fire was finally extinguished. All that remained was massive charring, including the body of the girl. She had been alive when the fire started, shown by soot in the air passages and a carbon monoxide count of 67% saturation in her blood. It was obvious what had happened. The stoked-up fire, flickering through the back of the stove had caused the wooden bulkhead to smoulder; this produced a lot of carbon monoxide, and it was this and the smell that had awakened the young man. It was unfortunate that his opening of the door (a natural reaction) led to the explosive conflagration of the smouldering wood. The explosive conflagration was actually witnessed by two independent and completely reliable witnesses on shore.

Of course there were spiteful rumours that both these young people were drunk or drugged or both. I was very pleased to be able to say at the Inquest that there was no alcohol and no drugs in the girl, a finding confirmed by the Forensic Laboratory at Bristol. Indeed it could, and should, be said that the young man, himself a partial victim of carbon monoxide poisoning, and in a consequently dazed condition, behaved in an exemplary fashion and made every attempt to save the girl. He did himself get extensively burned.

Although rarely fatal, carbon monoxide poisoning was not infrequently seen in nightwatchmen in the winter time, when they sought to keep themselves warm with the traditional brazier — a dustbin perforated with holes around the sides and filled with glowing coke, an ideal method of manufacturing carbon monoxide. The glowing bin would be positioned to the windward side of any prevailing breeze, ideal for the inhalation of the gas. Many nightwatchmen sacked for sleeping whilst on duty were probably most unfairly dealt with. It is recorded that a medical student (not one of mine) answering a question in his forensic paper wrote, 'It is not uncommon for nightwatchmen who sit for long hours contemplating a red hot brassiere (sic) to be overcome.'

The following case might also be regarded as a cautionary tale, and one of just retribution brought upon the offender himself, but also unhappily on half his family.

In 1958 there resided in Penzance a householder and five other members of his family. Not being possessed of the highest moral standards, not being well off financially, and being a mechanic, he conceived the idea of by-passing his gas meter, which he successfully accomplished. This worked very well for some time. Amongst the household gas appliances, however, there was a gas boiler, used for washing clothing. The boiler stood in the corner of the kitchen, and its gas tap was behind, and very loose. One evening the wife, either in a hurry or not very neat in her habits, threw a pile of dirty clothing on to the top of the boiler. Some fell behind, knocking on the loose tap and turning on the gas. Audible hissing of escaping gas was muffled by the clothing. Three out of the six of that household died that night, including the meter tamperer himself.

Another unlucky wrongdoer, although in another connection and not associated with accidental poisoning, was a young man in St Agnes. Noting that the occupants of a bungalow were away, and that the downstairs lavatory window hopper had been left open, he decided to burgle the place. Prising up the hopper still further, he climbed up a nearby drainpipe and let himself in through the opening. Unfortunately for him, he elected to go in front foremost. In sliding down, the 'V' of his braces caught in the upright peg of the window fastening, and there he was suspended in mid-air. His struggles to free himself were reflected in large numbers of deep scratch marks up and down the wall made by his frantic efforts to try and find a foothold. Unfortunately, the more he struggled, the tighter the hopper closed on his chest, and he died of suffocation due to fixation of his chest by this hopper.

The early symptoms of carbon monoxide poisoning are very similar to those of alcohol intoxication. For years and years, prior to the establishment of the statutory level of 80 milligrammes of alcohol per 100 millilitres of blood, above which a motorist could be prosecuted for driving with excess alcohol in his blood, the defence almost invariably was that the driver's motor car had a leak in its exhaust system, and this caused carbon monoxide to enter the car and poison the driver; hence his erratic behaviour. A motor mechanic could always be found to say that he had found a fault in the system, which of course he had immediately repaired because of its danger. Unfortunately this precluded any tests that could be made on the car to prove that there had been a leak at the material time. I, of course, always agreed that carbon monoxide could cause symptoms and behaviour similar to alcoholic intoxication, but invariably added that motor car exhaust fumes cannot put alcohol into the blood. However, carbon monoxide entering the car in this way could aggravate erratic behaviour due to alcohol. In the early days of these blood tests there was no statutory limit, but a level of 150 milligrammes of alcohol per 100 millilitres of blood was generally accepted as the limit for safe driving — almost double the present standard! These blood alcohol levels were calculated from the analysis of urine samples, it then being held that to take a blood specimen might constitute an assault on the person. When the statutory limit of 80 milligrammes per 100 millilitres of blood was established by the Road Safety Act of 1967, the Act also legalised the taking of blood samples. With this, the defence of carbon monoxide poisoning went out overnight. The blood samples were not only examined for alcohol content, but were also spectroscopically examined for carbon monoxide. Until this happened, this carbon monoxide loophole was sufficient for most juries, and many magistrates; convictions were difficult, if not almost impossible to get. I remember one notorious Court in which we almost never got a conviction. When at last we did manage to get one, we adjourned to suitable licenced premises and suitably celebrated. I forget if we reached the 150 milligramme level.

Many ingenious explanations have been put forward by anxious drivers who have been found to be 'over the limit' as to how they might have come to this state. I could write a hilarious book on the subject. Most of the explanations put forward have been completely without merit, and I have refused to touch them.

Occasionally however, a case presents itself that does seem to have merit, and then I will take it up. I have had instances in which completely reliable evidence as to the amount of drink taken could not possibly have raised the blood alcohol content to the level determined by analysis. These remain a mystery, but no analyst can guarantee that he is invariably right. We all make mistakes unwittingly, even when the greatest care is taken.

A number of cases have undoubtedly occurred where a person accused of a drink-driving offence has been the victim of a playful but dangerous prank. More seriously, it might be a dirty trick played on a friend — or enemy. I refer to the type of case where a perfectly respectable person, knowing his own alcoholic limits, is out for an evening with friends. Unknown to him, his drink is 'playfully laced' by the addition of spirits. Vodka is tasteless in beer, or even lemonade, and the same may go for gin. Whisky is rarely used, as its taste is difficult to disguise, although I have known it to have been used in Coca-Cola. A single measure of spirits will raise the blood alcohol by 16.6 milligrammes per 100 millilitres. This can make all the difference between an alcohol level that is safe and one that is not. I have had many such cases. The worst is almost incredible. A young Persian officer seaman, a Muslim forbidden alcohol, was entertained by a 'friend' in the latter's home. They consumed Coca-Cola in large glasses holding some 15 ounces — three-quarters of a pint. 9-10 ounces of Coca-Cola were poured into the visitors glass, topped up with 5-6 ounces of whisky. The effect was disastrous. The young Muslim became completely intoxicated and crashed his car at a roundabout as he was leaving. Fortunately for the young man, his 'friend' came to Court and confessed his part in the affair, and he saved his licence, but not his fine. Good hospitality is one thing, but this kind is criminal — and a statutory offence.

This line of defence is now being overdone, and the courts are looking very askance at it; but it still goes on, and I know some of them are genuine.

I was a little sceptical and concerned over a case of a physiotherapist, who after a party, ran his car into a hedge on the way home. He rather severely cut his forehead, and according to his story, being afraid of infection, he poured neat spirits liberally onto his handkerchief and applied it to his head. Quite a lot, he said, ran into his mouth. Found shortly after the accident by police, he was given a breath test, which he failed, and was then taken off to the police station for a blood test. This showed a blood alcohol content of 100 mg./100 ml., above the statutory limit of 80. I was asked my opinion. I understood that he had used neat spirit on his head, the spirit coming from a bottle that he used in connection with his work. Potable spirits, whisky, gin, rum etc. contain about 33% alcohol. One ounce will raise the blood alcohol level by 60.0 mg./100 ml. Only about a third of an ounce of neat alcohol would therefore be required to put 20 mg./100 ml. of alcohol into his blood. I thought it just possible that he might have swallowed this amount in the circumstances, and this would have put his blood above the limit. Without it, it could have been less than 80 mg./100 ml. I gave my opinion accordingly, and the Jury found him not guilty. Later, I heard that the Judge, Adie-Sheppard, was furious with me. Although the defence of 'lacing' still goes on, it is being overtaken by the new 'hip-flask' defence, resorted to by a motorist who consumes alcohol after he has returned home. Of course there are many genuine cases, and I have been involved in many of them, with variable results. Also there are spurious cases where it is quite impossible for the Defendant to have behaved and drunk what he alleges he did. These of course I will not touch.

The common case is that of a motorist who has had an accident or has been reported by another motorist for erratic behaviour, who reaches home and then has a stiff drink to steady his nerves. Under the old law (Road Traffic Act 1972) he could not be approached to give a blood sample because he was not driving or attempting to drive his motor car at the time; in fact, it was safely stowed away in his garage. Under the Transport Act 1981, by Section 7 of the substituted Act — 'Where a Constable in uniform has reasonable cause to suspect' — that a person *has* been driving or attempting to drive or been in charge of a motor vehicle on a road or other public place with alcohol in his body, he may require him to provide a specimen of breath for a breath test — or a blood sample. This allows the police to test drivers even after they have arrived at their home and put the car away. When the test is done, the driver is often found to be over the limit. His explanation, as given above, is that he consumed alcohol after arriving home, to steady his nerves. This excuse requires a lot of investigation. Often it is found that the amount of alcohol said to have been taken after arrival at home cannot possibly be related to the result of one or other of the analyses, intoximeter, or blood test. I have been presented with many of these, and just throw them out. However, there are occasions when the amount said to have been taken coincides very closely with the result of the analysis, and then I do think there is a case for the Defence, especially if there is some collateral evidence, such as the finding of bottles and glasses.

7

Drownings

Unexpected deaths are not uncommon during the holiday season amongst visiting and sometimes native bathers. Apparently perfectly hale and hearty, their bodies are nevertheless recovered from the sea, generally dead. Treatment of the apparently drowned has gone through a great revolution since my early days. Then, forty or so years ago, if anybody was fished out of the sea presumed drowned, artificial respiration was carried out for five hours or more, long after rigor mortis (death stiffening) has set in and the eyes had become glazed. Undaunted queues of willing helpers in lines kept up the artificial respiration for all this time, and almost invariably someone was able to feel a pulse returning, and efforts were redoubled. Most of the victims had their chests crushed in and ribs broken by these efforts before the body reached me. One of the basic troubles was that at that time some first aid books encouraged this mammoth exercise. Nowadays the mechanism of drowning is much better understood, following the classical researches of Dr Swan during the last war. These exhibitionist exercises are now mercifully replaced and restricted to the professional attentions of the many life and beach guards who have done a wonderful job of work in saving life in recent years. In the 1930s, when visitors to our resorts were a handful of the number that now descends upon the county during the holiday season, I dealt with something like fifty cases yearly of drowning whilst bathing. Now that number has been reduced to perhaps ten or a dozen, in spite of the enormous increase in numbers taking to the sea. It is a sad reflection how many who are found drowned whilst bathing have a very high alcohol content in their blood. People will still not heed warnings.

I am going to digress for a moment from case histories to scientific facts, because the mechanism of drowning is still not appreciated by the vast majority of people. It used to be thought that death was due to asphyxiation by the water inhaled into the lungs, and that if this could be got rid of all would be well. Rescued people were turned on their fronts and given vigorous artificial respiration. Sometimes they were hung upside-down and their backs thumped. Another method was to hold them by the shoulders and feet and rock them up and down. Other contortions were devised to drain the water from the lungs.

But this is not the mechanism of drowning, which is different in fresh and in salt water.

When salt water is inhaled, as from the sea, the water has a greater salinity, density (or scientifically, osmotic pressure) than the water in the blood. As a result, fluid is withdrawn from the blood into the lungs which then become completely waterlogged and airless. The blood itself becomes concentrated and sticky, and so does not go around so well, and with the lungs now waterlogged, no oxygen can get into it. In addition, some of the salt goes into the circulation, altering both relative and total amounts of the many salts that are a natural constituent of blood. It is on the proper maintenance of these salts that the heartbeat is partly regulated. Alter them drastically, and the heart stops. It can be kept going again perhaps by electrical stimuli, but by this time the damage is done, and anyway electrical stimuli will not correct the salt balance. After five minutes of this, irreparable damage has been done to the brain, and recovery is impossible.

When fresh water is inhaled, the opposite state of fluid movement in the body takes place. Fresh water, having a lower salt concentration than the blood, is rapidly absorbed into the circulation. When these lungs are examined, they are 'dry' and altogether different from the waterlogged organs seen when sea water is inhaled. But there is worse to follow. Dilution of the blood with water results in destruction of red cells. Given time these could clog the kidneys, but in the short time that it takes to destroy even a small number of red cells, potassium salts liberated from the latter enter the blood stream, and this is one salt that the heart just will not tolerate and it stops, and will not go on whatever remedies are applied. It may safely be said therefore that after five minutes restorative measures are hopeless, but for the sake of the possible 'outside' case, it is advisable to continue efforts for a quarter of an hour or so, especially by giving the 'kiss of life'.

Why do a post-mortem examination in such cases? Does it matter if they are drowned? Of course it matters. Quite apart from the soulless statistical aspects of the matter, many relatives are anxious to know exactly what might have happened, and if they had been brought out earlier might not the life have been saved. With 'snorkel' hunters, deep sea divers and the like, did something go wrong with the apparatus, and if so, could modifications avert further similar tragedies? Many people have insurance policies covering accidents, and drowning is an obvious accident. If death is due to drowning, the relations collect the money. The same applies to quite a number of motor car accidents; it is by no means uncommon for death to occur from natural causes such as a heart attack or stroke, and an accident to happen as a result of this.

One also wants to know whether or not alcohol or other drugs contributed to the tragedy.

As far as it is compatible with doing the job properly and thoroughly, one always makes a great effort to treat the body with respect and a minimum of mutilation. After all, they have been personalities, but what is left is really only their old clothes. In nearly all cases, a relative looking at a body after a post-mortem examination would hardly ever think that it had been disturbed. I add this to allay the fears of some people who I believe think that we put the body through a sort of mincing machine. Nobody need be afraid, although very occasionally one has to make a very exhaustive examination.

An odd belief surfaced a few years ago at the Liskeard mortuary. I had lost the sifter that I used to dust French chalk into my gloves. I asked my wife for a replacement and she gave me a tin that had contained meat tenderiser; I left this behind and was told later that a visiting funeral director, looking at the tin, said, 'He doesn't have to use that, does he?'

8

Shocks

Unlike my wife, I do not have any homicidal tendencies. She would shoot, or at least castrate anybody who was cruel to animals. However, I am pretty certain that on occasion, and quite without malice aforethought, I have hastened the end of a number of people.

One such occasion is very vivid in my mind.

Late one evening, my friend Dr Stewart of Grampound 'phoned me up in some distress. A very wealthy farmer had at long last been persuaded to make a Will, but before he had signed it, he had a stroke and was now deeply unconscious. Could I suggest anything? Well, a stroke means bleeding into the brain, compressing it in the unyielding skull, and stopping it functioning. To relieve this pressure by drawing off fluid from the spine is invariably immediately fatal, as it crushes the vital brain stem into the opening in the spine. But what about drawing off fluid above this vital part of the brain, and relieving pressure in this way — scientifically, a cistern puncture? I said I would have a go, and stuck a needle into the skull at its base. Within less than a minute the farmer recovered complete consciousness. He signed his Will, and Dr Stewart and I witnessed it.

We went downstairs to celebrate in royal fashion. I was just counting out my five pound notes when one of the daughters rushed downstairs saying that her father was dead. Of course what had happened was that by relieving the pressure in the skull, the originally ruptured artery had started to bleed again, this time to a fatal extent. I had obviously been instrumental in the death, but we did not report it to HM Coroner, as we should have done. The rest of the family were far too pleased to want to cause any difficulty.

I kept my five pound notes.

Attacks by inmates of mental institutions on each other are not uncommon, but they rarely result in such injury as to cause death. But old Miss Margaret Lilian Hefferman, aged seventy-nine years, of the Retreat Hospital, St Columb, was an exception.

She and her bed neighbour, a young woman, Winifred Coles, constantly squabbled over their respective beds, Coles always wanting that of Miss Hefferman, wherever she was located. Miss Hefferman was normally tucked very firmly in her bed by the staff, lying on her right side, making it difficult to turn her out.

At 3.40 a.m. on 14 June, 1968, she was found lying on the floor outside her bed, her head towards the foot and her feet and legs pushed rather underneath. She was removed to another bed in another room, given tea, and appeared to be alright apart from some slight shock. By 6.30 a.m. she was dead.

I found a large bruise, four inches in diameter, over the left forehead, and rather remarkably a dozen or more crescentic, deep abrasions going through the whole thickness of the skin of the face. They appeared to have been made by violent digging of fingernails into the flesh. No skull bones had been broken, and no damage done to the brain. The spine in the neck however had been broken by a violent backwards wrench, compressing and bruising the spinal cord at the point of fracture. It was also found that the bones of the spine were very soft, easily fractured. The next thing found was half a handful of hair torn from the scalp of the upper part of the forehead. This handful of hair was found in the hand of Winifred Coles when Miss Hefferman was found lying on the floor.

I had some conversation with Coles, but came to the conclusion that she was devoid of any normal intelligence or understanding, and quite incapable of rational behaviour.

There were bloodstains around her fingernails. This blood was subsequently grouped and found to be Group 'O' — the same as that of Miss Hefferman, but also that of the young woman herself.

There seemed to be no doubt that the young woman had got up on the material night and tried to remove Miss Hefferman from her bed. Finding her firmly tucked in and immovable, she seized her by the hair, pulling her head sharply backwards, fracturing her rather fragile neck. She finally pulled her out of bed, pulling some hair out in the process, and just flung her on to the floor. I understood that she then got into the vacated bed, having triumphed over an imaginary foe.

Matches are forbidden in these institutions, but sometimes an inmate will get hold of a box. This was the unfortunate undoing of one inmate. He was doing one of the necessary functions of life, standing up against a wall. Instead of making the usual minor adjustment to his trousers, he let them fall down around his ankles, exposing the ends of his shirt. This was too much for a passer-by, who applied a lighted match to the back end. The poor man died of very extensive burns.

When I was young, about fourteen, we lived in Leytonstone, within five minutes of Epping Forest. Tram cars ran along the almost deserted Whipps Cross Road by the Hollow Pond. One of the great delights of my great friend Arthur Bailey (killed in the First World War) and myself was to save up our pocket money and buy potassium chlorate and sulphur. The mixture, when struck, goes off with a most satisfying big bang. We used to put dollops of this mixture on the tram lines at intervals, and watch for the result. I don't think I need describe them, but within about a quarter of a mile all the passengers were out and walking home, and the fire brigade had been sent for.

One day I very nearly killed myself. I filled a twelve inch length of ¼" copper piping with the mixture, put a metal bung in one end, and hit the other. The result was devastating. Broken windows, police and the fire engine. I was deaf for days. I can still see that tube flying through my father's study window, going past my left ear and breaking the glass.

Roderick Pennycock, aged eighteen years, was not so lucky. He had been experimenting with exactly the same material, but on a much more sophisticated level. He used a length of copper piping, two and one-half inches long by one-half inch in diameter closed at one end. In the closed end a hole had been bored for firing. He used ball bearings as his cannon balls, with devastating effect, mostly in his bedroom. The inside of the door was peppered and splintered by ball bearings having been fired into it. Some idea of the power of the explosive used was shown by the fact that 'bullets' had been fired right through books an inch or more thick — something akin to the devastating power of a .45 revolver. Numerous ball bearings were scattered about the room, some showing the effects of fire on them.

On the morning of 26 September, 1973, the boy was found slumped and doubled up underneath his bedroom window at the foot of his bed. There was a ragged split in the right side of his head above the ear. Blood covered the head and face and had run onto the underlying carpet. Brain tissue was seen in the blood clots. In the room there was a bottle, almost empty, of potassium chlorate. There was an empty tin that had contained sodium chlorate weedkiller, and also a cup containing granular sugar. In the empty chlorate bottle there was cellulose wadding that could be used to separate an explosive charge from shot.

A second 'cannon' device was also found. This was a piece of brass tubing thirteen inches long and three-eighths of an inch in diameter. One end was open; the other end had been violently burst open. The burst end had originally been closed, but perforated with a 'touch' hole. How it did remind me of my own 'cannon'.

Subsequent examination of the body showed a penetrating wound going right through the skull from left to right. The entrance and exit holes corresponded in size to the ball bearings littered about the room. The skull itself was fractured, and the brain disintegrated. Death must have been instantaneous, in the position in which the body had been found. The offending ball bearing was never recovered. The force of the explosion driving a 'bullet' could be gauged by the finding that some of the brain had been blown right out of the exit wound.

There was no doubt that death was due to brain injury caused by a ball bearing having been fired from the shattered brass tube found beside the body. There was no singeing of the hair around the entrance wound, which suggested that the 'gun' was some distance from the head when it was discharged.

What had happened? Det. Supt Willmott was in charge of the investigations and we naturally put our heads together. Amongst other things found was a cardboard box with a 'V' groove in one of the short sides. Half the corresponding side at the opposite end had been blown away. The central wooden pillar of the window showed deep splintering at the bottom, and the glass was badly cracked.

It appeared to us that the boy had loaded his cannon, prior to firing it at a stack of books, and had mounted it on the cardboard box 'carriage'. Chlorate mixtures can act in two ways according to the way in which they are fired. Set alight through a touch-hole, the mixture burns as a propellant, and this undoubtedly was the ordinary method of firing. But these chlorate mixtures can also detonate with explosive violence as opposed to the more slowly propellant action when fired. It is surprising what little force is required to effect this detonation. A sharp blow will set it off. If the boy had stumbled whilst holding the contraption, knocking it on the windowsill, that would be all that would be needed to set it off. Mr Willmott and I came to the conclusion that this is what had happened.

Unkind remarks were made by some ill-wishers that the boy had killed himself as a result of 'examination strain'. There was nothing at all to suggest this. He had recently passed his 'A' level examinations, and had been accepted by a university. The direction of the shot through the head, and the distance of the 'gun' from the head when the explosion occurred, in our view completely put out any suggestion of suicide. What a tragic loss of an enterprising youth.

Very many years ago, indeed when I was still in London and teaching at the Westminster Hospital, I was sent for to perform a post-mortem examination. Arriving at the wooden hut on the top of the hospital that served as a mortuary, I found my victim sitting up on the table. Thinking that this was a prank on the part of the students, I gave the body a blow on the chest, only to find that when his body went down, his legs came up. He was indeed dead, and had a spine deformed to a right angle by old tuberculous infection. I said to my post-mortem room attendant, Mr Faulkner, that this was going to be very awkward. He replied that it would be, and that it was also awkward for the relations. I said why? Well, he replied, it is going to be very expensive for them. Again I said 'why?' Well, he explained, there would have to be a special coffin, something like an upright piano case; this would not only cost a lot of money, being a special order, but it would look a bit peculiar when carried into the church for the funeral. Furthermore, they would have to dig a triple grave to accommodate the thing, and what could I do about it? The penny dropped. In the days when medical school museums were being created, anything exceptional was retained for teaching purposes. We had already got a sufficiency of bent spines, but I asked Mr Faulkner to approach the relatives and ask if I could have this one for teaching purposes as it was rather special. The only difference they would notice, of course, would be the next time they saw him, he would be flat. They were delighted, and in due course the spine was removed. Whenever we did this, the practice was to stiffen the body afterwards with a length of broom handle, for otherwise it was very floppy. I asked for a broom handle, and was told that we had run out of them. Well, go and get something else. Mr Faulkner reappeared with a couple of feet of one-inch gas piping, which did the job excellently. A few days afterwards, Mr Faulkner came to see me white and trembling, and I asked what was the matter. He replied that the relations, after consultation, had decided after all to have the body cremated, and that when the ashes were raked out, out came a couple of feet of iron piping with them. All hell broke out. They were not amused, but neither of us heard anything more about it.

Not unexpectedly, I have had a number of similar shocks. At Wadebridge some years ago, I was asked to do a post-mortem examination. It was in the summer time, and very hot.

Having arrived at the primitive post-mortem room there, I found no body. I was told that it was still in the coffin. So I said, 'get it out'. The Coroner's Officer replied that he couldn't, as it was so swollen that it was tightly jammed. There was only one thing to do, lift the whole thing up on to the table, and do the examination in the coffin, which I did. To my enquiry as to when the burial was to take place, I was told that it was going to be a cremation, in several days time. This presented a problem, as I was convinced that the coffin would burst long before that. So, I asked for a sack of sawdust, which was duly presented, and I spread it evenly throughout the coffin. To my surprise and consternation, I found that the sawdust contained a large variety of stones. I removed as many of these as I could find, but was informed later that some must have been missed as the remains, after cremation, had wrecked some of the crematorium machinery.

A new hazard for crematoria is apparently the presence of cardiac pacemakers inserted into the hearts of some people with heart disease, who have worn these contrivances for many years with supreme benefit. Ultimately, of course, these people die, and if they are cremated, their pacemakers are liable to explode violently and cause very considerable damage. Before I knew this, I let one of them go into the furnace; fortunately on this occasion nothing happened, but I had a certain amount of acrimonious correspondence about the matter with 'Authority'. Incidentally, they then cost about £4,000, and can be used again.

Another case that caused me anxiety occurred at Penzance. A youth of some sixteen years of age had been 'killed' in a motor car accident. When I opened his chest, I found his heart still beating feebly — but only at a rate of sixteen beats per minute, quite insufficient to maintain life because of an insufficient blood supply to the brain. This is the basic (frog) beat of the heart, a muscle phenomenon, uncontrolled by any nerve mechanism; it does however illustrate that all our tissues do not die at the same time — fortunately, otherwise there would be no heart, kidney or other tissue replacements. When I mentioned this to a meeting of pathologists some years later, one after another got up to say that they had seen the same thing, but had been afraid to mention it. I must add that even without my interference, recovery was utterly impossible.

9

Mercy Killings

I had another very anxious time when I arrived at the hospital one morning to find Miss O'Donnell comforting a white, shaking and almost inarticulate laboratory porter, one of whose duties was to look after the mortuary and its body refrigerator store. He had told her a story, and both of them said 'Come and look at this'. 'This' was the body of an elderly man in the refrigerator. He was not lying peacefully on his back. He had turned over, and his fingers bore markings of intensive scratching. Scrutiny of the hospital records and enquiries amongst the staff left no doubt that the latter had every reason to believe that the man was dead before he was removed from the ward; he had terminal cancer, and had been unconscious for several days. Although apparently revived by the cold, it is likely that his terminal actions to escape were hopefully more reflex than conscious. I have heard of similar occurrences in other hospitals. Fortunately, we had at the time a very sympathetic coroner, and very understanding relations. Now, with recently agreed criteria of death, this kind of accident is most unlikely to occur again, and nobody, patient or relation, need feel any qualms on this account.

This rather macabre diversion brings me to another point, and that is the modern tendency to preserve life at all costs even for a few hours, or perhaps longer, when death from incurable disease is inevitable. Intensive care and massive manpower are sometimes used to do this, even to unfortunates who have suffered irreparable brain damage. Undoubtedly some of these efforts pay off, but in the majority of cases the agony of suffering relations is merely prolonged. I believe that old, incurably diseased and suffering ladies and gentlemen should be allowed the dignity of a quiet and peaceful death. On occasion, I have helped them to have it — 'Thou shalt not kill, but needs not strive officiously to keep alive'. There is nothing to be afraid of in dying. What is left are only the old clothes of those we once knew, and it is only these that I cut up. I do not think that anybody should be allowed to die like a trussed-up chicken. Being somewhat cynical, I have always thought it curious that such intensive steps are taken to keep people alive on this planet when their religious beliefs are that there is a much better world awaiting them. 'There is a happy land', but they do everything possible to keep out of it.

One thing that does make me spitting mad is the crowd of gawping idiots who gather at the scene of an accident and wallow in the blood and sorrow that accompanies it. The more the blood, the better the occasion. Equally my strictures go to the press and television reporters who wallow in and parade the grief of relatives of those who are suffering. Of all the stupid questions that are asked, nothing sends me so far up the wall as the inane, 'What do you think happened?' to a poor victim who could not possibly give an answer. Whilst I am about it, also the press and television pictures of suffering humanity; who on earth wants to see a mother crying over her dead husband, child or whoever? I suppose, human nature being what it basically is, primitive and vicious in spite of the veneer of civilisation, given a taste of blood the human pack is in full cry. Disgusting.

People at both ends of the span of life are the most vulnerable to be done away with when they become a nuisance or are not wanted. Old people can become senile, dirty, gaga and a burden to their relatives, even if not a terrible trial, curtailing their freedom and social life. They are old and feeble with a tenuous hold on life. What easier than to put a pillow over their face one night? They were expected to die anyway. Or perhaps they are found dead in bed one morning with an empty bottle of sleeping tablets or aspirin beside them; perhaps a few are found on the floor, and one even in the mouth. Only the risk of detection by post-mortem may help save the lives of these unfortunates.

Into this category fall the so-called 'mercy killings'. They are a reflection of some of the most tragic of human experiences. They are not all that uncommon, and are generally brought to light by the confession of the person doing the killing. In these circumstances, my experience is that the Courts invariably take a lenient view of the crime, considering that the mental trauma suffered, sometimes over many months, by the perpetrator of the act as sufficient punishment. What does one do in the case of a middle-aged man, completely paralysed in all his limbs as a result of an accident, helpless, praying for death, and in the end asking a devoted woman who has been looking after him with complete unselfishness, to give him an overdose of sleeping tablets that have been prescribed for him? In the event, his overstrained nursing companion yielded to his importunities and gave him his longed-for overdose. Only a minimal one as it turned out, ten tablets of sodium amytal, not sufficient to kill a healthy man, but quite sufficient to kill him. Even more tragically, it turned out at the post-mortem examination that he had a severely damaged heart and might have died at any moment. The companion was not convicted of murder.

On another occasion, a young man put some pressure on the neck of his mother dying of cancer and in great pain. He went immediately to the police and told them what he had done, and had intended doing. The pressure had been so light, and had caused such little bruising that I might have missed it altogether; it was barely visible across her windpipe; that was all that there was to be seen; no broken bones, or severe injury. This case was a little remarkable in another way. It followed the Assize trial of Miles Giffard for the murder of his mother and father. The Giffard trial took six days. This trial, also for murder, took exactly ten minutes, and no custodial sentence.

There is some reason for thinking that the death of Ernest Massey was a sort of mercy killing, but not quite. It was an attempt to get him out of his lodging into the local up-dated workhouse at Redruth, once known as The Grubber.

Massey was a thoroughly dirty old man — in the physical sense. He was seventy-nine years of age, and lived in an isolated village, Porkellis, some few miles from Falmouth. He messed all over the house whenever he thought to do so, or did not think about it. He was senile, filthy, objectionable and undoubtedly a nuisance. He also had the objectionable habit of sticking his fingers into anything sweet, licking them and carrying on until disturbed.

He was looked after by a middle-aged housekeeper, who had been a cowhand, and who had also looked after his late wife until her death; she had also promised the late wife to look after the old man until he came to his end, objectionable as he was becoming. Also in the household there was a rather dominant female friend of the house-keeper. Miss Hargreaves was the housekeeper, Miss Boston her friend.

Massey had been failing for some time. He was visited regularly by his doctor, who became increasingly urged by the housekeeper to get him removed to the geriatric hospital, Barncoose, at Redruth. Unfortunately, no bed could be found for him anywhere, and he had to stay in Polkerris. On one occasion, the doctor was asked if it was likely that there would be an inquest if the old man were suddenly found dead. The doctor replied that an inquest would be unlikely.

On the morning of 19 January, 1962, the old man messed his bed with everything that he had available. The housekeeper changed everything, and the doctor was sent for, but he did not arrive during the morning. Later, the old man had a bottle of beer, and for lunch some soup, after which he was left alone. At about 3 p.m. he collapsed, and the doctor was sent for urgently; he arrived within a short time, only to find the old man dead: in his opinion, he had been dead for from one to two hours. There was no indication whatever that death had been a violent one, and it was not unexpected. But for two things, the doctor would have been perfectly happy to have signed up the death as due to natural causes; one was that the deceased had not been seen by him for more than a fortnight, and the other, much more important, the housekeeper reported that on the previous night she had found the deceased sitting on the stone floor of the kitchen, having apparently fallen whilst looking for some beer. He did not appear to have hurt himself by this fall. He got up by himself, taking his beer with him, and put himself to bed. He had fallen on other occasions in a similar way, but had never hurt himself. In view of the whole of the circumstances, however, the doctor thought the case should be reported to HM Coroner.

On the following day I carried out a post-mortem examination. There were no injuries to be seen, and I found none internally. There were no bruises that might have been caused by a fall on to the stone floor, but inside, everything was a dusky brown colour. There was only one answer; the old man had been poisoned by one of a group of drugs that changes the normal blood pigment (haemoglobin) into a brown variety (methaemoglobin). Some drugs can do this, but there were none of these in the house. There are photographic chemicals that can do it, but these again were easily excluded. The most likely cause would be poisoning by the common weed killer, sodium chlorate. A tin of this was found in an outhouse. It had been opened, and a little had gone.

Chemical examination of the internal organs showed no chlorate present, but this was not unexpected, as this substance rapidly decomposes in the presence of organic matter of which the whole body is composed. However, I did find some chlorate in the urine, and this clinched the opinion that death was due to chlorate poisoning, and that chlorate had been taken certainly within twenty-four hours of death, and probably much less. It was not possible to say how much had been taken, or with certainty over what period of time, but it must have been over a period of some days. The destructive action on the blood does not commence at once, but it continues for as long as any of the poison is left in the body. Death usually occurs in from one to ten days, with an average of four-and-a-half days; it might be expected to be less in a very elderly person.

A rough calculation based on the amount of chlorate found in the urine suggested that something like 1/6 oz. had been taken during the last twenty-four hours of life. About one-half ounce is generally accepted as a lethal dose, but it would be less in an old man.

Two ounces of chlorate were missing from the tin of weed killer found in the outhouse of the home. The tin had been opened on several occasions (notches in the lid), so that it is most unlikely that anything like the two ounces that were missing had been taken at one time. If administered at one time, the taste would have been intolerable and promptly rejected. Because of the taste, it is unlikely that he had ever at one time taken as much as a poisonous half-ounce dose as there was no history of gastro-intestinal upset, apart from the terminal vomiting and soiling of the sheets.

It appeared therefore from the total amount missing, and from the absence of any gastro-intestinal symptoms requiring medical attention during the few days before his death, that the old man had received repeated small doses of the poison over a number of days, and that the sixth of an ounce that it was estimated that he had had in his terminal hours of life represented something like the amount that he was having daily during those terminal days.

Massey was well known to have the habit of stealing food from all over the house, sugar and sweet things in particular; these indeed had to be locked away from him. It was strongly suggested by the Defence that Massey might have found the tin of weed killer in the outhouse, and because of its granular resemblance to granulated sugar, mistaken it for sugar. It has a salty, but not unpleasant taste, but it is not sweet. However, an old man with a vitiated palate might possibly have been deceived and mistaken it for sugar, but I thought it unlikely, and most unlikely to be repeated.

Sodium chlorate can be put into various beverages, particularly soup, without markedly affecting the taste, provided that large amounts are not used. The result is just over-salty. One ounce in a pint of any beverage is wholly unpalatable, and nobody would drink it. Half an ounce in a pint of tea is noticeably salty, but this can be disguised by adding a lot of sugar. With smaller amounts, the taste is almost unnoticeable. The results are similar when the poison is added to beer or ale, but it makes the drink froth a lot and go very flat. Still, it can be drunk. It is just tolerable to the extent of one-half ounce in a pint of lemonade, especially if sweetened, and in soup or Bovril it is not noticeable in amounts of under one-half ounce to the pint, excepting that the drink has a rather excessively salty flavour. This gives plenty of scope for adding repeated small amounts of the poison to ordinary and accustomed household beverages.

A search of the house revealed amongst other things a beer mug with dregs in it. In these dregs I found a grain of chlorate per pint. This did not suggest that any large amount of poison had been put into the old man's last drink, but it did suggest that a much larger quantity had been put into a previous drink. Massey was not noted for cleanliness. At the subsequent trial it was suggested by the Defence that he had been in the habit of spitting into his beer — a quite reasonable assumption. The possibility was accepted, but if true, there must have been a very large amount of poison circulating in his body at the time, indeed a poisonous amount.

After the finding of the chlorate in the beer, the housekeeper was questioned by the head of the CID, Supt Roberts. She made a statement that Massey had become an increasing encumbrance and nuisance in the household on account of his general senility and filthy habits. She had made repeated requests for his removal to a geriatric hospital without avail, and the position was becoming desperate. Two days before he died he had played up beyond her endurance, so she put the weed killer into his tea. She had purchased the weed killer some three weeks before to deal with an overgrown path. She said that she had no intention of killing her lodger, but only wished to make him so ill that he would have to be taken to the hospital, where she hoped they might keep him until the time of his natural death. She gave him small doses just to make him ill, and not a large one to kill him.

This statement of course confirmed my opinion that small doses of weed killer (sodium chlorate) had been given to the old man over a period of some days, probably over some three to five days, somewhat longer than her admitted two days. It had certainly not been given in one massive dose. This would suggest that it had not been given to kill, but only to make him increasingly ill, to guarantee his admission to hospital. Unfortunately for her, she was not aware that this is a long-acting accumulative poison, not showing its effects for perhaps several days: seeing no immediate results from her efforts, she continued to ply him with the poison, possibly increasing the daily amounts up to the time of his final collapse.

Miss Hargreaves was tried for murder at the Spring Winchester Assizes in 1962. At her trial she withdrew her confession — without which it is possible that no proceedings would have been taken against her. Anyway, this withdrawal prolonged the trial from a few hours to three days, at the end of which she was found guilty of manslaughter and sentenced to two years imprisonment.

The Defence naturally and quite rightly had been that the old man had himself put the chlorate into his drinks, mistaking the crystals for sugar, of which he was inordinately fond. This the jury did not believe.

The case was followed by a massive correspondence between girlfriend Miss Boston and every conceivable authority connected with it; she even accused me of having committed perjury. Nothing came of this tirade.

I am quite sure that Miss Hargreaves did not intend murder.

I am sure that Gordon Horace Trenoweth was not contemplating murder when he was surprised rifling the till of a tobacconist's shop on Christmas Eve 1942. He was unlucky. In those days the law was administered with much more harshness than it is now, and he paid for his foolishness by suffering the extreme penalty. Although I helped to convict him, I think his sentence was too severe for his crime. However, the Court of Appeal did not think so.

10

'Twas Christmas Eve . . .'

This is reprinted from the Bossinney Books publication, *Murder in the West Country,* by kind permission of the proprietor, Michael Williams.

☆   ☆   ☆

Christmas Eve Crime at Falmouth
F. D. M. HOCKING

Albert James Bateman, aged sixty-one years when he died, had been an accountant. On retiring some six years before his death, he had taken a tobacconist's shop, close to the harbour and docks at Falmouth, where he ran a thriving business. He was an extremely methodical man, of absolutely regular habits. He always opened his shop at 9.00 a.m., and never went home to lunch before 2.30 p.m. so as not to miss any lunch-time trade with the dockyard workers. Invariably he returned to his shop at 3.30 p.m., sometimes accompanied by his wife, who assisted him. He was a very fit man, enjoying good health, and keeping himself fit by doing daily exercises. Mrs Bateman said that she always told her husband that if he was ever held up, to hand over his money and not put up any resistance; but he had been an athlete in his young days and always said he could look after himself. But on Christmas Eve, 1942, this was precisely what he was not able to do.

During the morning of 24th December that year, Mrs Bateman deposited something like £160 at the National Provincial Bank, Falmouth. That afternoon, being busy with Christmas trade, he did not go home for lunch, but was taken sandwiches to the shop by his wife. He was then perfectly well and fit.

Mr Bateman's invariable habit was to leave his shop between 5.45 and 5.50 p.m., giving himself time to get home to hear the six o'clock news on the radio. He always walked, and took the same route home. On this Christmas Eve he did not return in time for the six o'clock news, but his wife was not unduly worried, thinking that in the circumstances trade had been brisk. By 7.30 p.m. however she had become anxious, and feeling that something was wrong, she hurried down to the shop. It was closed, locked and unlit. Thinking that perhaps her husband had gone home by another route, although very unlikely, she ran back to the house only to find that he was not there. Taking with her a duplicate set of keys, she returned to the shop, but again all was blackness and quietness, and knocking on the door produced no response.

Leaving the shop, she ran down the street, running fortunately into two policemen. They returned together to the shop, opening the door with the duplicate keys.

Blackout time was approximately 5.45 p.m. The shop was in darkness, and the blackout curtains had not been drawn. Police Sergeant Bennetts switched on his torch, and by the light of it they saw Albert James Bateman lying in a pool of blood around his head, on the floor behind the shop counter. He was fully clothed, and had his overcoat on. His face appeared to have been battered in. As the blackout curtains had not been drawn, it seemed that Mr Bateman was about to leave for home at about 5.45 p.m., as was his usual habit when he was struck down. Dr Harris, called to examine the body, pronounced him dead, and thought he had been dead for two hours or so.

Across an inner passage from the tobacconist's shop there was a tailors and outfitters shop where Mrs Phyllis Evelyn Cooper was an assistant. In her evidence, she said that it was normal practice for Mr Bateman in the evening before going home to come out of his shop, pick up the doormat from outside his own door and carry it to a cupboard under the stairs. Then he banged the door to, and it became locked. Finally, he would go back to his shop, put on his overcoat, change his cap for a trilby hat and leave for home. On this particular night, she heard all these habitual things happening, and assumed that Mr Bateman had left as usual. All that was found by Sergeant Bennetts confirmed that Mr Bateman had behaved in his normal manner on that Christmas Eve, but just when he was about to leave his shop, he had been confronted by an intruder who attacked him.

Superintendent Thomas Morcumb, in charge of the Falmouth Police Division was at once sent for, and he in turn sent for me, the Cornwall County Pathologist. Together we made a preliminary examination of the body, which was then removed to the Falmouth public mortuary for a post-mortem examination.

This examination showed evidence of asphyxiation, by the blueness of the features, and there were numerous injuries present to the face and head. There was a large bruise on the point of the chin, splitting the flesh down to the bone, and a light bruise over the larynx or Adam's apple. The left cheek was heavily bruised, and the upper jaw bone underneath had been fractured. The lips were split, and so was the skin over the left eyelid. The skull had been fractured at the back, and there was a large associated bruise in the scalp, and mottled bruising of the brain. The deceased had worn both upper and lower dentures; these were smashed into a large number of fragments; two were found lying on the floor of the shop close to the head, others were embedded in the blood clots in the back of the mouth. Blood in quantity had run down the air passages into the lungs, and these air passages had become completely obstructed. Death was due to suffocation due to the inhalation of blood from injuries to the mouth and face whilst lying unconscious as a result of blows to the head causing concussion. At least two very heavy blows had been struck to the face, one on the chin, possibly sliding down to the larynx, and the other on the left cheek. The fracture of the skull and damage to the brain could have been caused by the deceased falling backwards after having been struck in the face, possibly by contact with the wall or shelving behind him, as a result of the blows to the face. It is also possible that some of the injury had been done by stamping on the face, after falling. In any case, the blows could not have been self-inflicted, nor could they have been caused by any fall in the premises — there was no disturbance, and no sign of any blood on any object on to which the deceased might have accidentally fallen. The injuries were therefore due to a vicious assault, and death was due to this assault, and the assailant was therefore guilty of murder. Temperature recordings and other signs confirmed that death had occurred at about 6 p.m. the same day.

The hunt was now on for the murderer — and we were lucky.

A general examination of the premises had shown that there was no apparent disturbance such as would have occurred if there had been a fight. The shop had not been ransacked; £14, in notes, was found on the deceased, and £15 9s. 4½d. in silver and copper in an attaché case on a shelf behind a plywood screen. On the counter, in the till and other odd places there was scattered cash to the value of seven shillings. According to Mrs Bateman, however, at least £25 was missing. The motive for the crime therefore undoubtedly appeared to have been robbery; the assailant, presumably knowing something of the habits of his intended victim, waiting until he disappeared into the back premises of his shop to lock up. He then rushed into the shop, grabbed what money was in the till, but on leaving was confronted by the tobacconist on his return from shutting up before he could get away. Mr Bateman, being an old athlete and no coward, might have shown fight, but encumbered with his overcoat was no match for his assailant, who struck him down and ran off.

And now we come to the most important clue that was to lead to the assailant and his subsequent conviction for murder.

On the counter of the shop there were two significant objects. One was a bloodstained handkerchief, recognised by Mrs Bateman as having belonged to her husband. The blood on it was of his group, and it would appear that he had taken it out to staunch blood running from his face as a result of a first blow.

The second object was a 0.455 Mark II Webley revolver, first seen by Sergeant Bennetts near the till. At the request of Dr Harris he broke it; all the chambers and the barrel were empty, and no expended cartridges were found nearby. Mrs Bateman said that she had never seen the revolver before. It had not been fired shortly before its discovery — there was no smell of the products of combustion of cordite or gunpowder. Without doubt, it had been left behind by the assailant, who had gone into the shop with it, intending to frighten and hold-up the tobacconist for money, but not finding him there had put the weapon down, rifling the till with both hands, and then fleeing in some panic after his vicious assault, forgetting altogether about the weapon.

The gun was subsequently packed up and taken to Scotland Yard for examination for finger-prints. None were identifiable apart from those who had handled it since its discovery in the shop, for a reason that will be apparent later.

The number on the gun was 33748.

This immediately rang a bell in the memory of Superintendent Morcumb.

At the outbreak of war Falmouth Docks had been taken over by the Admiralty. The Armed Forces had commandeered a great deal of civilian equipment, including the 130 ton yacht *Ceto* that belonged to Earl Fitzwilliam. She had been converted into a compass calibrating vessel and had become H.M. Yacht *Ceto*. Rather pathetically, she was armed with three Lewis guns, four rifles, and one Webley service revolver No. 33748.

Ten months before the Bateman murder, in February 1942, it was reported to the police that this revolver was missing. It had been taken, together with all the other arms from the *Ceto* to the ammunition stores at the docks; these arms had been lifted by crane and loaded into a Royal Naval covered truck just before dinner time on 27th February. In the words of the storehouseman, 'When I returned to the store just after 12.30 p.m. I saw the load from the *Zeneth* (which had removed the arms from the *Ceto*) had been deposited in No. 13 store. I went to the canvas bag in which I had placed the revolver and found that it was not there.'

Some dozen people who had been engaged in moving the arms were interviewed, but nothing came to light. However, one of the dock labourers who had actually unloaded the jib-crane had a police record, having been sentenced whilst very much younger for acts of larceny. He would have a good opportunity of stealing the revolver. However, he agreed to his home being searched. This was done, and nothing was found.

His name was Gordon Horace Trenoweth, aged thirty-three years, of Mallin's Cottage, Falmouth.

It was therefore decided by Superintendent Morcumb to interview this docks labourer again, and at 3.45 a.m. on Christmas Day he and Inspector Martin called at his home. He was in bed at the time, and alongside the bed was a suit of clothes and a pair of brown shoes. On examining the suit, what appeared to be blood stains were seen on the right sleeve, and small specks which appeared to be blood, on the shoes. In view of this, he was detained and taken to the police station.

He was asked to account for his movements during the previous afternoon and evening. He replied that he was down town patrolling and shopping all the afternoon, and then went to Truro on the 7 p.m. bus. Two packets of Woodbine cigarettes (that were to figure later in the investigations) were found on him. He was offered a Players cigarette, but said that he preferred Woodbines, and had bought those found on him at Pearce's shop in High Street — which was subsequently disproved. He had been told that a man had been found with severe injuries to his face and then he made the most significant statement. 'I bought the cigarettes at Pearce's, I was not in that man's shop.' Asked to account for £5 9s. 9d. in his possession he said, 'I don't want to say anything about the money.'

He explained the presence of the blood on his clothing by saying it must have been from a bleeding nose.

By this time, I had arrived at the police station, and, with consent, examined the detained man. There was no sign of any recent nose bleed. Tests on the hands with chemical reagents that indicate the probable presence of blood, showed that there was probable blood on the back of the right hand and at the side of the nail of his third right finger. He was agitated.

Superintendent Morcumb then told me that Albert James Bateman had been found dead in Arwenack Street, Falmouth, with face injuries; that he, the detained man had failed to explain how he got blood on his clothes, account for his whereabouts during the material time, or account for the money in his possession. On Christmas Day 1942 at 10 p.m. Superintendent Morcumb charged Trenoweth with the wilful murder of Albert James Bateman, to which the accused replied, 'I am not saying anything now.'

The jacket, waistcoat and trousers taken from the accused, as well as a shirt were handed to me for further examination, together with the Webley revolver. My report is as follows:

'I had observed on the right cuff of the shirt the accused was wearing a mark that appeared to be a washed-out bloodstain. Later laboratory tests on this stain showed that it had been caused by human blood. Bloodstains on the suit were found in the following places: on the middle button of the waistcoat, a small drop; on the right cuff of the jacket, seven circular drops of blood, up to one-quarter of an inch in diameter; they were of human type. Nothing of significance was found on the shoes.

'The Webley revolver proved to be a veritable Forensic Scientist's paradise. Already, a preliminary examination of the weapon in the shop had shown the presence of a number of coloured fibres adhering to the oiled parts. Later examination showed heavy mineral oil on all the moving parts, and stuck in this oil, coloured fibres and a number of miscellaneous objects, to be described below.

'The suit was of good quality, not heavily worn. In particular the linings of the trouser pockets were by no means unduly worn thin. At the bottom of the left trouser pocket however, there was a tear two and one-half inches in length. The material had not been worn thin, and only the fibres in one direction had been torn. The inference therefore is that this hole had not been worn, but had been torn. The inference is obvious. Placed in a sound trouser pocket, the whole of the butt, and part of the cylinder (magazine) of a Webley revolver is exposed and very obvious. The revolver itself is about a foot in length, the barrel accounting for some six inches. If the barrel is pushed through a hole in the end of a pocket, only six inches remain in the pocket itself, and this is easily concealed. The gun hangs securely in such a position in spite of its weight, owing to the strength of the unworn cloth. It was suggested that the accused had carried the revolver about with him, concealed in this way, through the shopping centre of Falmouth on this Christmas Eve, with the intention of threatening some shopkeeper into parting with his takings. This method of concealment would also account for the fact that no recognisable finger-prints were found on the gun, they having been rubbed off by the motion of walking. That none was found on the butt would be explained by the rough surface of this part of the weapon, and the fact that it had been handled in this part by a number of Police Officers and other persons, including the Pathologist himself.

'Further examination of this torn left trouser pocket revealed a lot more. The edges of the tear were lightly smeared with mineral oil having the same physical (fluorescent) characteristics as the oil on the moving parts of the revolver. Moreover, a very large number of coloured fibres and miscellaneous microscopical objects were found in this pocket, mainly around the edges of the tear.

'A few coloured fibres and other microscopical objects were also found in the right pocket.

	Revolver	Left trouser pocket	Right trouser pocket
Cotton fibres	Blue-grey	Blue-grey	
	Undyed	Undyed	Undyed
	Black	Black	
	Blue	Blue	
	Red		Red
	Pale green	Pale green	Pale green
Wool hairs	Undyed white	Undyed white	Undyed white
	Dark mauve	Dark mauve	
	Light mauve	Light mauve	Light mauve
	Medium mauve	Medium mauve	
	Dark grey-green	Dark grey-green	

	Revolver	Left trouser pocket	Right trouser pocket
	Medium green	Medium green	Medium green
	Light green	Light green	
	Yellow		
	Orange	Orange	
	Red	Red	
	'Eosin' red	'Eosin' red	
	Pink	Pink	
	Dark blue	Dark blue	Dark blue
	Medium blue	Medium blue	Medium blue
	Pale blue	Pale blue	
	Slate blue	Slate blue	
	Coarse light blue		
	Mauve to red	Mauve to red	Mauve to red
Miscellaneous	Unburned and partly burned tobacco on revolver and in both pockets		
	Portions of feather	Portions of feather	Portions of feather
	Black horsehair		
	Skin flakes	Skin flakes	Skin flakes
	Insect hairs	Insect hairs	
	Thin brown human hair (not the accused's)	Thin brown hair	
Wood fibres	Blue-grey	Blue-grey	
	Grey	Grey	
	Unstained	Unstained	Unstained
	Pink		
		Yellow	
		Black	
			Green
Flax	Dark green	Dark green	
	Light brown	Light brown	

'A comparison of the objects found on the revolver, and the two pockets is shown in the table above.

'Hairs and fibres from which the accused's suit were made were found on all the objects examined.

'From the above, it will be seen that:

'Five out of six cotton fibres on the revolver are found in the left-hand pocket.

'Sixteen out of eighteen wool hairs are similarly found.

'Eleven out of fifteen miscellaneous objects are common to both places, and that flax hairs also correspond.'

I reported 'If these findings are considered in conjunction with the contents of the other pockets of the accused's suit, it will be seen that a very large number of small objects are common to the revolver and the left-hand trouser pocket, and are not represented elsewhere excepting in very much less degree in the right-hand pocket, and are almost wholly absent elsewhere. I infer from this finding that all these objects could have been originally attached to the revolver, some closely, by reason of the fact that they were embedded in oil, some lightly deposited on the various surfaces and not attached. It is these latter that would be more easily removed by rubbing. In my opinion, it is most probable that the revolver found on the premises of the murdered man Bateman had been concealed in the left trouser pocket of the accused.

'Examination of tapings and rubbings from the rest of the accused's clothing showed the presence of a number of coloured fibres and miscellaneous microscopical objects, but very little of the kind found on the revolver and in the trousers.'

There remained the problem of where the revolver had been since it had been lost from H.M.S. *Ceto* and its discovery in Mr Bateman's shop.

Accordingly, Inspector Martin and I went to the accused's home to investigate the probability that it had been concealed there all the time. Mallin's Cottage faces the waterfront of the Fal estuary at Falmouth. It is approached down a narrow passageway where in sailing ship times men and youths were shanghaied for service at sea. The upper part of the house is a huge sail and spar storing loft, and when entered appeared to be full of the unwanted junk of generations. Searching amongst all this miscellaneous material there was eventually found a strip of multi-coloured carpet. Brushings from the carpet examined microscopically showed the presence of all the hairs, fibres and miscellaneous objects found on the revolver and in the trouser pocket of the accused.

This was sufficient to prove the continuity of theft of the revolver, concealment at his home, and ultimate use of it in

Mr Bateman's shop by the accused.

There can be little doubt that the above findings would have been sufficient to bring about the conviction of the accused for murder. But there was more to come.

When the accused was first interviewed at his home in the early hours of Christmas Day, his clothing was searched, and amongst other money and things, four £1 notes were found. One of these notes, H 59D 650932, had been torn at one corner, and neatly repaired, by a piece of white paper stuck across it. Mr Bateman was a man of known meticulous carefulness, and had been seen on a number of occasions to repair torn notes. In fact, he kept a bottle of gum, and a pair of scissors in his shop specifically for this purpose. On the day of the murder, a Mr Sowden called in the shop and saw Mr Bateman repairing a pound note with a piece of paper. On 31st December, Sergeant Bennetts and Detective Constable Eden (as he then was) searched Mr Bateman's shop and raked through the mass of waste paper that one would expect to find in a tobacconist's shop on a Christmas Eve. Their efforts were rewarded. They found a piece of a crumpled bill head, with a corner sharply cut out, that appeared to fit exactly the piece used to repair the pound note found in the possession of the accused. The note, gum and cut bill head were sent to Mr Parkes, the Director of the Forensic Laboratory at Bristol. He reported that gum on the note, and gum on the bill head was identical in composition, and that when the crumpled bill head was flattened out, the missing part corresponded exactly with the piece of paper used to repair the pound note.

This was the evidence that was given at the trial of Gordon Horace Trenoweth for murder at Exeter Assizes on 11th February 1943, presided over by Mr Justice Tucker. The trial lasted for five days, and the accused was found guilty. In spite of a recommendation to mercy by the Jury, he was not reprieved.

There was some additional evidence against the accused that was not given at the trial, it being considered that the evidence connected with the revolver and pound note amply sufficient, and the additional evidence rather complicated.

The additional matter concerned the Woodbine cigarettes found on the accused when he was arrested.

These, and other packets of Woodbines were sent to Mr Parkes at Bristol for examination. This proved lengthy and complicated, but did prove that the cigarettes found on the accused were part of a delivery made to Mr Bateman, and to nobody else in Falmouth, including Pearce's where the accused said he had bought them.

The greatest tribute in this case must go to the late Superintendent Morcumb. Had he not acted energetically at a time when most people were preparing for the joys of Christmas, the accused might have got rid of all the essential evidence against him by the following morning.

I I

Infant and Child Deaths

At the other end of the lifespan, infants are particularly vulnerable, and it is becoming increasingly realised that baby-bashing is on the increase. It is an emotive subject.

Like all pathologists, I have been involved in a number of these. One of the worst concerned Tracey Jane Hackleton, aged five years. For the three weeks before the child's death, her mother had been living with a Naval friend as man and wife, although he was already married. He appears to have been very fond of the child, and wanted her to regard him as her father. However, the child would have nothing whatever to do with him. On New Year's Day 1975, the trouble started all over again, the child obstinately refusing to have anything to do with her so-called 'father'. Tempers obviously got out of hand, and very severe slapping followed. There was no indication that any blows with a fist had been struck. After this onslaught, which altogether lasted for some hours, the man went for a walk to cool off. On his return, Tracey started screaming again, and then went 'funny' and limp, and afterwards fainted. She came around, but was sick after drinking tea, and was then put to bed. This rumpus had been heard by a neighbour, who sent for the police. When they arrived, however, everything was peaceful, and they left with the advice that a doctor should be called — which was not followed. In the morning, the child was dead. Attempts to revive her by mouth-to-mouth breathing did nothing, and reactions to pinpricks and actually to biting were negative. What do they do, then? They decide to hide the body, bury it; and the suggestion came from the mother. How did they do it?

They dumped her fully clothed into an old oil drum, closed the open end with a blue plastic sack, and threw it on its side in a rhodendron thicket at Polbathick; they then made a statement to the Plymouth Police that they had taken the child to Plymouth, where she apparently got lost. No sign of a child of this description being forthcoming, enquiries were made and the body ultimately recovered.

The post-mortem examination was done by my friend, Dr A. C. Hunt of Plymouth. Without going too deeply into rather revolting details, the following injuries were found. Two-thirds of the face was swollen and dull red from multiple bruises; two bruises on the front of the chest, and an abrasion at the root of the neck; multiple bruises in both groins, on the hip bones, both buttocks and the lower back, where there was confluent bruising; multiple bruises on both arms and both legs, in many cases running into each other. There was a fracture of radius on the right side, and X-ray examination of this suggested that it had been done some three to four weeks before death. On the front of the left shin there was a distinct patterned bruise consisting of two half-circles, having the appearance of biting — confirming the statement that the male partner in this crime had endeavoured to 'bring the child round' by biting her, as well as sticking pins into her. All the injuries (apart from the fracture) had been made within the last twenty-four hours of life, again confirming the statements made by her mother and rejected 'father'.

I was called in by the Defence to see if anything could be said on behalf of the two adults concerned. It was the easiest job I have ever been asked to do. There was just nothing to be said in extenuating circumstances. I confirmed all Dr Hunt's findings; together we examined the preserved brain, and bleeding into it was found. The cause of death was this head injury, due to multiple blows rained on the head.

There could appear to be no excuse whatever for the malicious onslaught on this child, and yet one could have seen it developing.

A man deeply involved emotionally with the mother of a young child might easily desire that child to accept him as her 'father', and be very upset at being rebuffed. Small children can be irritatingly perverse, and a time can be reached when control snaps. This might be an explanation, but it would be no excuse. The mother's conduct would appear to be wholly inexcusable.

I do not think that any point will be served by describing any other cases of baby-bashing. It is distressing from all points of view, not least for those who have to investigate them, and I will say no more about them.

The death of infants from overlying is now extremely rare, a happy reflection of increasingly improving social conditions. I have however had several, mostly connected with drunken parents having their babies in bed with them. One case does stand out in my memory. It occurred in Chacewater. There was a family of six children, including a baby a few weeks old. Apart from the husband, for whom there was obviously no room, the whole of the rest of the family slept in a double bed. Mother, the baby and three children properly in the bed, the other two children, head to foot, across the bottom. It was not unlikely that the baby was suffocated.

One has heard of cats lying across babies and suffocating them. I have had only one such case, although at first it appeared to be one of simple suffocation. The baby was found dead, having apparently moved or crawled down deeply below the bedclothes, which were rather heavy. A peculiar feature however was a number of apparent pinpricks all over the face. The penny dropped; obviously a cat had crawled over the infant, who had tried to get away by sliding down the bed. As is the nature of cats, this one most likely went to sleep on top.

Much more common were babies suffocated by having been put to sleep on unsuitable mattresses — the old 'downy' type, how lovely and soft for baby. Also how lethal; it has only to turn over and find it impossible to breathe through. These cases were extremely worrying. Did the baby turn over, or was it turned gently, so as to leave no marks? We could only do our best, largely guided by other circumstances. This does not happen now with the new, hard and perforated mattresses.

Equally baffling are the 'cot deaths' which cause us so much trouble. Every one presents a problem. Was it a natural death, or was there something sinister about it? Only when the cause has been found shall we be perfectly happy. So many of them show signs of suffocation.

If my memory serves me rightly, and this is only a post-childish memory, mothers whose babies were found dead excepting from a certifiable cause, and especially those that showed signs of suffocation, were automatically convicted of murder, and many of them hanged. Then, more mercifully, the charge was reduced to manslaughter, and now, with enlightenment, no charge at all. It is a rather sad reflection on those not-so-far distant times.

We have had very few cases of children poisoning themselves by helping themselves to mother's 'sweets', otherwise her pills. I can recall only two. One was the straightforward taking of mother's green iron pills, which indeed do look like sweets. The other caused me much more anxiety. A small boy was said by his mother to have got hold of a bottle of fizzy aspirin (dispirin) tablets and took a lot as a fizzy drink. He soon became unwell and was rushed to hospital where fortunately he was sick, bringing up most of the drug. He had a toxic, but not lethal amount of the drug in his blood. He made a complete recovery and was returned home. The same evening, however, he again became drowsy and restless, and during the night had increasing difficulty in breathing. He was seen by his doctor who was not alarmed, but shortly afterwards was found to be dead. The post-mortem examination showed all the classical features of aspirin poisoning, and aspirin (5 milligrammes per 100 millilitres of blood) was still present in the blood, when I would have expected most if not all to have been eliminated. However, one can never be certain of this. I nevertheless had the nasty feeling that this child might have been given another drink of 'fizzy' aspirin after he had recovered from the first dose, just to make sure. Precautions had of course been taken to cover any suggestion of criminal behaviour by taking the child to hospital, and later by calling the doctor.

Several children have died from eating poisonous berries.

One of the first, aged seven years, on holiday from Wiltshire, became very ill, with cerebral symptoms of indefinite character and difficulty in breathing. He had a convulsion and rigidity, and died on his way in an ambulance to hospital. At the post-mortem examination, no sign of any disease could be found, His stomach contained a mass of blackberry seeds, but no other recognisable parts of plants. Chemical examination, however, showed the presence of the alkaloid coniine, the poisonous alkaloid of hemlock, so that he had eaten of this plant, as well as blackberries.

Another small boy was found dead with his stomach crammed full of holly berries. Holly berries are not recognised as containing any poisonous substance, but I could find no other cause of death, and tests for other kinds of poison were negative.

Equally unlucky was Susie Jennifer Bate of Valhalla, Tresco, Isles of Scilly. She and her sister filled themselves up with the berries of the plant Solanum Aviculare. Both became extremely ill, but the elder sister recovered. The younger one unfortunately did not. Portions of not only the seeds but also of the plant were found in her digestive tract, and chemical examination of the tissues subsequently showed the presence of the powerful poisons atropine and solanine.

I believe that after this, there was a massive purge of the plant throughout the islands.

The case of R-v-William Thomas Menheniot was of an entirely different kind. There had been no maniacal bashing about and no fountains of blood flowing. It was the end result of years of impatience with a rather dimwitted son by a quick-tempered irascible father, who constantly overdid such punishment as he considered necessary after frequent failures of the boy to comply with his wishes. There was never any intent to murder, although the jury eventually decided that murder had been done.

William Thomas Menheniot had gone to St Mary's, Isle of Scilly, with his family of five children, the youngest of which was Stephen, a backward youth. All the children had been at one time or another in the care of the Council, Stephen finishing up with the East Sussex County Council. Menheniot at the time of Stephen's death was managing a daffodil farm at Holy Vale, St Mary's, and lived there with the boy and his daughter Elizabeth, Mrs Rayner. Menheniot was undoubtedly a fiery extrovert, not suffering fools gladly, and his backward son no doubt irked him to the point of exasperation. Witnesses said that the boy was badly treated, beaten repeatedly, treated as a lackey, doing all the housework and generally treated worse than a dog. He had had a knife thrown at him, tea was thrown over him, and he was repeatedly punched. One witness said that he had seen Menheniot hit the youth with a heavy length of wood. On another occasion, the boy had been seen tethered to the greenhouse by a length of rope. He was seen to have been knocked to the ground by a tray flung at him. Even the daughter Elizabeth said that she had seen her father throw a shovel at the boy, and on another occasion a length of iron scaffold tubing, which caught him between the shoulders. Not an endearing line of behaviour, and if some of the stories of the assaults were to be believed, the boy would have been literally 'black and blue' almost the whole of the time he was in that home. And yet, although he was about in the locality almost the whole of the time, and in and out of the town of St Mary's, none of this was noticed. Only one person thought that he had been monstrously ill-used, and that was his dentist, Mr Forrest, who had on one occasion to repair broken front teeth and prepare a plate to cover the deficiency. The excuse given was that the boy had fallen off a tree — and indeed the boy made no complaint to the dentist. Stephen obtained employment in the town, at the Co-operative store; nobody there complained of his appearance, and indeed several came forward at the trial to say that they had never seen anything wrong with him. He went regularly to collect his Social Security (when unemployed), but again nobody commented or complained about his appearance.

Stephen himself never complained to anyone. Nobody alerted the Social Security people. Nobody complained to the police, and the police themselves, who must often have seen the boy, made no complaint. His own sister Margaret, who said at the trial that she had hated her father, said that she had frequently seen the boy knocked about, but not badly enough to make any complaint or alert any authority.

Stephen himself never made any complaint to any authority — police, social services, friends or acquaintances. Undoubtedly the boy had been knocked about, but nothing to the extent that some witnesses would have the Jury believe.

Stephen returned in 1972 to St Mary's from Sussex, where he had been in the care of the East Sussex County Council, in spite of a warning by the council's childrens' officer, who regarded the father as a dangerous man with an uncontrollable temper who would not be able to cope with the boy's slowness and backwardness.

Things came to a head around Christmas time 1975, when Stephen was nineteen years of age. He disappeared. Menheniot gave it out that the boy had left the island for work in Sussex, and produced a forged letter to prove it.

Matters then settled down until tragedy struck the daughter, Elizabeth, who was in hospital at St Mary's following a stroke. It was she who told the police about a grave in California Field, part of the property that her father was managing.

As a 'result of information received', the police went to this field, to a swampy part at one end, and there, under logs, brambles and flowers that had been planted over the top, they found a shallow grave containing the almost completely rotted body of a youth, subsequently identified by his clothing, as well as the circumstances, as Stephen Menheniot.

My friend Dr Hunt made the investigations on behalf of the police, and I was asked by the Defence to look into the matter in their interest.

Dr Hunt made a post-mortem examination on 18 May, 1977 and I followed this with my own examination on 24 May. We agreed the findings, which were, briefly:

Fractures at the back of the fifth, sixth and seventh left ribs.

These fractures had all been caused some two to three months before death, and had only recently united, with signs that the ends had probably rubbed together for some time before union took place, causing considerable pain.

There was a fracture of the seventh right rib, probably done only a few days before death.

The right upper canine tooth on the right side had been

very recently knocked out, possibly even very shortly before death.

Dr Hunt gave it as his opinion, and I agreed with him, that these rib injuries appeared to have been caused by at least four separate blows and at least three different times. Much discussion took place at the subsequent trial as to how these injuries could have been caused. Kicking with a shod foot, falling from a tree on to a projecting branch or other object were all agreed as possibilities, as was also a submission by the Prosecution that some could have been caused by an iron scaffold pole having been flung at the boy, as described on an occasion by Elizabeth, Mrs Rayner, who said that she had witnessed such an assault.

In conclusion, Dr Hunt gave it as his opinion that there was no evidence as to the actual cause of death, and this of course was obvious, as practically all the soft tissues and internal organs had disappeared. He ascribed death, non-specifically, as due to injuries done to the chest by blows, enumerating the possibilities. Before the Coroner, Mr Geoffrey Robins, he expressed the opinion that no definite cause of death could be stated, and with this I agreed.

It was at this stage that Dr Hunt and I for the first time departed from our usual course of mutual agreement on the interpretation of facts as revealed by a post-mortem examination.

The causes of death by rib injury outlined by Dr Hunt were stated to be (i) haemorrhage, (ii) air getting into the chest cavity, or into the blood, and (iii) pneumonia.

These are all extremely dangerous conditions; there could be almost immediate death from air getting into the circulation. In any case, the boy would have been very ill for perhaps days before his death. I agreed that he could have died in this way, but for the history of the last day of his life.

I went to Holy Vale, St Mary's, and had a talk with Mrs Rayner in the presence of PC Oram. What she told me then, she subsequently repeated at the trial of her father, with one exception that I will come to.

The home was almost indescribably sordid, untidy, unkempt and inadequately furnished, but it was clean.

Mrs Rayner described the dead boy as mentally

subnormal and dull. She also said that she did not think her father was wholly normal, being subject to outbreaks of violence directed mainly at the boy. The father and son were always having 'bloody rows', and at times came to blows.

One night, about Christmas 1975, father and son had a row in the downstairs passage. She said this was a verbal row, and subsequently pressed by me, she repeated that it had been a verbal row. After she had intervened, 'Dad went up to bed with the TV and the boy went upstairs to bed in another room, adjacent.' Subsequently she added that the boy had had a bath (downstairs) before going up to his room. Shortly afterwards, the boy went into his father's room to have his legs dressed. It appears that he suffered from the not uncommon skin complaint of sensitivity (eczema) to daffodils (lilies), well known amongst the islanders as 'lily rash'. That the father did these dressings for him does suggest that he had a care for his welfare and comfort, in spite of the outbursts of temper. The dressing of the legs was confirmed at the post-mortem examinations by the finding of bandages around the lower legs.

The usual procedure for the dressing was for the boy to put one foot after the other on to his father's bed, whilst the bandages were being applied. On this occasion, according to the only witness we had, Mrs Rayner, the boy was not standing very still; this irritated the father, who, in Mrs Rayner's words, 'yanked him round'. The boy fell against the wall opposite, banging his head — 'his head went hard against the wall and he fell down' — she also added, in her examination in chief at the Crown Court trial, that 'it was an accident'. After the boy had fallen down, he did not get up, but crawled into his own bedroom. There he lay on the floor, groaning. Mrs Rayner found him on the floor and told her father. Together they lifted him on to his bed. He was semi-conscious and dazed, and kept on mumbling. He could, and did answer on several occasions when spoken to earlier in the night, but subsequently became increasingly unconscious. He became cold, and his sister gave him a hot water bottle. Either father or sister went into him approximately every half hour, and found him breathing, but still moaning. This moaning disturbed Menheniot, who repeatedly shouted out at him, apparently without effect. When Menheniot went into him at about 3 a.m., he found the boy dead. This presented a real problem. Menheniot said that they could not call a doctor, because of marks on the boy. These marks were naturally the subject of much investigation at the trial, but all Elizabeth would say was that there was a mark low down on the boy's back. However, marks or no marks, no doctor was called, and father and daughter connived to bury him on the farm. The place originally selected was found to be too hard to dig up, so they took him, the day after he died, first of all in a motor car, and then on a farm wheelbarrow contrivance to the swampy field from which he was subsequently exhumed.

The Defence relied wholly on Mrs. Rayner's account of the happenings on the fatal night to rebut the accusation of murder, and submit that the boy's death was accidental, as a result of the unexpected fall against the wall when his legs were being dressed.

A blow on the head does not necessarily result in fracture, or serious internal (cerebral) bleeding. But a blow on the head can cause concussion, and varying degrees of unconsciousness, and in this state, especially if neglected, fatal things can happen. These may be listed, as I gave in my evidence, as (i) suffocation by the restless and partially unconscious boy turning over and burying his face in bedding; (ii) suffocation by the inhalation of vomit, a very common happening in these circumstances; and (iii) suffocation due to lying on the back, when the tongue falls backwards and obstructs air entry to the lungs. One of the cardinal principles of first aid treatment of the unconscious or semi-conscious is to ensure that there is an adequate airway and that respiration is not obstructed. Nothing of this kind was done for Stephen — most likely through ignorance.

My opinion was based entirely on the statement of Mrs Rayner. This statement was essentially that, up to the time of having his legs dressed, Stephen behaved in a manner perfectly normal for him. When I said that Stephen had probably come to live philosophically with his home conditions, I was really taken to task by prosecuting Counsel! However, I survived. It was only after the bang on the head that his behaviour immediately became abnormal, even for him. He was obviously injured by this blow, and as already said, such injury could have indirectly caused his death. There was no reason to suppose that Mrs Rayner was lying over this occurrence. The events of the evening must have burned themselves into her recollection. She did not depart from her story, and as was emphasised at the trial, she was there as a witness, and the facts were likely to have been indelibly imprinted on her memory. Almost at the end of her examination in chief, however, she made a statement that contradicted one of her earlier statements, a contradiction that caused us (and me in particular) some concern. Up to the end almost, Mrs Rayner had insisted that the final quarrel on the night of the death had been a verbal one. Now, in almost her last sentence, she corrected this by adding that there had been 'rabbit punches' to the chest. This of course was nuts and figs to the Prosecution, who now additionally alleged that these blows had refractured the latest broken bone and had driven it into the lung. This last-minute pronouncement by Mrs Rayner did cause me some considerable worry, as she had not mentioned it to me when I interviewed her. Refracturing of a previously healed fracture was of course possible, but it is difficult if not impossible to drive a fractured rib into the lung unless great force is used, as sometimes occurs in a motor car accident. I maintained that if this had happened, the boy would have become immediately, or very shortly afterwards, extremely ill, and would not have behaved as he did up to the time of going to the bedroom to have his leg dressed. In fact, after this alleged 'rabbit punch' he had a bath before going upstairs, and no complaints.

My final opinion, and this was agreed by Dr Hunt, was that no definite cause of death could be given with any certainty because of the advanced state of decomposition of the tissues. But I thought (of course) that my opinion more satisfactorily covered the events of the evening, and that death was therefore accidental — as indeed Mrs Rayner said when giving her own evidence.

Naturally we went for a second opinion, either to back me up or to point out my mistakes and refute my opinion. Prof. Keith Mant of the Forensic Pathology Dept of Guy's

Hospital was asked for his opinion after reading the various depositions. He agreed with me, and came to the Crown Court at Bodmin to say so.

Nevertheless, the whole of my theory depended entirely upon the veracity of Elizabeth, the daughter and sister, and this was emphasised over and over again by the Judge. If she was to be believed, then the probability was that Stephen's death was accidental. If not, then the probability was that the boy had been murdered.

Only the members of the Jury knew how these opposing theories presented themselves to them. In the event, they did not believe Elizabeth, and in consequence, me. They brought in a verdict of murder. It was a majority verdict, eleven to one. I wish I knew who the one was who supported me! Menheniot was sentenced to life imprisonment, with an additional five years to run concurrently (how else could it be done?) for obstructing HM Coroner in the execution of his duty.

The case naturally went to appeal. This was presided over by the Lord Chief Justice, Lord Widgery, on 5 February, 1979. Their Lordships unanimously threw out the appeal. It was my last visit to London until 1987.

Stephen was twenty years of age when he died after a lifetime of abuse. For this, Menheniot undoubtedly deserved severe punishment, but I do not think he ever contemplated murder.

A complete transcript of the trial has been written up by John Purchas under the title, 'Death on the Isles of Scilly. The Grave in California Field', published by Dyllansow Truran, Redruth, Cornwall.

12

Simple Murders

Most cases of murder that I have had to deal with have presented little or no difficulty from the forensic point of view. They have consisted mainly of violent bashings on the head, knifing and strangling, and a few firearms injuries.

But juries do sometimes bring in rather peculiar verdicts. Shortly before I arrived in Cornwall, two elderly people were found battered to death, both with severe head injuries, in the yard of their home near Redruth. A heavy billet of bloodstained wood was beside them. The jury brought in a verdict that they had had a quarrel and fight, and had killed each other. It rather reminded me of the story of the verdict of an Irish jury (whether true or apocryphal, I do not know) who, having inspected a body, came to the conclusion that death had been due to natural causes, but they thought that the post-mortem examination had contributed to it.

Forensic evidence that is put forward at a trial can be of the simplest, easily understandable by the most dim-witted. For example an old lady was found battered to death in her home at Camborne on 14 September, 1954. She was lying outstretched on the floor of her sitting room, with her head propped against the front of a chair. There was blood almost everywhere, including streaks going across the ceiling. Tufts of hair had been torn out and thrown about. Also on the floor there was a heavily bloodstained small hatchet — obviously the weapon used, and subsequently proved to be by linear markings at the sides of cuts in the skull bones that fitted irregularities in the cutting edge of the hatchet. Multiple blows had been rained on the unfortunate woman; she had raised her arms to ward them off before being finally struck down by blows on her head.

There were two men in the house as well as the battered woman, and each showed bloodstains on their clothing. Both were therefore suspect. When the shirt of one of them was examined, it showed, besides blood splashes and smears, a large accumulation of blood in the right armhole. The shirt of the other occupant showed no such staining. The interpretation was obvious. The wearer of the shirt stained in the armhole had held the little axe with which the murder had been committed in his right hand. Multiple blows had been struck on the scalp, a very vascular part of the body. The weapon became heavily bloodstained, and every time the arm was raised to strike another blow, blood ran from the weapon down the arm and into the armhole. This suspect took an overdose of barbiturates, and in spite of being rushed to hospital, and given vigorous treatment, died there, thus saving us a lot of trouble.

Murder by stabbing with a knife or other implement is not uncommon. When the wounds are multiple, there is little difficulty in coming to the conclusion that they could not have been self- or accidentally inflicted. When there is only one single stab wound, difficulties do arise. If it is into the side of the body by a single sideways swipe, there is not much trouble, but where there is a single thrust into the front of the body all sorts of questions arise. The Defence is always that the deceased ran or fell onto an outstretched knife held in a position of defence during a quarrel. It is indeed rather surprising how easily a pointed knife will pierce clothing and enter a body if only lightly thrust against.

During the evening of Saturday, 17 August, 1974, a youth, Philip Roy Moore, aged sixteen years, went to the Blue Lagoon Entertainment Centre in Newquay with some companions. The atmosphere hotting up, the youth left his jacket in the cloakroom. When he came to leave, he found that his jacket was missing, and was told that another youth had just gone out with it. Hastening after him, Moore caught up with him; there was an altercation, and Moore was seen by a companion to slump to the ground, whilst the other youth ran off. Moore's companion saw that he was bleeding, stopped a passing car and had the injured man taken at once to the Newquay Hospital, where he died a few hours afterwards. This companion also alerted the police, who were on the spot at once, and chased a young man they saw running away. During the chase, the police heard a faint 'click' from over a garden wall, and later investigation revealed a flick-knife in the garden. The fingerprints of the pursued youth were on it, and the blade was bloodstained. He was apprehended and taken to Newquay Police Station, and later charged with murder. Still later, he was convicted of that murder.

Examination of the knife showed that it was one stolen that morning from St Ives, and tests on it showed the presence of blood. The knife was one inch wide, with one very sharp cutting edge, the other being squared off. It was pointed, and the cutting edge was five inches in length; indeed a lethal weapon.

Post-mortem examination of the dead youth showed a single stab wound through the clothing and into the chest just below and inside the left nipple. There was no surrounding bruising, nothing to suggest a fierce fight before the stabbing; no injury anywhere else on the body. The entry wound was one inch wide, sharply cut on one end and bluntly cut at the other, corresponding to a wound inflicted by a knife sharp on one side only. The knife had passed almost vertically upwards, missing a rib, and going through the upper part of the lung, which was deeply cut four-and-a-half inches above the entrance wound. Internal bleeding had been massive, and this was the cause of death.

The Defence naturally was that there had been a fight, although there were no associated injuries, and that the dead youth had fallen on to the knife held outwards in a defensive position, or had otherwise fallen on to it during such a struggle, and that his death was accidental.

The Prosecution would not accept this; neither did the Jury, for the following reason.

The knife had entered the body by an almost vertical upward thrust, and had been pulled out again in almost exactly the same line. This was shown by the form of the wound. As already stated, this was in the form of a single cut just over one inch wide. The cut was rounded on one side (closest to the nipple), due to the blunt side of the knife tearing the skin open. On the opposite side, there were two sharp nicks in the skin in the form of the letter 'M', each nick being about ⅛ inch deep. This peculiar appearance was obviously due to the knife being thrust into the body, and then pulled out in almost the identical direction, i.e., a rapid up-and-down thrust. If the dead youth had fallen against the knife, or run against it, the knife would have gone in at approximate right angles to the body, and struck the underlying rib, which it did not do. Alternatively, it was suggested that the dead youth, jumping up on to the person he thought had stolen his coat, got the knife stabbing him almost vertically as he came down. This could not be accepted, as if he had been wounded in this way, his body would have fallen away from the person holding the knife, which would have been torn out of the body, leaving a gaping wound and much internal damage. The only way in which jumping on to the knife in the way suggested could have caused the injury as found would be if the injured man, after receiving his wound, jumped up again in exactly the same line to free his body from the knife. The jury agreed that this was not only highly improbable, but beyond all the bounds of reasonable possibility.

On such little things, as the form of this little 'M' shaped wound, can depend liberty or imprisonment for life.

There is nothing wrong about being a lesbian, and nothing unusual in the fact that, like all loving couples, lesbians sometimes fall out and quarrel. But they must be law-abiding, and not stick knives into each other in a fit of temper. But this is just what finished very permanently the friendship of Mrs Joyce May Dunstan Reynolds and her girlfriend, Miss Mary Scorse, on 16 January, 1952.

Mrs Reynolds wanted to end the association. Miss Scorse did not, and there were rows with increasing frequency over the matter. These came to a culmination on a day in Redruth, when Miss Scorse approached her late friend and attacked her with a sheath knife. Three blows were struck, two resulting only in superficial wounds. The third, however, penetrated from the bottom of the breast bone almost to the backbone. There had been some struggling before this was finally accomplished, as there were bruises around the right wrist of the attacked woman, suggesting that she had been trying to shield herself from the blows that she saw coming, but had had her arm tightly gripped. A heavy blow, probably a punch from a fist, had also fallen on to the left side of the chest. Mrs Reynolds did not die at once. She was taken to the Camborne-Redruth Hospital for observation; her condition progressively deteriorated, and operative intervention was imperative. In the late evening she was operated upon by Mr O'Donnell (who later became my father-in-law); I was present and noted the injuries, confirmed at the subsequent post-mortem examination. The internal wound ran inwards for some five inches. It went through the lower part of the breast bone, front abdominal muscles, through the liver and into the pancreas, narrowly missing the main blood vessel (aorta) at the back of the abdomen. Internal bleeding was profuse, necessitating two blood transfusions (not commonly done in those days). Wounds of the pancreas are particularly dangerous as they let out digestive juices from the damaged organ, and these play havoc; in this case they played fatal havoc, as was anticipated. The young woman recovered from the immediate operation, but it soon became obvious that she was dying. I then had what I think was the most distressing experience I have ever had. The police naturally wanted a statement from her regarding the events that had led up to this tragedy. It became my job to convince the girl that she was dying, and had no hope of recovery, and persuade her to make a dying declaration to Det Insp Roberts (as he then was) in the presence of a magistrate.

At the trial at Exeter, the inevitable submission was made that the dead woman ran on to the knife which had only been held out in a threatening gesture to try and force a reconciliation. However, the bruising around the wrist of the dead girl, and the fact that three attempts had been made to stab her, turned the scales against the accused. She was sentenced to death, but the sentence was not carried out because she was suffering at the time from acute pulmonary tuberculosis. She was described by her Counsel as 'a dying woman'.

The knife used, which had been thrown away but was recovered, was a sheath knife with a blade five inches long and seven-eighths of an inch wide, tapering to a point. It was completely new, protective grease still being on the blade. It was stained with blood of the same group as that of the dead girl, and there were also fibres on it from the clothing that had been penetrated before the body had been reached. There were pink woollen fibres similar to those of a vest that had been worn, and dark green woollen fibres similar to those in dark green bands in a jersey, also part of the clothing of the dead woman. Miss Scorse's fingerprints were on the handle.

13

Poisoning Again

A mining engineer and his wife retired to a cottage in the St Annes, Callington area, famous for the vast Consols tin mine. This mineral area also produced a large amount of arsenic from the smelting works, so much so that this poison became at one time a major export through the Morwellen docks.

Mrs engineer in due course died of acute gastro-intestinal irritation. At the post-mortem examination, no disease was found, but there was massive inflammation of the intestinal tract. In view of the history and the possibilities, the organs were taken for further examination. This showed that shortly before her death, she had absorbed a poisonous dose of arsenic. There was no sign of any chronic poisoning, for example there was no arsenic in her hair. Asked if he could account for this, the engineer husband thought for a long time. Finally, he came up with an explanation. He was a mining engineer, interested in old mine workings; the St Annes district is riddled with these, and he spent a long time investigating them. One day, his wife was taken with a minor illness, and kept to her bed; he looked after her, including doing the cooking. She rapidly deteriorated in health, and ultimately died, no doctor having been called. Thinking back, he thought that he might have accidentally contaminated his wife's food. He was in the habit of walking along the old mine adits and chimney stacks; the walls of these are almost completely lined with arsenic, and cones of the powder are (or were) found underneath the stacks. It was quite possible, he thought, that in rubbing along the walls, his clothing could have picked up some arsenic powder. Preparing his wife's food, no doubt some of this powder might have dropped into it. Asked why he himself had not suffered at all in the same way, he explained that he did not fancy his own cooking, but always went out for his meals.

Examination of the husband's clothing showed the presence of many crystals of arsenic similar to those in the mine adit. They were on the outside, in the coat pockets, trousers and waistcoat pockets and in the turnups of the trousers. His story of having picked up the arsenic by rubbing against the adit walls was therefore completely compatible with the findings, and with the handling of the deposits. Later he said that he had carried arsenic about in his left-hand coat pocket for some considerable time. Very careless indeed for a presumably knowledgeable, educated mining engineer. The analysis did indeed show much more arsenic in this left-hand pocket than in any of the others; indeed, if this had been the main supply, it would not be unreasonable for some to be transferred to other pockets.

The exact amounts found were:

Left coat pocket:	1.15 grains
Right coat pocket:	0.00072 grains
Left trouser pocket:	0.5 grains
Right trouser pocket:	0.004 grains

The case went to the Director of Public Prosecutions, but after much consideration he decided that there was no case to answer.

In December 1953, we had another case of arsenical poisoning from the same district that caused us some considerable concern. An old lady living at Albaston, Gunnislake, had had periodic attacks of diarrhoea, vomiting and thirst over a period of at least eight months. The latest attack had been a serious one, and her doctor suspected arsenical poisoning by a Belgian lodger who had been in the house since the attacks began. When I examined her, she certainly showed signs of chronic arsenical poisoning, and when her urine was analysed it was found to contain 0.4 parts per million of arsenic. This was not very much, but it should not have been there, and might even have been the residue from an intake days, or even weeks before. To sort out how long arsenic might have been given to her, a tress of her hair was taken and the arsenic content estimated at inch intervals — approximately two months growth per inch. As the tress was fourteen inches long, we could go back something like twenty-eight months at least. The result was most revealing. There was arsenic in the hair over the whole of its length, varying in amount from five to as much as twenty parts per million. This of course absolved the lodger, who had been in the house for only some eight months. But where had all this arsenic come from, if she was not taking it voluntarily, or if someone was not trying to poison her? The explanation came from the old lady's habits. Being country bred, she believed in natural sources for her daily requirements, and would not drink piped water. Much more suitable for her was water in the rain water butt, collected from the roof. In this arsenic-laden countryside, the dust contains a certain amount of the poison, and this dust, settling on the roof and then being washed into the water butt, eventually got into her system, at times in mineral poisonous doses. Analysis of the dust on the roof at this time (winter) showed an arsenic content of five parts per million, and in the water butt there was eight parts per million. We made an attempt to correlate the differing amounts of arsenic in differing lengths of her hair with wet and dry periods over the past two years, and there was a rough correspondence.

Incidentally, the urine of her son, also living on the same premises, was examined; arsenic was found only to the extent of 0.02 parts per million, a negligible amount when compared with the old lady's 0.4 parts per million. The explanation was obvious, and confirmed by the son. He preferred tap water to rainwater!

At about this same time, I examined fish from the upper reaches of the River Tamar, draining this same area. I found in them arsenic to the extent of 1.5 parts per million, three times the amount normally found in similar fish from the lower reaches.

The presence of so much arsenic in the soil of Cornwall, particularly heavy in granite areas, has bedevilled many a case of possible arsenical poisoning, not least the notorious one at Lewannick, when Mrs Hearn was accused of the murder of farmer's wife, Mrs Thomas, in 1930.

On 20 August, 1963, I received two samples of 'herbalist mixture' from Chief Insp. Jenkin (as he then was. Later he became Assistant Chief Constable). They had been given to him in the following circumstances, detailed in this letter from him to me as follows:

On Monday, 12 and Tuesday 13 August, 1963, a man and woman as described in the attached statements were in the Porthcurno area. In the course of their visit, the couple met a lady and later a gentleman. The man described himself to these people as a herbalist, and on noting that they were showing signs of illness, offered to prepare a mixture which would improve their health. He sold one bottle of mixture to the lady for £5, and one to the gentleman for £2. 10., this being the initial payment, the amount asked for being first £8, then £5.

Both bottles contain approximately one pint of a most dubious liquid. The liquid is foul smelling, and during the short period it had been in the possession of the police it appears to have been fermenting and a growth had appeared on the surface. No other people in the district appear to have been approached.

The lady's statement (abbreviated) said that she met this couple, and the man said to her, "Your breathing is very bad; I can fix that for your." 'I suffer from rheumatism, and the man noticed this and said, "I can cure you of that right away, I will bring you a bottle for it." 'I thought the bottle would cost about 5s., and I was prepared to pay this to get rid of him. The following day, he brought the bottle and I said, 'How much is it?' and he said, "Five". I said "Five bob?" He said "Five pounds." My husband paid it.'

The following day, the itinerant herbalist accosted the gentleman, who said he had been ill since an accident in 1955, having had an ulcer removed, and having jaundice. The man said to him, 'I am a herbalist and I can give you a bottle of medicine, and if you take it for a month you will be a new man. I have sold a bottle to the lady for £8, and she is like a new woman.' They haggled a bit about the price, eventually settling on £2. 10 immediately and another £2. 10 later on, provided that a written agreement was given that the stuff would cure him!

The 'herbalist' was never seen again, but his mixtures were analysed with remarkable results.

The lady's mixture consisted of a decoction of roadside plants, seeds and grasses, bits of which were all mixed together. To this decoction there had been added an approximately equal quantity of urine. The plants isolated included some dangerous ones, including foxglove (digitalis) and belladonna (atropine). A dead fly was floating on top, together with moulds. I reported that the mixture was worthless and dangerous.

The second bottle was not quite so bad; it did not contain any urine. It was, however, a similar decoction of wayside plants and grasses, including foxglove and belladonna. This time tea had been added instead of urine. Large numbers of yeasts and bacteria were present, but none of these was pathogenic — likely to cause disease. Again I regarded the preparation as worthless and dangerous.

Unfortunately nothing more was heard of the itinerant herbalists.

It would have been difficult to produce the two exhibits in Court. Both exploded by fermentation.

Most decoctions of this kind, and I have examined many of them, were sold by so-called herbalists to anxious overdue girls and young women — for obvious purposes. All of them useless for the purpose, unless definitely poisonous. A useless fraud battening on the frailty of young women.

One of these was a young woman who bought a six-ounce bottle filled with a viscous, very dark brown fluid, and also some pills labelled 'French Capsules'.

The mixture contained a large number of drugs reputed to have an abortifacient action, viz. aloes, liquorice, oil of Cardamon, myrrh and potassium carbonate. The French Capsules contained iron sulphate, gamboge, emodin and chrysarobin, all having a reputed similar action.

It is a pity that these girls did not recognise that (at the time) no drug, or combination of drugs will, when taken by the mouth, cause a healthy uterus (womb) to empty itself unless taken in poisonous doses. Most of these decoctions or medicines were sold at grossly inflated prices, advertised as tonics or faith cures, obviously disguising their real double purpose, one to produce an abortion, two to make a vast profit for the vendor battening on the frailties of young girls.

In November 1963, a gypsy, Samuel I----- by name, noted that a local resident had a bad leg. This was in St Just. He told the unfortunate sufferer that he had just the thing for him, and produced two bottles, one a Vat 69 whisky bottle, the other plain. This lot he sold for £5. 5. 0. Examination of the contents showed that the smaller bottle contained Cartwrights Nerve & Bone Liniment, and could be purchased for two shillings from local chemists, and the larger (whisky) bottle contained about eight ounces of paregoric worth about three shillings.

It is really remarkable how gullible the public can be on occasion.

In October 1943, a Mrs Rowe of Truro thought she had become pregnant when she should not have done. Worried, she went to the Queen of the Truro abortionists, whom we had been trying to catch for a long time. Mrs Juliffe treated Mrs Rowe generously, with the result that she was found dead in her home. The post-mortem examination showed that she had been poisoned, and further examination of the organs showed the presence of massive doses of abortifacient drugs. Not only was this a tragedy, but a further tragedy was that Mrs Rowe was not pregnant. When found dead, there were still in her possession the following: eighty-five black capsules, eighty-six dark brown gelatine coated capsules, a box of yellow pills, four gold pills, eleven magenta pills, six silver pills and silver 'blood pills'. Examination of these pills showed that they contained practically all the known (supposedly) abortifacient drugs; you mention it, they were there.

Mrs Juliffe was duly apprehended, and in her possession there was found a wonderful large box containing massive numbers of the pills found in the possession of the late Mrs Rowe, together with needles, probes, bundles of wax tapers and all the paraphernalia of the professional abortionist. The box measured some two feet by eighteen inches by about four inches deep. Mrs Juliffe went up, I think I am right in remembering, for two years for administering noxious drugs with the intent to procure an abortion. Meanwhile, I had possession of her box of tricks, and regarded it as one of my most colourful forensic museum pieces. On her release from prison, Mrs Juliffe demanded her stock-in-trade back, and although I protested, I was told that I had to give it up. As far as we know, there was never another abortion traced to this woman.

The case had a sequel many years afterwards. My wife and I, soon after we were married, decided to give a cocktail party, and we wanted it to be rather exceptional. It was. Remembering Mrs Juliffe's outfit, I recalled the delightful odour of many of the essential oils that she had used. I made a very dilute concoction of these and added the mixture to the conventional cocktail. Although present in only very small amount, the result was literally staggering. But the flavour was deliciously distinctive. Later on it became known as 'Hocking's Varnish', and was in great demand. Nobody thought of prosecuting me for adding 'a noxious substance' to their drink.

Some years after I had given it up (it was too much of a success), my wife and I went to a luncheon party. I had a Bishop's wife on my left, and opposite were the Bishop and my wife. It was a very sticky party, so to liven things up a bit I told the story of my special cocktail. Neither the Bishop nor his wife were amused. She turned her back on me, and the Bishop did the same to my wife. However, the others enjoyed it, and the party then became a great success.

Many are the people who have died of acute or chronic alcoholic poisoning, with blood alcohols in the region of 5-600 mg./100 ml. The worst of these was a lady who lived in the Wadebridge area. She had lived for the last three months of her life on three bottles of gin a day, to the exclusion of all other food. Incredible. She was a skeleton when she died, and her liver was the most perfect example of pâté de fois gras that I have ever seen.

One of these alcoholics should never have died. He was a taxi driver, and on one Christmas Eve he had been well employed and well-compensated for his services. Late that night he was found slumped over the wheel of his taxi, unconscious, and obviously deadly drunk. A doctor was repeatedly called to see him, and repeatedly refused to come out. The next morning, the driver was found dead, still in his taxi. I was furious, and at the subsequent inquest gave my opinion of the doctor's behaviour in no uncertain terms. The coroner did not back me up. Later, I heard that the doctor was threatening to sue me for unprofessional conduct, or slander or something, but nothing came of it.

Poisoning by cyanide was not very common, possibly because it is believed to be probably the most painful way of ending a life. I remember one foolish girl who developed an unrequited passion for her chemistry master, and in despair took cyanide from the laboratory and ate a spoonful of it — quite a lot. Cyanide poisoning is reputedly almost instantaneous, but this is not necessarily so. I recall the case of an elderly man, a resident of Newquay, who disappeared for some weeks in the autumn. He was discovered on the top of a corn stack which was being demolished for threshing — you can see how long ago that was! There were no injuries, no natural cause of death, so a post-mortem examination was necessary. Demolishing of the corn stack had been stopped. In his stomach I found a quantity of cyanide; no trace near the stack of any bottle from which he could have taken it. However, searching the surrounding field, underneath a hedge we found a bottle containing liquid. Examination showed that the liquid was a strong solution of cyanide. The bottle was far too far away from the stack to have been thrown from it. The only explanation was that the deceased had drunk his suicide draught somewhere near the hedge, gone to the corn stack and climbed on to the top. Rather a remarkable performance considering the supposed rapid action of cyanide.

I have investigated many fish, mainly salmon, killed by cyanide used by poachers. This is a useful poison to use, because it evaporates away on cooking. A cyanide killed salmon brought to me was therefore always a welcomed asset. There was also a generous supply of salmon killed by stunning for scientific investigations for a variety of reasons.

Most of my work with the old Cornwall River Board was confined to a running battle between that Board and the

China Clay Industry, which at that time was causing serious river pollution with their waste products. I must say that we fought without acrimony, and that as a result of our combined efforts practically all the rivers of Cornwall are now running clean and clear.

The other activity that I undertook on behalf of the River Board was to investigate every river and beach in the County for signs of pollution. The result was staggering. I found every beach and river heavily polluted with sewage, some of them to a gross extent. We were just about to raise all Hell about it when a report by the Public Health Laboratory Service said that they had made a similar investigation over much of the country, and that although they agreed with my findings that serious sewage pollution was occurring, there was no evidence that there was any risk to health. In fact, as far as I can recall, only one minor outbreak of typhoid fever was ever traced to rivermouth pollution down here, not in Cornwall.

One curious cyanide poisoning occurred on the River Camel on 6 July, 1976, when there was the possibility of poacher activity. It followed the removal of silt, gravel and weeds from the river bed. The dead fish were seen immediately below the disturbance, and I found cyanide to the extent of 0.22 parts per million in the gills. The only explanation seemed to be that the clearances had disturbed an old wasp's nest that had been treated with cyanide. (I have dealt with fish poisoned by poachers by many means, but I am not disclosing these.)

We had a curious death in the old Royal Cornwall Infirmary on 8 September, 1957. A Mrs Kathleen Burridge had been admitted; she had a long medical history of gastric upsets, and was finally operated upon as an emergency two days before her death, when part of her stomach was removed. She recovered very well from the operation, and was progressing favourably until 4.15 on 8 September. Just after tea, and just after her visitors had left, she suddenly collapsed, and then jumped out of bed shouting that she had just drunk poisoned tea, was going to die and wanted a post-mortem examination to be made. This was in complete contrast to the provisions of a will of an elderly gentleman, in which he specifically said that in no circumstances should

I be allowed to do a post-mortem examination on him. Unfortunately, his death was not a natural one, and I was duly requested by HM Coroner to do just that, which I did. He had been involved in a motor car accident; there were no suspicious circumstances. But to return to Mrs Burridge. She had visual hallucinations, seeing black spiders — there was no possibility that this was a chronic alcoholic hallucination! She continued to be violent for about half an hour, then gradually relapsed into unconsciousness and died an hour afterwards. No immediate diagnosis could possibly be made, but the House Surgeon did recall that a similar, but milder attack of hallucination had occurred on a previous occasion after visitors had left.

At the post-mortem examination I found some inflammation of the stomach and first part of the intestine, possibly not unusual considering her recent operation. Possibly much more significant, the end of her gullet was not only inflamed, but the lining membrane was partly shredded and blistered, very definite evidence that something very nasty had been swallowed. There are plenty of plants and fungi growing in this country that can cause hallucinations, and an extract of one of these could easily have been given to her. They are tasteless in tea. Hysterical hallucinations could be ruled out as the unfortunate woman did indeed die. It is well authenticated that a person can will his or her death. I have experienced one. When I was still at 'Westminster', a young Englishwoman came home from Jamaica where she had been living for some years. For some reason she fell foul of the natives, and a spell was put upon her by a local witchdoctor, who said that she would die at a certain time on a certain day. Naturally she was very worried, and asked to be thoroughly examined. She entered the hospital, and we all fell upon her. Sir James Purves-Stewart K.C.M.G., M.D., F.R.C.P., neurologist. Dr (later Sir) Adolph Abrahams M.D., F.R.C.P., Dr (later Sir) Arnold Stott M.D., F.R.C.P., Consulting Physicians, Dr (later Sir) Peter Kerley M.D., F.R.C.P., radiologist, Mr (later Sir) Stanford Cade F.R.C.S., surgeon, Mr (later Sir) Rock Carling F.R.C.S., surgeon, and me — not knighted and never likely to be. We did every possible known investigation on her, and found nothing wrong. She died at the appointed time, on the appointed day.

This is reminiscent of a story told by the same Sir Ernest Rock Carling. During the 1914-1918 war, as an army surgeon, he was examining a minor war injury in a young soldier when a message came that the young soldier's twin brother had been killed. He immediately said, 'I must go with him,' and promptly died.

But none of this seemed to apply to Mrs Burridge. I decided that this was too much for me alone, and that I wanted some support. I therefore not only investigated for poisons myself, but I sent half of the material to Mr Parkes, Director of the South Western Forensic Laboratory at Bristol. We both drew a complete blank. Looking back now, I often wonder if our present-day scientists with their new sophisticated methods might not have found something. The result might have been very different. As usual when in a jam, I sought the advice of my friend Prof. Webster. I quote from part of his letter to me, as it reveals so much of his kindly helpful character. 'With regard to the last part of your letter, I strongly advise you to insist on Parkes coming to give his negative evidence. Why should you carry the can? You live in the county, he does not. I should insist on Parkes being called and then say from a pathological stand-point the cause of death was unascertainable. For a chemist and pathologist to admit the limitations of science is no disgrace, but for you to say natural causes is for you to run the risk of some conscious-stricken idiot coming forwards at some future date and saying, "I gave her so-and-so".'

And so the mystery remained, and an open verdict recorded.

The carelessness of people with electrical fittings, lighting and heating appliances is quite incredible.

One lady in Redruth electrocuted herself whilst using an iron with a broken handle exposing both leads and with the earthing wire disconnected. The leads had been fastened into the sockets of the iron by match ends. The lead to the iron was also in a deplorable state.

Another lady incinerated herself in an aluminium caravan at Doublebois. The whole fire lasted only about a quarter of an hour, during which the aluminium shell self-combusted, the glass melted, and she was reduced to practically nothing

— a better job than is done in the some crematoria. The cause? A lamp made out of a jam jar, with screw lid. A hole had been roughly bored through the lid and an old lamp wick loosely stuck through it.

A young wife, only twenty-six years of age electrocuted herself whilst hanging out washing on a wire joining her caravan to a tree. Unfortunately, the line had been stretched across the main electric lead to the caravan, and the wind had caused the insulation to fray away, with the obvious consequence that the clothes line became alive.

An almost similar accident befell a young man cutting his hedge with an electric hedge clipper; he did not notice that the main lead to his bungalow passed along the top of the hedge, and he cut it with fatal results.

Almost unbelievably, Mrs Francis Vera Johns had an electrician husband who made her an electric fire. It had no fire guard, the element (a single one) was broken, the reflector consisted of a bent piece of tinplate, and the whole thing was not earthed. Mrs Johns appears to have fallen in the room, struck her shoulder on the corner of a table, and continued her fall onto the electric fire.

Deaths due to attacks by animals have fortunately been very rare.

As far as dogs were concerned, I have had only one, a boy of five who was savaged and killed by an Alsatian. On several occasions, however, dogs have attacked and done considerable damage to their owners after the owner's death, and sometimes this has caused considerable difficulty.

Two people had been attacked and killed by pigs, both being very considerably mauled. One unfortunate old man, aged eighty years was seen to slip in his pigsty, knock his head badly and was presumably rendered unconscious. He was seen, but before help could arrive, the pigs did the rest.

One man was kicked to death by his horse. He was last seen walking across one of his fields carrying a laden bucket in one hand. Later, he was found kicked to death by his horse. He had obviously stumbled in a hole in the ground, broken his ankle and was unable to move away.

14

A Tragic Murder

The most dramatic utterance in any Court used to be the death sentence — 'The sentence of the Court upon you is that you be taken from hence to a lawful prison, and thence to a place of execution, and that you there be hanged by the neck until you are dead, and that your body be taken down and buried within the precincts of the prison within which you shall last have been confined before your execution, and may the Lord have mercy on your soul.' This usually took about twenty seconds. I have known it last for less, and in the case of Miles Giffard, the Court and people in the gallery hardly had time to get on to their feet before it was over.

Just as dramatic, and probably more so, was an incident during the trial of William Douglas Biddick for the murder, by strangulation of Peggy Iris Moore and her daughter Donna Marlene Moore on 16 March, 1959, at New Mills, Laddock. Counsel had asked me how long the pressure would have to have been kept up around the neck before death occurred. I replied at least two minutes, and probably more. In his address to the Jury, Prosecuting Counsel invited them to consider just how long this could be. Taking out his watch, he said words to the effect, 'Let us start now.' In utter silence throughout the whole Court, not even broken by a cough, he looked fixedly at his watch. After half a minute had gone he said, 'One half-minute has gone.' At the end of a minute he said, 'A minute has gone, and the pressure is still being kept up.' At the end of two minutes he said, 'The pressure has been kept up all this time, at least, do you think he did not intend to end the lives of these two people?' Try it yourselves, and see how long two minutes can be.

To me, my most fascinating trial was that of James Camb for the murder of Gay Gibson, already told. The fascination was that there was no body, so that the imagination had free reign to run loose and we could indulge our imaginations to the full — a favourite pastime of mine.

To most Cornishmen, however, the case that aroused most stir and interest was that of Miles Giffard for the murder of his mother and father on 7 November, 1952. The interest was partly in the viciousness of the onslaught, but mainly in the mental make-up and background of the boy and the social standing of the whole family. The mental aspect of the murder has been well and truly dealt with by my friend, the well-known author, Colin Wilson, in, amongst other writings by him on the subject, his chapter, 'Miles Giffard of St Austell' in the publication, *Murder in the West Country*, again Bossiney Books. In this article, Colin Wilson gives a most learned and reasonable discourse on the psychological background to the whole affair. The case really all turned on common sense, and not the everlasting opposing opinions of psychiatrists.

In this connection, I will digress for a moment.

Many years ago I was involved as a medical witness in a case of buggery. Many hours of this trial were taken up by a psychiatrist giving evidence for the accused as to his mental state. He was followed by an equally eminent psychiatrist called by the Prosecution, who gave evidence of exactly the opposite kind. In his summing-up, the learned Judge (I regret I forget who it was) said to the Jury something like this: 'Gentlemen of the jury, you have listened for many hours to an eminent consultant doctor giving his opinion on the mental state of the accused. For about the same time you have heard an equally eminent doctor saying exactly the opposite. Now, don't you think that these equally learned doctors cancel each other out, so I propose that we deal with the matter on the facts of the case only, and ignore them.' I could not have agreed with him more.

The same disagreement was a feature of the trial of Miles Giffard. The opposing psychiatrists cancelled each other out, but the family General Practitioner, Dr Hood of Truro, 'put the boot' in with a downright straightforward assessment of the sanity of the whole family, whom he had known for twenty years or more. His commonsense assessment that there was nothing basically wrong with Miles's mental make-up was summed-up by Mr Justice Oliver in his final words to the jury — was Miles Giffard mad or bad? The Jury decided that he was bad.

The first intimation of tragedy was the discovery of the body of Charles Giffard at the bottom of a hundred-foot cliff at the east end of the beach at Duporth, immediately opposite my present home. He had been found by a local china clay worker on his way to work, spreadeagled across a large boulder and obviously extremely injured. His head had been split open and his brains spilled over adjacent rocks. Beside him there was a heavily blood stained iron wheelbarrow. This discovery was made in the early hours of the morning of 8 November, 1952. He immediately contacted the local policeman, PC Mutton, who passed the information on to the Assistant Chief Constable, Mr Reggie Rowland.

Mr Giffard was far from being a popular person with the police, or indeed with almost everyone else, in contrast to his wife who was universally liked. It is alleged that the conservation went something like this: PC Mutton: 'Charlie Giffard has been murdered.' Mr Rowland: 'Serve the b----r right.' A pause. PC Mutton: 'What did you say, sir?' Mr Rowland: 'What did you say?' PC Mutton repeated himself. Mr Rowland: 'Well, something will have to be done about it, and at once.'

Meanwhile the household servant girl, Barbara Orchard, had also telephoned the police. The previous evening had been her night off; she had spent it with her boyfriend, who had seen her home at about 9.30 p.m. As she was entering the house, she saw Miles Giffard drive off at speed in one of the family cars, a Triumph, which he had some difficulty in reversing, a common defect in that particular car; he had in fact reversed into the house before driving off. She was a lucky girl. Had she arrived earlier, she would probably have suffered the same fate as the owners of the house. Finding nobody at home when she returned, she was not alarmed as it was comparatively early in the evening, and her employers were not infrequently out late. She went to bed. On getting up in the morning, however, she found both Mr and Mrs Giffard missing, and there were suspicious bloodstains in the kitchen.

Det. Supt Julian, Supt Johns, other police officers and I arrived at Carrickowl in the middle of the morning and inspected the premises, with the following findings.

Facing the garage, the left-hand door was seen to be closed behind a black Standard 8 saloon motor car. The right hand door was open, and the garage space behind it was empty. It was normally occupied by the Triumph car in which the maid had seen Miles Giffard drive away the previous evening.

On the garage floor, along the front edge of the open part, there was an irregular water line, heavily stained with blood and ending in a mass of bloodclots and bloodstained earth. Six feet out from the garage there was a similar washed-out bloodstain, including bloodclots and a tuft of hair, later identified as part of the scalp of Mr Giffard.

Outside the garage, running in a direction towards the garden gate, there was a single wheel track that appeared to have been made by a heavily-loaded wheelbarrow. Following this track, we found a number of very heavy blood drops and clots on either side, all the way to the gate, near which some potted plants had been knocked over. Just on the house side of the gate there was a large pool of blood on the left-hand side, and a smaller one on the right. The gate itself and the posts were all heavily smeared with blood on the side facing the house. There were three large pools of blood on the path immediately behind the gate. Still following the rut in the path, the wheel track led slightly downhill towards the cliff overhanging Duporth beach. There were heavy blood drops, and some bloodclots at intervals on both sides of the track. Some of the drops and clots were sizeable, suggesting that the barrow, carrying a heavy load of a bleeding body, or bodies, had been rested at intervals because of its weight.

A handkerchief very heavily stained with blood was found

just outside the gate, on top of the adjacent hedge. It suggested that it had been used to wipe hands heavily stained with blood, which being slippery, would have affected the grip on the handles of the wheelbarrow.

Following the wheel marks still further towards the cliff edge, we came to an open patch of grass which had been partly beaten down. On the grass were three large pools of blood and bloodclot, each some six inches in diameter. By the farthest pool there was a collection of personal belongings, identified as those of Mr and Mrs Giffard.

There were:
    A man's hat
    A lady's hat (Mrs Giffard)
    A man's wallet — empty
    A bundle of letters
    A bunch of keys
    A collection of loose coins

Everything was heavily bloodstained; somebody's pockets had been rifled.

At this point the wheel marks divided, one branch bearing right in the seaward direction, the other slightly to the left across recently ploughed land and leading directly to the cliff edge and the rocky beach 120 feet below. At the side of this track there were drops of blood, and a heavily bloodstained man's glove. Going on to the cliff edge and looking over, we saw the body of a man spreadeagled across rocks below, and an iron wheelbarrow beside him.

Going back to where the wheel marks divided beside the bloodstained articles, we followed the right-hand branch and noticed that it was doubled. One mark was moderately deeply indented, but less than half seen in the track immediately leaving the house. It ended at the far cliff edge, some one hundred yards from the junction in a grassy patch above an almost sheer drop into the sea.

There were occasional projections of rock in the cliff face; on one, some six feet down, there was a dark red smudge some nine inches in diameter. Lower down at about twenty feet below, there were two similar-sized smudges. They appeared to have been made by blood, but considering the difficulties of the terrain, we did not investigate further. Looking over, we could see no body, but the tide was in. The returning track, to where the personal articles were found, was hardly impressed into the soil.

The inference was obvious. The wheelbarrow had been loaded with the bleeding bodies of both Mr and Mrs Giffard — it was a large wide barrow, and would just about accommodate them, although the man was heavily built. This load had first of all been overturned at the gate because it would not go through unless tipped sideways. It had been overturned again at the place where the belongings were found, probably because Mr Giffard was underneath and his wife on top, and it would not have been easy to have got at his pockets with this arrangement. Mr Giffard's pockets had been rifled after the bodies had been thrown out. Leaving him there, Mrs Giffard was wheeled to the cliff edge along the right-hand track, and thrown over. Returning to Mr Giffard, leaving only a very faint wheel track, his body was then placed again in the barrow, and the whole wheeled to the cliff edge and thrown over. Looking over the edge of the cliff, we saw a man's body spread-eagled over a large boulder, with an iron wheelbarrow beside him.

Proceeding to the beach, we examined the body first seen from above. In spite of the considerable facial injuries, it was recognisable to those police officers who knew Mr Giffard, the Clerk to the St Austell Magistrates and a well-known solicitor. He was lying on his back, fully-clothed but with the clothing drenched in blood and considerably disarranged. The head was completely crushed in at the back, and the brains spilled out over the adjacent rocks. It was obvious that he had arrived headfirst from above. Beside him there was the battered, heavily bloodstained wheelbarrow, for long preserved in the yard of the Bodmin Police Station.

As we were leaving the scene, we saw two police officers carrying the body of a frail elderly woman along the sand from the seaward end of the beach. The body was that of Mrs Giffard, immediately identified. It had been found wedged between rocks after the tide had gone out, and almost immediately below the point above where the beaten down and bloodstained grassy patch had been seen.

We returned to the house, and made many other significant discoveries.

First of all, we examined the Standard 8 car behind the closed garage door.

There were three heavy pools of blood on the floor of the garage underneath the running board on the driver's side, and another in front of the offside rear wheel. There were drops of blood on the offside front mudguard, and heavy splashes both inside and outside the windscreen. Inside the car, on the driver's seat; a pool of blood had soaked into the carpet, and another pool had collected all along the inner edge of the running board. Inside the driver's door there were blood splashes all over the window and lower half. Most significantly, there was a torn gash in the cloth covering the lower half of the door.

It now seemed perfectly obvious that Mr Giffard had been heavily attacked whilst he was getting out of his motor car. He had been beaten to death and then trundled in the wheelbarrow to the cliff edge over which he was subsequently thrown.

What kind of a weapon had been used? We searched diligently but could find nothing. But there was a peculiarity about the Standard car. As well as being smeared with blood, there were streaks of muddy clay thrown all over the windscreen and bonnet from the direction of the front of the car on the driver's side. This mud had been flung approximately horizontally at the car. On the top of the bonnet there was found a solid core of similar mud, almost bullet-shaped. It was cylindrical, one inch in length and three-quarters of an inch in diameter. Looking around, we found a stack of iron pipes of varying length standing at the side of the garage; the ends were buried some inches in the ground. These lengths of piping had an outside diameter of an inch, and an inside one of three-quarters of an inch. Using one of them as a potential weapon and striking towards the garage door in a simulated attack, mud was thrown off from the outside in a pattern similar to that seen on the Standard car, and more importantly, from the end a bullet-shaped core of more completely dried mud emerged. This core was exactly similar to the core found on the bonnet of the car. A pipe of this kind was therefore the likely weapon used, but the actual one could not be found — then. After Miles Giffard had been arrested, he made a statement including the fact that he had indeed used one of these pieces of iron piping with which to attack his parents, and that he had later thrown it, together with bloodstained clothing that he had been wearing at the time, into the river, at Fenny Bridges on the Exeter-Honiton road. Searching there, the police recovered both the clothing and the length of iron piping. This weapon measured two feet six and a half inches in length, and weighed three pounds. There was no blood on it, or hairs, but having lain for some days in running water, this would be hardly expected. However, mud inside it exactly matched mud in and around the pipes found in the garden.

The clothing was heavily bloodstained.

We then examined the kitchen and back kitchen of the house and found many bloodstains. In the kitchen there were heavy bloodstains on the door jamb and over the front of the stove. Over the middle of the floor there were semi-circular sweeps of watery blood, and similar sweeps were on the floor in front of the stove. They appeared to have been made by attempts to wipe up heavy bloodstains with a wet cloth. Splashes of blood were also seen on the walls, spattered about the floor and sink in the back kitchen, and there were smears on the taps. The obvious inference was that there had been a murderous attack on somebody, obviously Mrs Giffard, and that that person had been severely injured.

The two post-mortem examinations were carried out that same evening.

As far as Charles Giffard was concerned, it appeared that he had been attacked whilst getting out of his motor car, and before he had actually got out, with only his head protruding and his right arm lifted up to ward off blows. Four blows had fallen on the face, splitting it raggedly open, one on the right collar bone, and one or more on the top of the head very severely bruising it, and undoubtedly rendering him unconscious. Both eyes were blackened. A very important injury was severe ante-mortem bruising of the back of the right hand, extending some six inches up the arm. There was very marked swelling but no laceration, suggesting that a heavy blow or blows had fallen on to his arm, partly protected by the bloodstained glove later found on the pathway. This would be the result of the attacked man holding up his arm to ward off blows being aimed at his head. The cuts on the face had the appearance of having been caused by blows with a ragged-edged instrument, such as the piece of piping found.

The whole picture was perfectly plain. The assailant was waiting in the garage for Giffard to return, probably with the iron pipe concealed behind his back, and that when he (Giffard) opened the door and was getting out, head first as usual, he was attacked and belaboured with this iron pipe until he became unconscious, and probably dead. He was then disposed of as we have already seen.

We do not know the exact time of this onslaught, but it was probably about 7-7.15 on the evening of 7 November, 1952. Within minutes, Mrs Giffard arrived home, dropped a friend, left her car (a Triumph Renown) in the drive and went into the house. This friend, Mrs Wilson, must be reckoned one of the more fortunate people about at that time; if she had gone into the house with Mrs Giffard, it is certain that she would have met the same fate.

Miles was now in a quandary, facing immediate discovery. It was never supposed that he intended to kill his mother, but now it was a fight for his own survival and he had to get rid of any possible accuser. So he hit his mother over the head almost as savagely as he had done his father, but not quite. The bloodstaining in the house was nothing like that seen in the garage, nor were the injuries as severe. Both Mr and Mrs Giffard had the same blood group (group 4), so that we could not really sort out the origins of the various blood splashes, but any such exercise was not really required and would only have been a waste of time.

The post-mortem examination of Mrs Giffard showed that she had two very large bruises in her scalp, with considerable swelling. The scalp had also been split. A split scalp always bleeds profusely. These injuries probably did not cause death, but they would certainly have caused unconsciousness. Other, very extensive injuries all appeared to have been caused at about the time of death, as there was little associated bruising. Almost certainly they had been caused when the body was flung over the cliff and by sliding down a rough cliff edge. My opinion was that Mrs Giffard had only been knocked out by the blows on her head, and not killed in her kitchen. She was therefore alive, but of course unconscious, when she was thrown over the cliff, when she received fatal injuries. The only time that I saw Miles Giffard show any sign of emotion during his trial was when I said this.

What was the background of all this? It is this that has caused so much controversy, both at the trial and subsequently. Almost the last words uttered by Mr Justice Oliver, who tried the case, to the jury were, was Miles Giffard mad, or was he bad? The jury decided that he was bad. In this, I am sure that they were largely influenced by the impeccable evidence given by his own family doctor who had known him and the family since his birth, the late Dr Hood of Truro. Dr Hood had known Miles, baby, child, boy and youth, since he had brought him into the world. Dr Hood had also been the parents' doctor and knew the whole set-up from the all embracing view of the old-type general medical practitioner.

Miles had been a failure at practically everything that he had taken up. He had to leave Rugby School because he did not fit in, and he singularly failed at several menial jobs that he took, including peddling ice cream in Bournemouth. He lived largely by bouncing cheques and borrowing from his friends. On more than one occasion he stole money and jewellery from his mother and sold it, always to be forgiven. In the interval from November to March of the year previous to the murder, he had fecklessly got through a legacy of £750. Hardly any wonder that his father, a pillar of the establishment, became increasingly exasperated with him. Giffard himself was a hard, not likeable man, determined that Miles should follow his profession of solicitor; Miles wanted to be a professional cricketer; he would have been hopeless as a solicitor, and well he knew it.

The crunch came shortly before the murder when Miles, shabby and penniless, returned to Cornwall to receive an ultimatum from his father to work as a decent citizen in the family office, or else. . .

To add to his difficulties, Miles had fallen desperately in love with a young woman, Gabrielle Vallance, who appears to have been a good influence in his life, and who had agreed to marry him provided he got himself a stable job. Unfortunately, a sixteen-year-old youth of Gabrielle's acquaintance was also making passes at her, and this aroused Miles's intense jealousy. Now, threatened by his father's ultimatum, he could not return to London and Gabrielle, and this is what it was said 'finally closed the doors on his sanity', aided by half a bottle of whisky, possibly taken to give him 'Dutch Courage'. Drunkenness, however, was not pleaded in mitigation at his trial.

This was no 'spur of the moment' attack, but a deliberately conceived one, evidenced by the planned waiting with a lethal weapon in his hands for the return of his father. He had previously written to Gabrielle — 'I have had a hell of a row with the old man. As usual, he is right. He says he will cut me off without even the proverbial shilling. Short of doing him in, I see no future in the world at all.' In the later afternoon of the day of the murder, Miles telephoned Gabrielle to say he was coming to London that night, and three hours later he rang again to say that he was coming in his father's car. To provide himself with funds he had again stolen his mother's jewellery, which he sold in London for £50. He spent the day happily and relaxed with Gabrielle; they went to see the film 'Limelight', and had a meal. Later, in a Chelsea pub, Miles again asked Gabrielle to marry him. Her answer was not a definite refusal, but a request that he first got a job and became independent. It was immediately after this that Miles confessed to having killed his parents. Gabrielle did not believe him, but thought he was only saying this to impress her. However, at the door of Gabrielle's house, police were waiting the return of the couple. The position was a little more than delicate, because it was suspected that Miles was armed with his late father's revolver, which the police had discovered was missing from the home, and they anticipated a struggle. However, Miles gave in without offering any resistance.

At the commencement of his trial, Miles pleaded not

guilty, but changed his plea the following day. He had made a complete and comprehensive confession to the police, covering all aspects of the affair, and offered the only explanation that he had had a brainstorm — completely ignoring the obvious premeditation.

Two psychiatrists were called by the Defence, led by Mr John Maude QC, Dr Craig and Dr Rossiter Lewis. Dr Craig had known Miles since his youth, and regarded him as a schizophrenic; he was not surprised when he heard about the murders and said that, 'It fits into the picture of schizophrenia that he robbed his parents as well as murdering them.' I quote (with permission) Colin Wilson's report on the evidence given by Dr Craig. Miles had a long history of mental illness. As a child he had been subject to nightmares, and had often been punished for lying and stealing. The lying continued at Rugby School, where he also chewed holes in the bedsheets (? shades of Hitler) and wet his bed. He was expelled and sent home. His father was having a nervous breakdown at this time. At the age of fourteen years, Miles was sent to Dr Craig, who found him dull, apathetic and stupid. He seemed to be without emotions — it was impossible to upset him or make him laugh. His lying seemed to have no object; he lied as often as he spoke the truth. He was still suffering from nightmares and panic attacks. Craig diagnosed his complaint as a rare form of schizophrenia (which means simply that the patient had lost touch with reality); but an attempt at treatment was suspended because the doctor was afraid that it might only activate deep and violent disturbances in his mind. (The psychiatrist Jung often ended treatment of cases when he realised he was on the point of stirring up some latent psychosis that might destroy the patient.) The initial cause of the disturbance may have been a sadistic nanny, who locked Miles in a dark cupboard as a child, as well as beating him. The nanny had been dismissed, but by then it was presumably too late.

More recently, Dr Craig had again been consulted by Charlie Giffard, and had warned him that Miles was deteriorating. 'The doors are closing on his sanity,' was the phrase that he used.

This might have convinced the jury that there were

extenuating circumstances, but the prosecution, led by Mr Scott Henderson QC was adamant that Miles had planned the murder at least five days in advance.

Dr Rossiter Lewis caused further confusion by suggesting that Miles was suffering from hypoglycaemia, a condition of low sugar content in the blood; this often results in irrational behaviour, but there was no evidence whatever of any history of this condition. Dr Rossiter Lewis gave no explanation of how or why such a condition should have arisen on this one and only occasion. It was obvious during the trial that the Judge, Mr Justice Oliver, did not like Miles. After the question of hypoglycaemia had been raised, he threw down his pencil and remarked, 'I am very much afraid that I for one do not understand the position.' He asked the simple question, 'Would you say that packing clean clothes, getting rid of bloodstains, putting on clean clothes — is consistent with a man who knows he has done wrong?' to which the answer was 'Yes'. That was the end of hypoglycaemia. At one stage, Dr Rossiter Lewis had suggested five different reasons for Miles's behaviour. The Judge asked him which he really wanted. He was equally brusque with Dr Craig. 'Has it occurred to you that by throwing his parents over the cliff, Giffard might have thought to hide the wounds he had inflicted? That might lead one to a line of reasoning that Miles Giffard had wanted to cover up what he had done and that therefore he knew that what he had done was wrong?' To the Judge, that was the crux of the matter from the mental point of view.

To come back again to that very sane practitioner who had known Miles all his life, the eminently sane Dr Hood, who had been a life-long friend, doctor and confidant to the whole family, finally got the mental aspect away from the airy-fairy on to firm ground. He painted a picture of a comfortable middle-class home, marred only by one selfish and idle son who only wanted to play games — at which he was undoubtedly very good. Dr Hood had watched him closely throughout his whole life and had concluded that he was mentally abnormal only in that he was supremely selfish and lazy, and thought that his parents and the world generally owed him a living. To the question from the

Judge, 'Did Dr Hood think that Miles was mad or bad,' Dr Hood replied 'Bad'. This was one of the last questions that the Judge left to the Jury, and they had no hesitation in bringing in their unanimous verdict of Guilty. In all my lifetime, I have never seen such a magnificent performance in the witness box as that given on this occasion by Dr Hood.

The final tests of Miles Giffard's sanity came when he was examined by the statutory panel of psychiatrists before the death sentence was carried out. They found him sane, and responsible for his actions.

Charles Giffard was undoubtedly a Right Man.

This case is now being thoroughly reviewed by Mr J. C. H. Tully of Truro. He has had access to reports in Home Office files that were not available to either side at the time of the trial. His revelations may turn out to be sensational. I am sure we shall all look forward to them avidly.

15

A Determined Murderess

Another premeditated murder was that of Mrs Sandeman by her children's nanny, sixteen-year-old Elizabeth Sheila Ferguson.

During the 1939-45 war, many Naval personnel stationed at Plymouth and the adjacent Raleigh Camp were billeted out into rented temporary accommodation in the nearby towns and villages. Amongst them was a Naval Officer, Lt Sandeman, his wife and two small boys, living in a beach villa at Seaton, Downderry. The boys were looked after by the girl Ferguson, who had come with the family from Scotland.

In the middle of the morning of 10 October, 1942, the girl was seen walking across the bridge over the stream at Seaton from the direction of the villa, holding the children, one in each hand. They were all heavily soaked in blood.

Those who saw the girl immediately sent for the police, and kept observation on the house until they arrived. They saw nobody leave the house, but of course, somebody could have done so prior to their vigil. I arrived shortly afterwards.

When immediately questioned, the girl said that a maniac had entered the house and had attacked her mistress Mrs Eva Sandeman, with a knife. The girl went to her mistress's help, and was also attacked. One of the children that got in the way was also injured. The girl had managed to get away, and fled with the children to get help. She held up her hands, which were deeply cut, in confirmation of her story, and also showed a deep cut in the head of the elder boy. She added that she had gone back to the house after taking the children for a walk, to find the attack on her mistress in full sway in the hall.

Thinking that we had a homicidal maniac on our hands, and that he might still be inside the house, we sent in the most junior constable to investigate. Not being very brave myself, I took on the job of going round the house outside, looking for footprints. I found none. Meanwhile, the constable had gone from room to room, holding a broom-handle in front of him for defence, pushing the doors open with it, looking for an intruder. He found nothing in the way of an intruder, but he did find Mrs Sandeman lying at the foot of the stairway in a large pool of blood and obviously severely injured. When I was assured that it was quite safe to enter, I made a cursory examination of the body and noted massive stab wounds to the face and hands. Even a cursory glance showed that the wounds had been made with two different instruments. There were sharply incised cuts and stab wounds obviously made by a very sharp knife. Most of these had been made after death, as there was no associated bruising. The other wounds, with much bruising around them, had been made by a stabbing action with a much blunter weapon. In all, on later examination, I found no less than 126 stab wounds. They were mainly in the head, face and upper part of the chest. Very few in the back.

We did not have to look far for the weapons, because they were lying beside her. One was a very sharp, long-bladed breadknife. The other was a bill or reaping hook, normally kept in an outhouse and used for chopping wood. Most significantly, the blade of the hook had parted from the handle; all three, knife, hook and handle, were lying alongside the body.

Examination of the girl's cut hands did not suggest that the wounds had been made by holding up the hands to ward off blows with a knife or reaping hook. The cuts were at right angles across the fingers, close together on the inside of the lower parts of the fingers on both hands. Three or four were present on each hand. With the hand opened, they showed an irregular pattern, but with the hand closed, it could be seen that the lines of the cuts became continuous across the fingers; in other words, the knife blade had been drawn across the fingers, four times on both hands, with the hands clenched. The cuts had gone so deeply that the tendons of the muscle used for gripping had been severed.

All these findings and the absence of any men about the place made things look very different. The girl was questioned by Supt Frank Sloman on these points; she then told a very different story.

This was that she had come home from a walk with the children to find her mistress at the foot of the stairs with the reaping hook in her hand. For no apparent reason, the mistress attacked the girl with the hook, injuring her hands. The girl, then in a panic, ran into the adjacent kitchen, to pick up a knife from a dresser drawer, where it was usually kept, with which to defend herself. Not finding the knife there, she ran into the dining room, where she found it in a sideboard drawer, and then went back with it and fought it out with her mistress. Killing in self-defence in this way would have absolved her from any really serious charge. Accounting for the great number of wounds on the body of Mrs Sandeman, the girl said that she was so frightened, that she went berserk and didn't really know what she was doing. Reasonable enough, in a frightened girl of sixteen years. But the findings were at complete variance to this story. If this story had been correct, the first blood drawn would have been from the girl. Here we were in luck, because the girl and her mistress had different blood groups, Mrs Sandeman being Group O, the girl was group A. If her story were true, then a line of blood drops leading from the hall to the kitchen to the dining room, diminishing in number, would also have been group A. But, they were all group O. The drawers in the kitchen dresser and the dining room side board were indeed open; drops of blood in them were also of group O. Not a single drop of group A blood was found. In addition, there were very heavily bloodstained foot marks leading from the hall to the kitchen and back again into the dining room, where they faded out. The shoe pattern of these bloodstains fitted the shoes the girl had been wearing, so that when she ran into the kitchen, as she undoubtedly did, there was already a great deal of blood about in the hall, and that blood had come from Mrs Sandeman. Further, the girl had said that she had been attacked with the reaping hook, and had gone to look for the knife. But her injuries were typical of those made by a sharp knife, and not at all what one would expect from a relatively blunt reaping hook.

Well, of course we pieced together a story very different from the one told by the girl, and it was this evidence which was given against her at her trial for murder. The prosecution alleged that the girl had come from her walk with the children, determined to kill her mistress. The reaping hook was kept in a cellar by the back door, and she picked this up on her way in, attacking her mistress furiously at the foot of the stairs. The first few vicious blows on the head must fortunately have caused the woman to lose consciousness soon and would have felled her. The murderous attack went on until the blade of the hook parted from the handle, and both were thrown down and left beside the body. Not content with this onslaught, the now heavily bloodstained girl ran into the kitchen to get the bread knife from the drawer in which it was usually kept. Not finding it there, she ran into the dining room, leaving wherever she went a tell-tale line of blood drops and footprints, finally finding the knife in the sideboard drawer. Re-armed with this, she renewed the attack on her mistress, by now already dead, using the knife in a stabbing action; some of the cuts went deep into the chest. Blood is a slippery fluid, and getting on to the hands would lessen the grip until the hand finally slid down over the blade in one or more of the stabbing actions. This way the fingers slipping over the knife would be cut in continuous lines, as we found, and this went on until the tendons of the fingers holding the knife were also cut. Then the knife was transferred to the other hand, and the stabbing went on until this hand also became useless.

On this evidence, Elizabeth Sheila Ferguson was convicted of the murder of her mistress Mrs Eva Sandeman — for no reason that we were ever able to find out or even guess at. The girl was lucky in her Defence Counsel and in her jury. She was acquitted on the murder charge and given five years for manslaughter. She was completely unruffled throughout the whole of her trial and the previous interrogations. She served her sentence, but died soon after her release.

There was a curious sequel to this case.

The house became haunted, or was alleged to have become haunted. Nobody would live in it. Heavy footsteps were heard with nobody about, doors opened and shut for no obvious reason, windows opened and lights went on and off. A seance was held in the house, and a medium transmitted a message from Miss Ferguson to the effect that she could not rest until she had apologised to her mistress.

The local vicar was called in to clean up this lot, but whether he did not use the right words at the exorcism, or for some other reason, the happenings went on. Finally, they were stopped by an exorcism by the Bishop of Crediton.

16

Sexual Murders

Mrs Oldfield was just a little lucky.

On 4 July, 1958, Mrs Daphne Adeline Oldfield and her husband were on their honeymoon, staying at a small hotel in Bude. One evening, they went to a local dance, and Mrs Oldfield, an attractive young woman, not unnaturally spoke occasionally to young men there. This quite normal behaviour appears to have aroused the devil in her husband, who took her away. Leaving the dance, they went for a walk along the cliffs, starting almost immediately behind the hotel. At a point about half a mile along, the path approaches an almost vertical drop onto a pebbled beach 117 feet below. It was at this point that Mr Oldfield gave his wife a nudge and sent her over, presumably and hopefully to her death. Looking over the edge of the cliff afterwards, he saw that his wife had miraculously escaped immediate death, and was moving about on the stony beach beneath him. Hurrying back, he reached the beach and soon caught up with her. He then proceeded to belabour her over the head with a large stone; finally he took off his tie and pulled it around her neck. He left her for dead, but she survived all this, was found, and taken to Stratton Hospital, where I saw her the following day.

She had severe and multiple injuries, but was fully conscious. Of the injuries, there were three groups of significance. One group consisted of multiple jagged splits in the scalp on the top of the head, and a crush wound at the back, all consistent with her having been hammered on the head with a large stone. Almost certainly associated with these injuries were injuries to the backs of the hands, obviously held over the head to ward off the blows. The backs of both hands were extensively bruised, and there were ragged splits and abrasions. The fingers were similarly affected. Of significance was the fact that she was wearing engagement and wedding rings on her left ring finger; both of these had been crushed into an oval shape — an indication of the force of the blows rained onto the head. Other severe injuries were massive bruises and scrapes over the buttocks. These were in two groups, an upper and lower, the upper in the line of the body, the lower (also over the thigh) at an angle of approximately 45°. The scratches were filled with dark grey mud, and similar mud covered most of the clothing. Mud had also been scooped into the knickers that the woman had been wearing. A third, most significant group of injuries consisted of bruising and abrasions across the neck, strongly suggestive of an attempt at strangulation.

Examination of the cliff at the place over which she had gone showed exactly how these scrape injuries had occurred, and how her life had been saved as far as the fall was concerned. Although almost sheer above the point on the beach where Mrs Oldfield had been found, nevertheless there is a narrow indentation or gulley, where between the sheer cliffs on either side there is a slightly less steep slope filled with mud and stones that had accumulated from weathering of the rock on either side. The slope even here is something like 75°-80°, but the mud had collected in a series of rough shelves at intervals. On one of the shelves some six feet from the top, there was a deeply indented imprint of a shoe (or boot). Some forty feet down, the mud shelf had broken off irregularly; it showed marked scrape marks, and undoubtedly accounted for one set of such marks on the body of the woman. Still further down, there was another projecting rock shelf, not covered by so much mud, and this could have caused the second group of abrasions found.

Mrs Oldfield was heavily clad — fortunately for her. She had on a fairly thick and heavy blue coat, flowered skirt, pink cardigan, vest and underskirt, all heavily stained by the same mud as covered the cliff. It was obvious, and of course extremely fortunate, that her fall was not only broken in three places, but the blows on her body were cushioned by her relatively thick clothing.

The clothing of the husband was also examined. It showed mud stains similar to those found on the clothing of the wife, and there were also bloodstains on it of her group. Of more significance was his tie. It was smeared with blood at both ends, and both ends were crumpled, suggesting that they had been firmly gripped, as they would have been if, as the wife alleged, he had tried to strangle her with it. It was at this point that she lost consciousness and had been left, apparently for dead. The blood on the tie was that of Mrs Oldfield.

Mr Oldfield, after these events on the cliff top and beach below, returned to his hotel where he proceeded to take an overdose of the drug Carbromal. When found unconscious, he was also taken to the hospital at Stratton. His stomach was washed out, and the result handed to me; it was in this that the drug was found. On regaining consciousness, he was charged with the attempted murder of his wife and later duly appeared at Bodmin Assizes where he was found unfit to plead. He died shortly afterwards in a criminal mental hospital.

I have never in all my life seen such a change in a person as in Mrs Oldfield when she appeared at the Assize Court. She appeared to have aged fifty years.

Some murders, with a possible unbalanced sexual background, have been quite pointless.

Two of these occurred close together in Falmouth, one on 7 May and the other in March 1971.

On 14 March, 1971, a young girl, Helen Jean Veale, aged sixteen years, was found lying just inside the entrance to an old and long disused pillbox, left over from the war on the outskirts of Falmouth. She was dead, and from her body temperature it was estimated that her death had occurred between 7am and 9am that morning, about the time she would have been going to work. Her clothing was in great disarray and some had been violently torn. Her upper clothing had been pulled up, and her lower clothing pulled down to her thighs. Her trouser zip had been torn open. Her brassiere had been wrenched from her body, torn and thrown aside. Both shoes were off, one found inside the pillbox, the other outside. The fronts of the jeans from the knees downwards were heavily stained with mud, similar to that outside the box, and drag marks suggested that she had first been assaulted outside then dragged along inside. Beside the left hand, which was drawn up beside the head, there was a large irregularly-shaped stone weighing some two and half pounds. It was heavily bloodstained.

The post-mortem showed very numerous injuries, divisible into two groups.

There had been crushing blows on the face and left shoulder, done by a rough, blunt instrument, very obviously the heavy bloodstained stone found beside her. In addition, she had been stabbed twenty-two times — only one of them a superficial cut. There were stab wounds in the hands, their position suggesting that the girl had held them up to ward off blows aimed at her. There were three stab wounds in the back, two stopped from going very deeply by striking bone. The other penetrated the heart.

The weapon used to inflict these injuries was a knife blade about three inches in length, one half-inch wide, with one cutting and one blunt edge. Later that day a 'flick-knife' of this type was found amongst the possessions of a youth of seventeen years of age who was subsequently charged with the murder; a perfectly useless and sadistic crime.

Only one stab wound went through the two pullovers the girl was wearing, and none through the brassiere. It appeared therefore that the brassiere had been torn off before the stabbing commenced, and that the pullovers had been pulled up whilst the stabbing was done.

There was no evidence of any sexual assault. The girl was a virgin. There was no evidence either that the girl and the accused knew each other. The original charge of murder was reduced to manslaughter on account of diminished responsibility, and to this charge he pleaded guilty. However, he got the same sentence.

The enquiry had been a gruelling one for all the police concerned. When the arrest had finally been made, one of the detectives involved, who had flogged himself unmercifully for five days, collapsed outside the cafe that we had used as temporary crime headquarters. I naturally had him carried inside, made him comfortable lying on the floor, and sent for the ambulance. Before this arrived, he recovered, looking up at me bending over him, and not surprisingly shouted out 'Oh! No!'

Very similarly, an equally senseless murderous attack was made on a young girl (Valerie Ann Symons) aged seventeen years, also in the Falmouth area on 14 March, 1971.

She was on her way home at Mawnon Smith from a youth meeting in Falmouth on the previous night. She never arrived, and a search was started. In the early morning she was found at a site off the right-hand side of the hill leading from Swanpool to the Falmouth Golf Course. The body was just inside a gateway, on a stony path.

The girl was obviously dead, with severe injuries around her head. Her head lay closely between two very large stones; a third stone, flatter and not quite so large, lay across her face. This stone was heavily bloodstained. One of the large stones appeared to have been dropped close to her head, grazing her right shoulder.

Her clothing was not disarranged. The zip fastener of her trousers was undone, and later examination showed that her bladder was empty, suggesting the purpose for which she had sought some cover on her way home. Her upper clothing had been been pulled up only a little, and was almost completely undisturbed. There was no suggestion whatever of any fight. The ground was not scuffed up, she had not been dragged to the place, and there were no marks of abrasion or bruising on her hands, or on any other parts of her body. It appeared that the girl had been attacked and struck down without any preliminaries.

Post-mortem examination showed very extensive crush injuries to the head and face. There was some abrasion on the chest wall, probably due to one of the large stones having been dropped upon her whilst she was lying on the ground after being knocked down by blows rained on her head by the flat stone. Proof that she had been killed where she was found was shown by broken teeth scattered around. The girl was *virgo intacta*. There was no evidence of any sexual assault. It was a perfectly senseless murder by yet another youth of seventeen years of age, apparently perfectly mentally normal.

During the 1939-1945 war, the Housel Bay Hotel at The Lizard, along with many other Cornish hotels, had been commandeered for the use of HM Forces, the Housel Bay Hotel itself being occupied by a WAAF Radar Plotting team. The Station was commanded by a thirty-two-year-old Flying Officer, William James Croft, and amongst the personnel there was a dark-haired vivacious Welsh Corporal, Joan Nora Lewis.

Friendship between Officers and Other Ranks was frowned upon, and forbidden if there were any signs that the friendship had become intimate. It soon became evident that intimacy in every sense of the word had sprung up between these two, although Croft was already a married man with two children in Wales. Miss Freda Catlin, the officer in charge of the girls, tackled Croft about the association, saying that it was intolerable for morale and discipline. The affair must stop, and one or the other must go away. Croft's application for a transfer was refused by Higher Authority, so it was agreed that Miss Lewis should be posted to a Station in Devon.

The morning of 16 October, 1943, was cold and miserable. At about 5 a.m. the sound of a shot was heard coming from the summer house. After a short interval (about a minute or less), a second shot was heard from the same direction. Very shortly afterwards, Croft was seen leaving the summer house; he went up to the Duty Officer, Flying Officer Page, and told him that he had killed his girl. Croft next 'phoned a fellow officer, saying, 'I have shot Joan,' this conversation being overheard.

Indeed, it appeared very likely that he had done so.

Police Superintendent Thomas Morcumb and I arrived at the summer house at about 7 a.m., and there we found the body of Joan Lewis stretched out on the floor, and obviously dead. She had been shot twice, once through the left side of the chest in the region of her heart, and again through her head on the same side. On a nearby table there was a Webley revolver; it had been fully loaded. Two adjacent shells had been fired, and the firing pin had struck

191

a third shell, which had not fired and was still in position in the firing chamber. The girl was lying on the floor in a pool of blood around her head and chest, but the shot into the chest appeared to have been fired whilst she was sitting on a adjacent settee, as there was a bloodstained bullet hole through the material at the back at about the height of a shot into the chest at the level of the heart. A rather flattened 0.455 bullet was subsequently recovered from the back of the settee.

The body was removed to the RAF Headquarters at Predannack, where in the afternoon I made a post-mortem examination.

It was confirmed that the girl had been shot twice.

The first shot was the one into the chest, obviously aimed at the heart, but which it completely missed. The revolver had been fired some five or six inches away from the tunic, not pressed against the chest as would be more likely in a suicidal action. The distance from the body was proved by the degree of burning of the material, and the spread of unburned powder fanning out in a cone from the muzzle of the weapon. As is not altogether unusual in these cases, the bullet had not gone straight through the body in the firing line. Instead, the bullet struck a rib (the sixth), which it fractured. It then deflected upwards, completely missing the heart, and then went backwards, coming out at the side underneath the armpit. The explosion severely damaged the lower part of the left lung, and most important, the track of the bullet, injury by the explosion and subsequent bleeding had severely damaged the muscle over the upper part of the chest that is used in raising the arm. This point became the crucial argument at the trial at Winchester Assizes, when the Defence tried to make out that this was a case of suicide and not murder. The Defence accepted without argument that this was the first of the shots that had been fired. How could we be sure of that? There was no difficulty in coming to that conclusion; it was shown by the massive bleeding into the surrounding tissues along the line of the bullet track. This can be understood when it is remembered that the blood in the blood vessels is under considerable pressure. When an artery is damaged, blood seeps out of it under this pressure and infiltrates widely. If the same vessel is damaged after death, there is no blood pressure in it, and no infiltration of blood. In this case, there was wide infiltration of blood all along the bullet tract. The shot through the head would have caused instantaneous death. If this had been the first shot, then death would have taken place before the shot through the chest, and there would have been no infiltration of blood along the chest bullet tract. So, we have the first shot through the chest, not causing death. The shot could have been fired by the girl herself, although in a very awkward and unlikely way. It could more than equally have been fired by someone else.

Now about the all-important second, killing shot. The bullet had entered the skull three inches above and an inch behind the left eye. It had gone through the skull from above and in front of the left ear, emerging at the same level behind the right ear. It had been fired from left to right without a shadow of doubt, accepted by the Defence. If this point needs explanation, it is that when a foreign body, such as a bullet, enters a plate of bone such as the skull, the bone is compressed at the point of entry and a clean sharp cut is made. On the other side of the plate, the bone is expanded outwards in the form of a bevelled cone. In this skull, the bevelled exit hole was on the inside of the left side of the skull, and on the outside behind the right ear. Moreover, as again is usual, the exit wound was larger than the entrance wound because the bullet starts to spin after meeting its first obstruction.

From the complete absence of any burning of the skin and hair around the entrance wound, and from the range of spread of unburned powder, it was estimated that the revolver had been held at least eighteen inches away from the head when it was fired. This fact was also agreed by the Defence.

The obvious interpretation of these finding was that the girl had been shot twice by a 0.455 Webley revolver. One shot, the first, aimed at the heart from a distance of some five to six inches, had obviously gone wrong. This shot was fired whilst she was sitting on the settee, and it had gone right through her into the back of the furniture. Quite understandably, she fell from the settee onto the floor, and lying or kneeling there, the second shot was fired through her head. There were blood splashes and smears over the settee, confirming that she had been sitting there when she probably received the first of her injuries. A 0.455 bullet was found in a patch of blood adjacent to the settee.

I gave it as my opinion that the girl had died of gunshot injuries inflicted by some other person.

Now the legal battle was joined.

After saying, possibly in the tension of the moment, that he had shot the girl, Croft changed his plea and said that there had been a suicide pact, and Miss Lewis had shot herself. This in the first place might sound rather ridiculous, as the revolver was found on an adjacent table some yards from the body. The revolver was later examined for fingerprints, but there was such a confusion of them that it could not be positively said that the girl had handled the weapon. However, there it was on the table, and Croft said that the girl had shot herself some yards away, and presumably had put it there afterwards.

This may sound silly and impossible, but it is not, although it must be extremely rare. I recall a case, also during the war, at the RAF Station, St Eval. One morning a bang, obviously a gunshot, was heard coming from a Nissen hut used as sleeping quarters. The hut was under observation from the moment of hearing the gunshot, and two ratings immediately went inside. At first they saw nothing, but going to the end, they saw a mound in one of the beds, obviously a body. The bedclothes were drawn right up, and when pulled down they saw the body of a man with his arms folded over his chest. On the bedside table beside him there was Webley revolver with a recently discharged cartridge in situ — the cylinder was still warm. The man had been shot through the head, and must have died instantaneously. There could be no doubt that he had shot himself, and then, when presumably dead, he had put the revolver on to the bedside table, pulled the bedclothes over his head, and then folded his arms. Fortunately, this kind of matter was not brought up by the Defence at the subsequent trial.

Croft's final story was that rather than be parted, they would commit suicide together. In his statement he said, 'We woke about four-thirty. There was a moon, but the light was obscured by clouds. We could just distinguish each other. It was raining heavily, and blowing a gale. I placed the gun on our laps and then we clasped our hands together. We arranged that whoever felt like making the first move was to take the gun, use it, and the one left was to use it in turn.' He goes on to add that a shot awakened him and he found the girl grasping her breast. 'It is hurting me; go and get help.' He climbed out of the window (why the window, the door was open) and almost immediately heard a second shot. He returned to the summer house and put the revolver to his own head, but confessed that he could not pull the trigger. He tried a second time, but again failed. I will make a further comment on this later.

If this story was true, it would have been a good defence against the major charge of murder, and it was the defence that was adopted. Croft was tried before Mr Justice Humphries at the Winchester Assizes in December 1943.

I admitted that the girl could have fired the first shot into her chest, although I thought it unlikely. It would have had to be done with the muzzle five to six inches away. In this position she could not have had her finger on the trigger, but could have fired the shot with her thumb, an extremely awkward and unlikely procedure. The revolver was not easy to fire. When cocked, it required a pull of six pounds ten ounces to discharge it. When uncocked, the discharge pull was eighteen pounds.

However, I was adamant that the girl could not have fired the killing shot through her head. I will recapitulate on the reasons. It will be remembered that the first shot had injured the muscles on the front of the chest, the muscles that had to be used to raise the arm. Could it be conceived that such a damaged muscle would have been able to raise the arm above shoulder height, hold a heavy revolver twelve to eighteen inches away from the head and discharge it with the thumb? It would be quite impossible to have had a finger on the trigger. And anyway, where was the revolver? Held initially in an awkward position, it would have flown out of her hand on first discharge, and gone anywhere over the floor. Is it supposed that the girl, severely injured and in obvious great pain, grovelled in the dark over the floor until she regained her weapon, cocked it again, and then discharged it in an impossible position? Even if she had not lost the gun on first discharge, she could not have manipulated it into position for the second firing. It was this that clinched the matter. Mr Humphrey Edwards KC, himself a firearms expert, made me go through all sorts of contortions in the witness box to try and convince the jury that the girl could have shot herself using her right arm. The jury did not think so. They convicted Croft of murder, and he was sentenced to be hanged. His appeal was dismissed, but his sentence was reduced to life imprisonment.

I have already said that the defence was that this was a suicide pact, rejected by the Jury. Even if it had been, the final killing shot had been fired by Croft, and not by the girl herself, so that he was rightly convicted of murder. But what about the suicide pact? There are grounds for believing that there might indeed have been one, and that not sufficient use was made by the Defence of facts disclosed to them by the Prosecution. I believe I am disclosing such grounds for the first time, as they were not mentioned at the trial.

The weapon used was a heavy revolver, No. 132070, normally charged with cartridges 0.455 inches in diameter. On examining it, it was found to have been loaded with five cartridges of this size, and one slightly smaller, 0.450, normally cartridges for Smith & Wesson revolvers, which were also in use at the time. Two adjacent cartridges (0.455) — had been fired, obviously into Joan Lewis. But the gun had also been fired again. The cartridge next to the two 0.455 was the single 0.450. It was in the firing position, and indeed the trigger had been pulled on to it, as shown by an indentation on the cap and the mark of the firing pin in this indentation. Because of its slightly smaller size, this cartridge had slipped slightly down its position in the cylinder, thus lessening the impact of the striking pin, and preventing firing the primer. Did the finding not bear out Croft's statement that 'he tried to pull the trigger a second time, but failed'? This does tend to confirm the suicide pact, but it does not alter the fact that Croft shot his girl.

There is a final, most extraordinary and almost unbelievable sequel to this, related by my friend, Commander T. E.

Stanley, late proprietor of the Housel Bay Hotel, who writes as follows:

'Towards the end of January 1978, my wife and I visited Cornwall to negotiate for the purchase of the Housel Bay Hotel at The Lizard. This was to be our 'retirement home' and ongoing hobby in our new roles as hoteliers. During the period of handing over and actually taking possession of the hotel on 20 April, 1978, we were informed that not only were we acquiring the fixtures, fittings and other hotel impediments, but also the hotel's ghost!

'We were informed that the ghost of a young woman in WAAF uniform had been seen walking in the hotel gardens on numerous occasions (always in the month of October), seen by several people, both young and old alike: the girl was alleged to have been murdered by her lover in 1943 whilst billeted at the hotel as a member of the WAAF Radar Plotting team operating a small station at Bass Point (since demolished, but traces of the mast's base mountings are still visible). On seeking confirmation of the so-called facts, the actual story, well documented in press reports etc., came to light and will no doubt form a major part of the story. I do not therefore wish to dwell upon that particular part, but relate two other incidents which took place later.

'On 4 October, 1978, a Mrs W——————— from Stockport in Lancashire telephoned to book a single room for herself and a small lap-dog for a four-day "break". On arrival she proved to be a mature lady of some sixty years or so, and of ample proportions! October 1978 was favoured with exceptionally fine weather, and the good lady spent many hours in the hotel gardens with a book and her dog. On the second day of her visit (6 October), at approximately 3.30 p.m., she appeared at the hotel reception desk in a very distressed condition. She had been weeping, and her expensive mascara cosmetic had suffered in a most obvious way. However, having composed herself with the help of my wife and a few well-directed dabs with a hand towel, she quietly told us the following story, after first telling us that she was a Medium! She had apparently been sitting on the garden seat in the lower part of the garden when she heard a woman weeping. Realising that it was of a "spiritual" nature, she entered into a conversation with the unseen spirit, which informed her of the facts of the murder and identified herself as the young WAAF concerned and went on to say that she was waiting for her lover (also her murderer) to join her, as he had promised when they had made their suicide pact in 1943.

'Mrs W--------- who had, she alleged, never before visited Cornwall, was so intent on giving me the information which she thought would in fact be news to me, she obviously did not at any time realise that the event she was describing was in actual fact well and truly documented! However, she was allowed to go on thinking we knew nothing, and informed us that she intended to revisit the same spot at 9 p.m. the same night, as she had made an appointment to "meet the girl there"! I was asked to escort her down to the garden seat, now in pitch darkness, by the light of a torch. My instructions were to return in fifteen minutes' time to observe her without actually distracting her from her trancelike state, and if all appeared to be well, I was to return again after a similar period of time had elapsed and to remove her, *by force if necessary*, back to the hotel.

'As it happened, no force was required and she returned, albeit again in a distressed state, weeping etc., to the hotel where she wrote down details of her conversation with the "girl". I was most interested and intrigued to read within her "report" dates, times, names etc., which I knew to be correct from the well-documented story which appeared in the press reports of 1943, although I am certain that Mrs W--------- still had no knowledge of the true facts of the case. She returned to Southport a few days later without further enlightenment. At all times she wished to speak only to my wife and myself about her encounter with the girl, and was not in any way desirous of making financial gain from her experiences.

'The second incident occurred in August 1979, when a Mr and Mrs B------ arrived from Sheffield for an eight day holiday. Mr B----- was an artist, and his bread-and-butter work was designing murals in mosaic tiles for ceilings and walls of the houses and palaces of sheiks in the Middle East, a full time job but not as creative or diverse as he would have wished, apparently. In order therefore to fulfil his creative desires, whilst on holiday he insisted on carrying around with him, at *all* times, an artists' pad in which he sketched almost everything within sight! On the third day of his holiday, at about 2.45 p.m., he came up from the lower garden saying he had seen a young lady sitting on the lower garden bench seat dressed in a RAF blue uniform, skirt and blouse, looking particularly dejected and with a "faraway" look in her eyes, who appeared to be waiting for someone to join her. He commented on the fact that he could never understand why some of today's young people insisted on wearing articles of clothing from World War II, and enquired if the young lady was staying at the Hotel. I replied in the negative and gave the incident little thought.

'The following day, Mr B----- came to me again from the lower garden, and made further reference to the young girl, who he alleged was again sitting on the same bench as on the previous day; he had almost decided to speak to her, but something made him change his mind at the last moment and he had continued to walk back to the hotel where, of course, he spoke to me again. It was at this stage, I suddenly recalled the WAAF incident and decided to see the girl for myself, but, on reaching the bench seat, I found it empty and decided not to mention anything of what I suspected to Mr B-----, except to say that I thought he was pulling my leg about a pretty girl who just did not exist, as I hadn't seen her on the bench seat or even depart from the garden. He insisted that she *had* been in the seat, and he would look out for her around the hotel.

'The very next day at about 3 p.m., he came up from the lower garden, again saying that the same girl was on the bench seat. I immediately went to see for myself, but there was no sign of the girl when I arrived a few minutes later. I told Mr B----- that I was convinced that he was in fact "pulling my leg", and that no such girl had been seen, to which he replied "Oh! yes there was, because this time I sketched her," and he produced the sketch of the girl, tore it from his artists' pad and presented it to me! — and I still have it in my possession.'

I have seen this sketch, and with his kind permission, it is reproduced in the photograph sections of this book.

After this lapse of time, my considered opinion is that this was a tragic suicide pact that went wrong.

Judith Anne Enwright was the very attractive eighteen-year-old daughter of the proprietor of the Driftwood Spa Hotel, St Agnes. She had lived for a year or more in London with her boyfriend as man and wife.

Tiring of the association, she left him, and returned to her home at St Agnes. He followed her down, driving his own car, and there seems to have been a confrontation in the doorway of the house adjacent to the hotel. The young man attempted to pursuade the girl to return to him, but on her repeated refusal, he went to his car, returning with a 0.22 automatic pistol, threatening to kill himself if she did not return. What happened next was that two shots were fired, and the girl fell down, obviously severely injured in the head and chest. An ambulance took her to the Royal Cornwall Infirmary almost immediately, but she was found to be dead on arrival.

The post-mortem examination revealed that one bullet entered the chest almost exactly in its middle, and at right angles to the body, bearing slightly to the left, striking the sixth rib and then turning at right angles, embedding itself in the muscle at the back. In its course, it went right through the heart, and through the root of the left lung. Blood ran from the cut air passages into the windpipe, some was coughed up and ran down the front of the body and dress, showing that the girl must have been standing up when this happened. The second bullet entered her head two inches above the right ear, ploughing its way in a straight line through the brain to the opposite side where it was found. I estimated that both these shots had been fired from a distance of from six to nine inches from the body, and this was confirmed by Det. Insp. George Price of the Home Office Laboratory, who made a detailed examination of the weapon.

The shot through the chest was $3'10\frac{1}{2}''$ from the ground; that through the head was $5'3''$ from the ground level.

I thought the logical interpretation of these findings was that the young man, frustrated in his attempts to get his girl back, and determined that no other man would have her, deliberately shot her in the chest, and again whilst she was falling, through her head. But, as usual, one had to consider accident, suicide or murder.

Suicide was ruled out at once. The shot through the chest had been fired some nine inches from the chest wall — too far away for the girl to have held the pistol herself. As the chest shot had gone right through her heart, death would have been instantaneous, and she could not have subsequently fired the shot through her head. Moreover, and quite convincingly, her fingerprints were not found on the revolver.

Accident? There was no evidence of any struggle. There were three moderately large pools of blood in the doorway and on the doorstep, and others just outside. A large plant in the doorway was undisturbed, and loose plaster between the stones outside the doorway was also undisturbed. Two chair cushions were heavily bloodstained, but these had been put underneath the girl's head pending the arrival of the ambulance.

Expert examination of the pistol showed that there was nothing wrong with it. It could not be discharged by shaking or rough handling. It could be discharged only by pulling the trigger; the pull required was the normal three-and-three-quarter pounds. The magazine held nine 0.22 cartridges, a self-loading pistol of American manufacture.

A statement made by the accused, Eric Edwin Hawkins, affirmed that the shooting was accidental. He said that after an argument, he told the girl that if she did not come back to him, he would shoot himself. To emphasise this, he lifted up the revolver and started to move it towards his head. The girl in alarm grabbed out at the pistol, pulling it towards herself. In the struggle, the weapon fired whilst it was pointing towards the girl's chest. Blood welling up from the mouth, and running down the front of the chest proved that the girl was standing up when the shot was fired. So much for the first shot; the explanation was just possible.

During the trial, I had a serious row with Defending Counsel over this part of the evidence. I wanted to see how the average person reacted to this situation. I asked every member of my laboratory staff, separately and without any knowledge of what each other was doing, what they would do in similar circumstances. I stood with the revolver (unloaded) pointed at my head. Every one of them threw my arm away sideways or upwards. Not one drew the revolver towards themselves. When I mentioned this in the course of my evidence, I was howled down by Defence Counsel, although my own Counsel had wanted the evidence given. The Judge upheld the objection.

What about the second shot? At the trial I said that I thought that whilst the first shot might just have been fired accidentally, I found it difficult to believe that the second had been so fired. My opinion was that, frustrated, and madly jealous, Hawkins had deliberately shot the girl in the chest whilst they were both standing up. As she slumped down, he fired the second shot in rapid succession, and this caught her head as she was falling.

The late Dr Camps came down to give evidence for the Defence. In characteristic style, after taking the Oath, Dr Camps announced to the Court that he knew more about firearm injuries than anyone else in the country. He said that both shots could have been fired accidentally. The Jury did not believe him, and Hawkins was convicted of manslaughter. He got off with the light sentence of two years' imprisonment.

The Judith Enright case — the Ruger
automatic pistol (chapter 16)
police photo

Judith Enright case — the doorway where the
victim was shot (chapter 16)
police photo

The author (left) with Mr Russell (right) and his
solicitor (middle) (chapter 18)

photo taken by Robert Roskrow

Figures restored to key after etching (chapter 21)

Nanjarrow Farm
Below: the dining room (chapter 22)
police photos

The body of William Garfield Rowe lying in
Nanjarrow farmyard (chapter 22)
police photo

Housel Bay Hotel case — the summer house (chapter 16)
police photo

Housel Bay Hotel case — interior of summer house (chapter 16)
police photo

Housel Bay Hotel case — interior of summer house (chapter 16)
police photo

VIGIL HT
HOUSEL BAY.

Housel Bay Hotel case — an artist's impression
of the ghost of Joan Lewis (chapter 16)
courtesy of Commander T.E. Stanley RN

Firearms and ammunition found during the search of
Trench Cottages (chapter 22)
police photo

Cyrus Hoar (chapter 22)
police photo

The Hoar murder case — the staircase at the house (chapter 22)
police photo

Below: the bodies of Cyril and Doris Hoar (chapter 22)
police photo

17

Suicides

I think it is time to leave murder alone for a while, although I shall return to it.

Now to be considered are some of the suicides. I have always regarded these as the most tragic of people. Murdered people are also tragic, although a few of them seem to have asked for it. Mostly it is over for them in a few minutes. Not so the suicide, who generally has brooded in agony for weeks or months before finally deciding that life is no longer worthwhile.

I have already dealt with the lady from New Zealand who took the best part of 5000 tablets of barbiturate.

Now comes a lady from Hayle. She apparently decided to drown herself, but to do so in comparative comfort. There is plenty of water in the Hayle area, but she took a very unusual course. She took a chair with her, went to a very large covered water tank, took the chair down an iron staircase into the interior and sat on it whilst she drowned.

By no means all persons who take their own lives are unbalanced at the time. Indeed, many seem to have been perfectly rational, but have just come to the end of, to them, impossible conditions. Some indeed would appear to be perfectly rational, like this one. At one time there was a well-known trio of elderly gentlemen living in Bude; great friends who met regularly at the local. Perfectly reasonably and sensibly, one of them, Charles George Cloke, said that when he became tired of life, rather than be a nuisance to anyone, he would hang himself on a particular tree. A branch of this tree straddled .a Cornish hedge, which itself was some six feet high and about two feet wide at the top. This overhanging branch was some six feet above the top of the hedge — an ideal gallows. Came a certain day, and the old gentleman did not keep his accustomed tryst at the pub. His friends of course knew where to look for him, and set off in the direction of the tree. When it came in sight, there was no sign of the friend dangling from it. When they got close up, there he was, dead on the opposite side. The branch indeed had been broken off, but over a higher one, a rope dangled. When the post-mortem examination was made, it was found that the old man had fallen headfirst over the wall, breaking his neck. Now, the question was, was this a suicide, or an accidental death? There can be no doubt that suicide was intended, and the rope thrown over the lower branch, but this broke off because it was rotten. An attempt was then made to throw the rope over a higher branch, but in doing so, he slipped and fell, landing on his head. It was in the autumn, and the top of the wall was covered with long, slippery grass. The argument in favour of accident was that, having succeeded in throwing the rope over the upper branch, he might at the last moment have changed his mind and not put it around his neck, but unfortunately slipped. Lawyers, coroners and forensic pathologists are still in some doubt as to the proper verdict; the Coroner in the case brought in a verdict of accidental death, and I agreed with him.

People intending to hang themselves usually do it in easily accessible places, but I remember one who thought otherwise. On the treeless high moor of Carmenellis, between Helston and Redruth, miles from anywhere, there stood a dead tree with a single projecting branch at right angles — a typical gallows. One day an old man who had been missing for days was found hanging there. He had obviously been affected by the suitability of the surroundings.

One man went to great and extraordinary pains to drown himself in the wilds of the Land's End peninsular. He selected a large stone, about eight inches in diameter, from a Cornish hedge (we found the place), bound it round with binder twine, hung it around his neck, and then crawled some 200 yards on his hands and knees to a nearby stream, where he immersed himself.

One day I was sent for to do a post-mortem examination at Penryn — in one of the worst of the Cornish mortuaries. We were unable to find the caretaker to open up for us, but after considerable search the police officer found his bunch of keys, and duly opened up. The first thing we saw was the body of the caretaker suspended by the neck by a rope, immediately in front of the entrance. Whether or not he was making it easy for us to find the body and transport it to the mortuary, we shall never know.

Another unusual setting for a suicide occurred in Liskeard. An employee of the local abattoir decided to end his life, so he sat down amongst the carcasses that he had helped to slaughter that day, and blew his brains out with a humane killer.

It is curious, or perhaps not, how suicides tend to copy the method used by one similarly afflicted a short time before. When I was in London if one suicide ended his life by jumping in front of an underground train, then almost invariably, many of the next batch would do the same. The same followed a suicidal death by Lysol poisoning, or by use of the gas oven. The same pattern has been noticed in Cornwall.

This extends to the more bizarre forms of suicide.

Recently, a man came home from his work, expecting to find his wife and dinner awaiting him. He found neither wife nor dinner, but a note in his wife's handwriting saying that she had gone to see 'Liz'. Not knowing who Liz was, or how long his wife would be away, he waited until quite late in the evening before the pangs of hunger sent him in search of food. He found nothing suitable, so finally went to the deep freezer, kept outside the home. There he found his wife, stretched out and lying rather uncomfortably in the freezer, and obviously dead. She was lying on her left side, and had vomited.

The vomit contained a large amount of white powder. When the stomach was examined, it was found to contain a mass of similar powder, subsequent analysis of which showed that it was aspirin, some 250 grains being recovered;

obviously a very large and poisonous dose had been taken, and it must have been taken voluntarily as it would be impossible to force this amount of drug down a person's throat without resistance, and there was no sign whatever of any resistance having been offered. Death from aspirin poisoning is slow, and there would have been ample time for this unfortunate woman to have placed herself, rather uncomfortably, in her deep freeze. Her death would have been a gentle one, becoming increasingly drowsy as a result of the aspirin overdose, and later unconscious as the cold took effect. I am told that people who die from exposure to extreme cold just pass into sleepy oblivion — the experience of those who have been rescued.

Within a few weeks of this rather extraordinary happening, this mode of suicide was exactly copied by another woman, 'up country'.

Unfortunately, it is not every suicide who does, or can, take the pleasant way out. One I recall, in January 1954 (a Mrs Florence Menhenick) made a really maniacal attack upon herself.

She was found in her home at Liskeard with her throat raggedly cut, severing her windpipe but not her gullet, and avoiding the main blood vessels in the neck. There was a deep, rather ragged cut through the muscles at the back of the neck, and in the middle of this what appeared to be a stab wound three-quarters of an inch deep. There was also a split and bruise in the scalp on the back of the head, and another large bruise on the top of the head. There were heavy bruises on the upper left arm and in the fronts of both thighs and around the knees. In fact, the body appeared to have been generally battered and bruised all over the front.

A number of parallel, sharply incised cuts ran transversely across the inner aspect of the left wrist. Most of these were superficial, but one tendon had been cut. The main blood vessels were exposed but not cut.

Surprisingly, she was found alive but unconscious, and was taken to Freedom Fields Hospital, Plymouth, where she died without regaining consciousness. At the post-mortem examination the injuries noted above were confirmed, but there was another significant finding. This was marked corrosion of the lining membrane of the gullet; nothing was seen in the mouth or stomach, but it was obvious that some corrosive substance had been swallowed. I therefore took the gullet, as well as the stomach and other organs, and later examined them. I found some 15 grains of potassium oxalate (salts of sorrel) in the gullet, but none in the stomach. The amount found was not a poisonous amount, but it would have caused great discomfort and pain in the chest and throat.

The initial findings of the wounds in the neck and head and the multiple bruising at first suggested a homicidal onslaught on this woman, especially as a very large amount of money was found in the house. However, investigations in the house, combined with the findings at the post-mortem examination, suggested that this was a case of suicide in a state of frenzy.

Examination of the kitchen showed a mass of white crystals scattered over the floor. Analysis of these showed that they were potassium oxalate and had obviously come from a packet of the same chemical found in a 'Boots the Chemists' packet by the sink; this chemical is commonly used domestically to remove iron mould from clothing. On the draining board there was a cup with a broken handle; it contained a teaspoonful of watery liquid; analysis of this showed that potassium oxalate had been dissolved in it. Also on the draining board there was found a sharp knife, fairly heavily bloodstained. Further searching revealed a heavily bloodstained patch-hook lying in the front passage of the house. This hook was rather exceptionally sharp for an instrument of this kind. The hook at the end of the blade exactly fitted the stab wound at the back of the neck. There were masses of blood splashes all over the kitchen and back kitchen, but they were all confined to the floor and lower walls, none being at a height greater than two feet from the floor. This rather excluded an homicidal onslaught unless the woman had been lying on the floor during the attack. Nor was it consistent with the woman throwing herself about whilst trying to escape from a homicidal attack.

This was obviously a suicide, attempted first by poison, then cutting the wrist — an action which very rarely succeeds, although often attempted. (One successful suicide did it most considerately in his bath.) Finding the cut wrist unsuccessful, and in a most distressful state, and finding herself still alive, she next tried to cut her head off with the patch-hook, and still not succeeding, slit her throat.

The same kind of desperation was shown by Trewella of Nancledra. He tried three times to cut his throat, but unfortunately had selected a rather blunt reaping hook for the purpose — it was found bloodstained beside him. Failing in this way, he then hanged himself.

In 1964, Florence Kate Edwards of Padstow thought up a complicated way of ending her life.

She was found slumped in the doorway of her kitchen, with an overturned chair beside her. Above her, a two-inch nail had been driven into the woodwork above the door. On this nail, there was found a considerable fragment of thick twine. Around her neck there was a double loop of similar twine, knotted on the left side. It had not been tightly tied, as would have been done by a murderer, and there was no imprint of any upward turn. Although not tightly tied, the ligature was sufficiently tight to obstruct the return of blood from the brain. This was shown by suffusion of the face above the line of the tie, and bleeding spots in it, and in the whites of the eyes. Was this a case of suicide or murder? We decided on suicide for many reasons, and particularly because the ligature had not been tightly drawn, as it almost certainly would have been done by a murderer deeply indenting the neck, and causing extensive damage to muscles and other structures in the neck.

In this case there was no damage to the windpipe or indeed to any of the underlying tissues generally. We supposed therefore that this poor woman had prepared to hang herself from the nail above the kitchen doorway, the nail either already in situ or driven in for the purpose, to enable the job to be done. She had tied the cord around her neck, leaving a loop at one end to slip over the nail. She arranged a chair underneath the nail, presumably with the intention of climbing up on it, slip the loop over the nail, and then jump. Unfortunately, or fortunately, she had tied the string rather too tightly around her neck. This did no material damage, but the tightness was sufficient to obstruct the flow of blood from the brain, with the result that the brain gradually swelled, and with increasing loss of oxygen she became increasingly unconscious until she collapsed on the floor beside the chair, dead but not hanged. Fibres of the cord around her neck on the nail indicated that she had made an attempt to loop cord around the nail, but had failed owing to her increasing unconsciousness.

How long could it have been between the act of tying the cord around the neck and the loss of consciousness? Would there have been time for her to have completed the movements she undoubtedly undertook? My estimate was that she would have had some twenty to thirty seconds at least, and it is surprising how much one can do in this apparently short space of time. How do I know? The answer is that I have tried it. This takes me back to 14 April, 1959, when a Mrs Mary Ellen Richards was found dead in peculiar circumstances at her home in Porkellis, Helston. Her husband had gone to work normally that morning, and there was no doubt at all that he was there all the morning. He returned to his home at 1 p.m. and found his wife dead in their bedroom with a nylon stocking tied around her neck. She had been dead (from temperature readings) for only about an hour. She was found in a very strange position beside her bed. She was kneeling on the floor, with her forehead on the floor. A twisted nylon stocking had been wound fairly tightly around the neck, and knotted in front. The ends of the stocking were firmly grasped by both hands crossed in the front of the chest. The width of the line of compression in the neck exactly matched that of the stretched stocking, and ridges corresponded to the ridges in the stocking. There were no signs whatever of manual strangulation. There was some bruising around the mouth, nose and forehead, but nothing that would suggest a blow of weight sufficient to cause unconsciousness or even momentary dizziness, or mental confusion before the ligature had been tied. The marks were consistent with the head bumping about a little whilst she was lying against the floor. The question arose as to how long this woman could have moved about before finally collapsing. I decided to try. Flanked by my wife and a number of police officers, I sat on the edge of the bed and pulled a similarly stretched stocking around my neck and started counting slowly — second time. I got to ten when I began to feel 'muzzy', and got fairly easily to twenty when I found myself beginning to fall off the bed. Before becoming quite unconscious, I was rescued by my wife, who had quite a lot to say to the police officers for allowing me to go for so long. I am sorry that I was not sufficiently conscious to hear or appreciate the whole of it. However, I did then know that quite a lot can be done between pressure being applied to the neck and the loss of consciousness. The police told me later that they had never before heard so many words previously unknown to them. I think there is no doubt that this woman strangled herself, but the reason was never discovered.

Another woman who ended her life in Newquay in a somewhat similar manner gave us some concern. She was found dressed only in her nightdress on the floor of her bedroom. She had obviously been strangled by a ligature; the marks on the neck exactly matching the cord fitted at the top of the nightdress. When seen, this cord was quite loose; but it could easily have been twisted by somebody standing behind just by putting a finger through it and twisting it around. Fortunately we were able to find a deep crescentic linear abrasion at the side of the right jaw, with some bruising around it. This curved abrasion exactly fitted the curve of the nail of her first right finger. It was therefore a reasonable assumption that after tying the cord of her nightdress around her neck, and finding that this did not strangle her, she inserted her right forefinger underneath the cord and twisted it tightly, digging her finger nail into her cheek as she did so. I would have been happier if I had still found the finger in situ, but experiments showed that it could easily have fallen away after death. There were no suspicious circumstances.

Many, if not most people who take their own lives make several, and sometimes many attempts before they finally succeed.

It is unusual, however, for someone who had embarked on taking an almost certain way of ending his life to suddenly regret it, as it were half-way, and try and retrieve the position, and indeed almost succeed.

But this happened in August 1960. A late-middle-aged

man named Charles Curtis of Polruan, Fowey, had been depressed after losing his wife the previous Christmas. He was a quiet man, with a good home, and was a regular church-goer; he was well looked after by his son and a sister-in-law.

The son came downstairs one morning and found his father leaning against a cupboard, coughing up blood. He told his son to fetch a doctor 'before it was too late'. The room was completely undisturbed. A doctor and ambulance soon arrived, and he was taken to Tehidy Hospital, after an initial collapse and emergency treatment at St Austell Hospital on the way.

When he was examined at Tehidy, he was found to have a line of abrasion and bruising running across the front of his neck, turning upwards behind both ears — the typical marks seen when a body is suspended by a cord — hanging. X-rays showed a fracture of the larynx (voice box). Later, air escaped from the broken windpipe, and infiltrated the surrounding structures. These ultimately become infected, and he died a week after his admission to hospital. Asked to explain his injuries, he said that he had decided to end his life, and hanged himself with a fine rope. Having started on this, and there was ample evidence that he had indeed hanged himself, he suddenly regretted what he was doing, and cut himself down. How he did this, or with what instrument, was never revealed; neither was any rope found or the cutting instrument, but of course he had ample opportunity to dispose of those before he finally collapsed.

Similar determination, but not this time stopping half-way, was shown by a man (Percy Speare, aged sixty-eight years), who first attempted to cut his throat twice, then tried to hang himself, and finally finished up in his gas oven.

18

Accident, Suicide or Murder

Another one who nearly got away with it, but who would probably have tried again, was John James Collins, aged thirty-five years. He went to elaborate lengths to hang himself. He tied a long length of cord to a beam, and made a slip knot at the other end. Unfortunately the tie was very loose, and the cord was rather long. Getting up on to the top of a pair of household steps, he found the cord too long, so he wrapped it around the beam until a convenient length remained, and then jumped. As the loops of cord around the beam were so lightly drawn, when he jumped they just unravelled without any tautening until he was almost at ground level when the surplus cord ran out. He was found suspended by his neck in an almost horizontal position, only a few inches above floor level. He had been there quite a long time before being found as the blood had gravitated all along the dependent part of the body. This was a case of only just succeeding.

On 9 September, 1967, Albert Edward Scoble drowned himself in a most peculiar way. He put a bucket of water inside a dustbin, and up-ended himself into the bucket.

More recently, a well-known and very wealthy middle-aged farmer cut his hay and built a fine haystack. Attaching one end of a thickish rope to the top of the stack, he put the other end around his neck and jumped. There was no possibility of anyone else having been involved, or of accident, but there was no earthly reason why he should have committed suicide.

The night of 2/3 January, 1976, was a wild one with a south-east gale blowing full blast into the little harbour of Mylor.

The next morning, the body of Mrs Susan Mary Russell, a resident very close to the beach, was found on the beach below high tide mark. She was fully clothed, and her clothing was not more disturbed than could be accounted for by heavy wave action.

I examined her the same day (3 January, 1976). It was impossible to say exactly how long she had been dead as there was no knowledge of how long she had been in the sea. The appearances were suggestive of death having occurred in the late evening of the previous day, and this was in fact confirmed by her husband who last saw her late that evening.

It was assumed that she had drowned. How wrong can one be.

Externally, there were no injuries of significance; some nibbling by fish, which is not unusual, proved that the body had been in the sea. Only some light scratches on the face suggested that she had been lightly washed against sharp rocks or nibbled by fish. It might be thought that a body lashed about by a wild sea would be smashed against adjacent rocks, and hence any minor injuries completely smothered by more obvious injuries caused by rocks. So thought the person who dumped the body of Mrs Russell into the sea on that turbulent night. But a body, or a plank of wood, or anything that will float is not immediately and repeatedly bashed up against rocks during a storm. The floating object is washed towards the rocks, but much more often than not, is sucked back again into deep water, and no harm results. The fact that she showed no serious external injuries therefore did not exclude the possibility that she had been in the sea for a long time, probably hours, as the wrinkled appearance of the skin of her hands suggested.

My first surprise was that her face was very congested above the level of the middle of the neck, and that there were pin-point bleeding spots in the skin above this line and especially in the whites of the eyes — almost cardinal signs of severe neck compression, and manual strangulation.

My second surprise was that her lungs were 'dry' and did not present the waterlogged and boggy appearances most commonly associated with drowning in sea water. Then I found that she had vomited at the time of death, and that food almost completely filled her windpipe, blocking both branches to her lungs. No, she had not drowned. I confirmed this later the same day by taking fluid from the lungs (which were so dry that it was difficult to get any) and having its salt content estimated by Mrs Maureen Blackburn, Senior Technician at the Pathological Laboratory, Treliske Hospital. This showed a normal salt concentration, so no salt water had been inhaled, and there was no drowning, and death was due to some other cause. Her neck was next examined. This showed a bruise one inch long in the muscle that runs from the top of the breastbone to below the ear (the sterno-mastoid muscle) on the right side and level with the voice box or larynx. More significantly, the tip of the cartilage of the larynx in the same side had been fractured, with associated bruising, indicating that this had been done during life. There was also a bruise around the tip of the hyoid bone on the left side. She had severely bitten the tip of her tongue, and a severe bruise was found lying along the line of the left jaw. There was a bruise one inch in diameter in the upper chest on the right side, suggestive of a punch.

I gave it as my opinion that the injuries to the neck had been caused by heavy manual gripping, or manual strangulation, and that death was due to this and to suffocation due to terminal inhalation of vomit. Vomiting as a result of pressure on the neck is not uncommon.

I did toy with the possibility that, in great distress, Mrs Russell had rushed out of her house, possibly intending to end her life by drowning, and that after entering the water, in range and panic, she herself had violently gripped her neck, had vomited, inhaled the vomit and died of suffocation

I did not think much of this possibility, but put it to my more senior forensic experts. They had never heard of any such thing (and neither had I), and suggested that it would be impossible because of the pain caused by severe pressure on the neck. The matter was not mentioned at the trial before the Magistrates.

As it was after the amalgamation of the Police Forces, the Big Boys from Exeter now took a hand. They wanted my opinion confirmed, and so sent Dr Hunt, Home Office Pathologist, down to do another post-mortem examination. He agreed with all my findings and conclusions as to the cause of death, but then added a rider that I was never able to understand. He thought that there was a possibility that she might have had her throat manually gripped and rendered unconscious for some time. Whilst still unconscious, she was taken to the sea and thrown in. This caused her to vomit, which she inhaled and died as a result. In any case, he fundamentally agreed with me that her death was due to manual strangulation. But what I regarded as this somewhat bizarre theory, did throw a small spanner in the works by suggesting that the pathologists for the prosecution did not wholly agree.

We agreed that it would be advisable to have a long bone examined for the presence of diatoms. As I was an interested party, I thought it best to have the examination performed by an independent party. The bone was therefore sent to the South-West Forensic Laboratory at Bristol. They found nothing, and we thought that the case was cut and dried from the pathological point of view, and ended.

Not so. On behalf of Mrs Russell's husband, his solicitor brought in Professor Cameron, Director of the Forensic Dept of the London Hospital. He agreed with the findings, but did not express any opinion, and I have never heard that he did indeed express one. However, he did not attend at any of the subsequent proceedings, so that we assumed that he entirely agreed with us. He did, however, take away a femur for examination for diatoms, and thus started a series of arguments that went on for some ten months. By that time, everybody was fed up with the whole affair.

He sent the bone to the well-known expert on these things, Mr Ingram Hendey. He found fragments of diatoms of the kind that inhabit the Mylor harbour. This completely upset things, as the presence of these organisms in bone marrow is generally regarded as indicating the inhalation of sea water, and probably therefore of drowning. But we had a loophole. Although diatoms are found after the inhalation of water, there is no indication as to when they were inhaled. Silica is indestructable in water. They could have been inhaled a long time ago, and there was a significant history that Mrs Russell was deadly scared of the sea for a reason that one could only speculate about. Query, had she been nearly drowned when she was a child? However, we now had agreement on the strangulation but a difference of opinion as to the significance of the presence of the diatoms. So, off we went again, this time to the fountainhead of the significance of diatoms in bone marrow, Prof. Thomas of Ghent University. By this time he had only the breastbone to work on, but in this he found fragments of diatoms of the Mylor variety, and confirmed that these could have come only as a result of the inhalation of water — but again, when? It is significant that in all cases only fragments of diatoms were found; no whole specimens. This suggested the possibility that they had been there for a long time and had nothing to do with recent events.

All these matters were referred to Prof. Keith Mant of the Forensic Department of Guy's Hospital, London.

He agreed with the evidence of manual strangulation, that considerable force had been applied to the neck, and that this was essentially the cause of death. The injuries could not have been self-inflicted. He agreed with Prof. Thomas (and Prof. Timperman of the same University) that Mrs Russell might have been still alive when she was immersed in the sea, in spite of my findings that there was no sea water in her lungs. This fact appears to have been persistently overlooked by many of the investigators, but it was of prime importance, as I persistently tried to get across.

Anyway, after all this investigation, the police were convinced that Mrs Russell had been murdered by manual strangulation.

What was the background? It was an open secret that she and her husband had been on bad terms recently, and that in Mr Russell's own words, they had had a serious quarrel on the night of her death, and she threw her wedding ring at him, and then left the house. That was the last he saw of her until the next morning, on the beach at Mylor. He added that for several nights recently, Mrs Russell had left her home for about an hour, but he had no idea where she had gone, or what she did. After she had left on the final night, he found that some £500 was missing. Questioning all around failed to obtain an evidence that anyone in the neighbourhood had seen Mrs Russell about in the evenings; even a French lorry driver had been questioned.

With this background, and after months of indecision, the Director of Public Prosecutions eventually charged Mr Russell with the murder of his wife. The initial proceedings were heard before the Penryn Magistrates in the November following the death — some ten months afterwards. After hearing the evidence, they ruled that there was no case for Mr Russell to answer. The final proceedings took place at Truro in February 1977, when the District Coroner, Mr Carlyon, brought in an open verdict. So that case is still open.

But for a most unfortunate circumstance, the whole proceeding of the disposal of Mrs Russell's body might have been witnessed, and a great deal of trouble avoided.

On that stormy night, when it would appear that she had been thrown into a raging sea, either dead, or just alive, a near neighbour of the Russells heard a motor car drive on to the quay. Thinking that this might be one of the 'locals' going to secure his yacht, he thought he would go and help. He went to his garage to start up his car, only to find the battery flat. Had it not been for this he might have driven to the quay, and witnessed the whole affair. What an amount of trouble and expense this would have avoided!

A final act in this drama was the finding of the body of Mr Russell on the pavement below the window of a room he occupied in an hotel in Spain, on the morning of 28 February, 1985. He was at that time insolvent to the tune of a very large sum of money.

This case has never ceased to exasperate me and my police friends. Indeed it exasperated the Director of Public Prosecutions, who, I was informed, had considered bringing in a Bill of Indictment. It occurred after the amalgamation of the Police Forces of Cornwall & Devon. Shall I have the affrontery to say that if had been in the 'old' days, and had been left to Chief Supt Alfie Jenkin, Det. Supt Roberts and me, we would have had the whole thing sewn up in a matter of a few weeks, and dealt with at the next (Spring) Assizes. Instead, there was such a muddle over the medical and scientific evidence that it was ten months before the case came before the Magistrates, and over a year before it was dealt with by HM Coroner. Looking back, and having cooled off, I think that I can now appreciate, shall I say the wisdom of Their Worships in throwing the case against Mr Russell out. They must have come to the conclusion that after such a long time, and so much wrangling, no jury would convict.

It was five to one against me. I maintained throughout that she had been strangled, vomited, inhaled her vomit and died of suffocation. The others maintained that she had been strangled and thrown into the sea, apparently alive, in spite of no sea water having been found in her. Professor Cameron's view, as far as I am aware, was never made public. The case still rankles.

Accident, suicide or murder? It is sometimes difficult, but imperative to distinguish between these three possibilities.

Take the case of an elderly man, living in Lostwithiel. He was married to a much younger wife, and most unfortunately for him, he suffered from Parkinson's Disease, or paralysis agitans. A feature is progressive muscular weakness, without absolute paralysis.

One morning he was found dead on the floor of his sitting room. This was not unexpected, but his doctor thought the case should be reported to Coroner.

We went to the home and examined it; all seemed to be in order, but I do remember a rather curious feature. The cat had been put to sleep on a sort of pedestal table, covered by one of those perforated meat covers; it was there when we arrived, fast asleep.

The first thing that the post-mortem examination revealed was a very heavy blow on the upper chest. It had fractured the breastbone, also the upper ribs on both sides, and the lungs were bruised. Going further, there was found bruising in the neck, fracture of parts of the larynx, and obvious signs of manual strangulation. Naturally, the police required an explanation from the widow. She stated that her husband, being very weak in his legs, used to go downstairs sitting on his backside, bumping from step to step. If he was in a hurry, he leaned over the banister and slid down. On the day of his death, this had been his mode of progress, and on arriving at the bottom, he complained that he was not feeling very well. The wife did not witness this slide. He was assisted to the downstairs sitting room, and his wife asked him if he would like a cup of tea. He said, yes. At this time he was sitting on the floor. The tea was brought, but he was unable to get up into a chair. He was assisted up, then collapsed and died. Asked how she assisted her husband up, the wife replied that he was a very heavy man, and that she was a slight woman. This was obvious. Her method of lifting him up was to push a chair towards him, lean over the back, grab him by the neck and pull him up. Well, that of course accounted for the strangulation. What about the chest injuries? Examination of the banisters showed that they ended in the usual large spherical newel post, projecting about a foot above the level of the banister rail. If, as his wife had said, he had leaned over the rail that morning and slid downwards, it would be quite possible for him not to have stopped in time, and crashed into the newel post, crushing the upper part of his chest.

This explanation was accepted by HM Coroner.

One of the first that I encountered (not personally) had been a patient of Dr O'Donnell's. The doctor was sent for one morning and told that an old patient of his had, not unexpectedly, died, and could they have a certificate. Dr O'Donnell said yes, of course, after he had seen the body. They replied that there was no need for this; the old man had died of a haemorrhage, and that was that. Dr O'Donnell persisted and was finally taken to the room where the old man was lying in deathly state, covered up to the chin with immaculately clean bed linen. On turning this down, Dr O'Donnell saw that his old patient had slit his throat from ear to ear. Some haemorrhage!

One of my own cases occurred in Bodmin. Again an old gentleman had died suddenly, and his doctor was sent for to give the necessary certificate. He was not so thorough as Dr O'Donnell, and certified death due to heart disease. When the undertaker came to lay out the body, he saw that it had been shot clean through the chest! No gun of course was seen, but police investigation soon found one, a shotgun. It had been cleaned and polished outside, but examination of the barrel showed that it had been recently discharged. We assumed that it had been a self-inflicted wound because the muzzle had been held touching the chest, and it was difficult to suppose that anyone would allow another person to approach so close and fire a shot into his chest without thrusting the muzzle away. The shot had gone right through the heart and disintegrated it. Some heart disease!

Social consequences of suicide impelled William Henry Hocking (no relative of mine) and his family to try and conceal his self-inflicted death. He lived on a farm in the wilds of St Buryan, and was found dead one day beside one of the farm buildings. A doctor who was called certified that death had been due to heart disease. The police were not happy about this, and a post-mortem examination was made.

The deceased, fifty-nine years of age, was dressed in the following clothing: overcoat (done up), short coat, waistcoat, pullover, inner pullover, green shirt, white vest, trousers and pants. All the clothing apart from the shirt and vest was intact, but in the latter two garments there were corresponding ragged holes about one-inch in diameter, with burned edges. These corresponded with a ragged hole of similar size and appearance, and with burned edges in the chest, immediately over the heart. The appearances were characteristic of the point-blank discharge of a twelve-bore shotgun directly into the chest. Immediately outside the main wound there was a circular ring of bruising and slight abrasion of the same diameter as the muzzle of a twelve-bore shotgun, suggesting that the weapon used had been a double-barrelled gun, one side of which had been fired. The heart had been half shot away, and the left lung completely disintegrated. Cartridge wads and shot were found scattered about the chest cavity. There was no sign of any gun anywhere near the body, but one, completely cleaned and furbished up, was found in the home, again recently discharged. Nobody but the deceased himself could have gone through the complicated manoeuvres to get the barrel of the gun through all the outer clothing to the ultimate and penultimate garments, and the case was one of obvious suicide. But, as usual in darkest country, suicide had to be discounted. A rather peculiar feature of this case was that the deceased had carbon monoxide in his blood to the extent of 22% saturation; not a lethal amount, but one that could have affected his reasoning abilities. It was never found how this had come about.

Shortly after the introduction of the chemical DDT, a curious case occurred in Helston. DDT was a wonder invention, lethal to all kinds of parasitic infections, and to some minds, diseases as well. An elderly man living in the Helston area was found dead by his son one morning. Post-mortem examination showed him full of DDT. Hardly an accident or a murder; probably a suicide, but why? The answer was provided at the Inquest by his son. Dad had 'got religion' and sought to purify his soul by this new disinfectant. What it did to his soul I do not know, but it did no good to his body.

19

Sexual Offences

Of course it is no offence for a managing director or other high executive to take his secretary away with him for a working holiday. Unfortunately the strain appeared to be too much for many of them. They died suddenly, and their death had to be reported to HM Coroner. I think that in almost every case I was able to report that death was due to coronary thrombosis, and the very sympathetic Coroner did not pursue the matter any further.

However, on occasion there were complications. On one of these, a very superior director was spending a working weekend with his secretary at the Trebetherick Hotel near Wadebridge. He succumbed to what we called Weekend Executives' Disease. When his wife in London was informed of the particulars by the police, she replied, 'Well then, she can bloody well bury him.'

On another occasion, the Coroner's Officer informed me that the secretary had made a statement to the effect that whilst they were 'operating' he suddenly gave a great sigh. She said, 'I thought he was coming, but I suppose he was going.' I must say that I always regarded this statement with a certain amount of doubt.

There is no doubt that Executive Weekending is an occupational hazard. Anyway, a nice way to go.

I remember causing much consternation when I said in the Assizes Court at Exeter that on occasion sexual inter-course was a dangerous thing to indulge in. You should have heard the outcry, but it was the main plank in our defence of Camb.

Sexual offences have been of many and very various types, from the trivial, and sometimes indeed comic, to rape and murder. After treason and murder, rape is the most serious crime in the calender, punishable by death until the unfortunate repeal of this sentence, and even now by life imprisonment. When sentencing Anthony Francis Martin to fifteen years' imprisonment for rape, Judge Frank Martin said that the time had come to cry 'stop', with exemplary sentences which would prove not only a heavy punishment but a deterrent to others. The Judge went on to say that he had no doubt that many would consider the sentence he had just imposed very harsh, but the crime of rape was a cruel, heartless and abhorrent one. Whereas the murder victim had no memory of the crime, a rape victim must carry the mental and psychological scar for a long time, and perhaps for life.

In my early days, the incidence of rape in Cornwall was about one-fifth of the murder rate, and that was little enough. Unhappily, the position is becoming increasingly reversed, rape and attempted rape now running at a very high level.

But, I believe, as with murder, there are degrees of the offence, although the law does not allow for shades of grey. There is the type of brutal rape resulting in severe physical as well as mental injury, and perhaps death. At the other end is the girl or young woman out with her boyfriend, who encourages him almost to the bitter end and then takes fright, leaving him in a desperate state, when his inhibitions at last crack. Of course there is no legal excuse for the subsequent happenings, but surely the responsibility should be shared by the aggravating party.

Very often the story starts at about 2 a.m. The police 'phone me up to say that they have got a young girl in the station who says that she has been raped. My first question is, 'Is she grinning all over her face, or is she distressed?' If she is grinning all over her face, I say that she can keep until the morning. If she is distressed, I go at once. Examination will sometimes show evidence of injury, and if we find spermatozoa in the vagina, or elsewhere on the body, we are home and dry. Often there is no injury, which makes one wonder if the case is one of what I call rape by consent. However, the finding of spermatozoa, particularly if they are active, is proof positive of sexual intercourse, but not necessarily immediately recent. Active spermatozoa can survive for some days in comfortable surroundings. It is much more difficult to deal with an accused man. There may be contact fibres, blood, even semenal stains, but are these recent? Can it be proved that a man has had recent sexual intercourse? It can, but until recently it was rather difficult. A few years ago it was pointed out to us what we all knew, that the vagina is lined by cells resembling skin cells apart from the fact that they contain a starch-like substance, glycogen. The only other cells that contain this substance are found in the liver. So, what we do is to take a length of sticky tape and apply it to the accused's offending organ. If on subsequent examination we find glycogen-containing cells, then that person has had sexual intercourse since he last had a bath. According to the circumstances, I remove the tape very quickly, or very slowly.

A famous London gynaecologist once pointed out that this vaginal secretion is not only of great use to the forensic pathologist; it is of even greater benefit to the female species as a whole, because without it they would squeak as they walked. I mentioned this once in a lecture that I gave to the police. For months afterwards, WPCs were known in the Force as 'squeakers'. They did not seem to mind!

When lecturing to lay audiences, I regret to say that often I was guilty of more than a little inaccuracy. I used to say that any man who could reach as far as the liver must have been exceptionally well-endowed by nature. It brought the house down, but was of course anatomically quite impossible.

Unless there is confirmatory evidence, the proof of rape or indecent assault can be extremely difficult to confirm. Some sympathy could be extended to some (possibly only a few) who are accused of rape without there being any confirmatory evidence.

In mid-1987, a young girl accused an acquaintance of rape. He had accosted her on her way home, but as they were acquainted, there was no reason why she should object to his accompanying her. On the way, some sexual fiddling occurred, to which she made no objection. Later she complained that he threw her to the ground, and raped her. She asserted that she had been a virgin, and that the rape caused her acute and extreme pain, 'like being torn in halves'. The doctor who examined her the following day made a rather perfunctory examination, with the excuse that she was menstruating. However, the impression was that the girl might have been raped. I was asked my opinion, and reserved it pending the testimony of the doctor. In the witness box he said that the girl was not a virgin, that the hymen had been broken some time ago, and that there was no sign of injury whatever. So much for pain resembling being torn in halves. Collapse of case, as far as rape was concerned. But that poor young man endured months of extreme anxiety, for which there was no compensation.

He was convicted and fined for an indecent assault.

Some few years ago there was an outbreak of teenage schoolgirls wearing yellow golliwogs as a kind of broach. I believe the habit started in Sheffield and spread from there. It was thought to be an innocent and probably temporary gimmick, until one day a school mistress discovered that it was a badge of sexual maturity, presented to girls who had had sexual intercourse. Naturally all Hell was let loose, and these girls were brought to me in their dozens to be examined. The result must have been disappointing for them. Hardly anyone showed signs of sexual interference. It was all a matter of status. I think that I might have done something to stop the habit. Word probably got about that to be examined by me was most unpleasant, and not worth the wearing of a golliwog.

Accusations of incest can sometimes lead to curious situations.

Quite recently (January 1973) there was a problem family living in Plymouth. A teenaged girl, an epileptic, accused her elder brother of having raped her. The particulars were, that in a household of, father, mother, and three children, the boy assaulted and raped his sister in the kitchen. The girl apparently did not call out or otherwise disturb the family. She said that her brother pulled her trousers, pants and tights down to her knees, pushed her against the wall, pulled her legs apart, and had intercourse with her for ten minutes. He also had pulled his trousers and pants down to his knees. She was a small girl, some 5'6" tall, whilst he was a tall boy. I went in for the Defence, and said intercourse in such a position was impossible. With the girl's legs pinioned together by her clothing, they could not have been separated. She added that there had been full penetration. The boy, with his knees equally pinioned, would have been quite unable to get anywhere near her, considering the differences in their heights. The more he bent down to attain her level, the farther away from her he would be bound to go. I was of course asked in cross-examination whether or not I had ever seen couples standing up in doorways having intercourse. Of course I said I had, but never with their knickers and trousers around their knees. The Court Rooms at Plymouth Crown Court open on to a long wide corridor. When I came out of the Court Room, this corridor was empty excepting for two policemen, whom I saw standing up against a wall, trying out the exercise as I had described it. They agreed with me that the girl's statement was impossible. Unfortunately for the young man, although he emphatically denied what his sister had said, he did admit to having had intercourse with her in a more likely position in the bathroom, which she promptly denied. The outcome was that the Jury found him guilty, but the Judge took the extremely lenient view of the proceedings and sentenced him only to a term of probation.

Very great difficulties arise in dealing with epileptic people, who can imagine and believe all sorts of things. Equal difficulties also not infrequently arise with elderly ladies who bring false accusations of rape, or at least of indecent assault against perfectly respectable men, either from wishful thinking, or in some cases a genuine belief that they have been assaulted. Some misguided souls even go to the length of injuring themselves to prove the accuracy of their stories. These take up an awful lot of time and waste it. Bloodstains on soiled garments often do match with the story, but injuries suffered could not possibly have been caused in the way alleged.

Accusations of sexual offences are so easy to make, and often so difficult to disprove. However, we have had many successes, both ways.

Take for example this one, the antics of a young woman so bizzare as to tax one's credibility

In March 1946, there was a young, recently-married woman, twenty-one years of age, who began to miss her husband who was on active service. Having acquired missing pleasures from other sources, she became pregnant, and of course had to account for this unfortunate development. So she went to the police and said she had been raped. She was brought to me, and naturally I listened to her story. She described how an unknown American soldier entered her home, uninvited, and a serious struggle took place when the object of his visit dawned upon her. There was a struggle that went on for five minutes in a normal fully-furnished room — and yet, when I saw her a day or so afterwards, there was not a mark on her. She said that she had finally been borne down onto the hearthrug, when she fainted. When she came to, the man had gone. She found herself with her skirt pulled up around her waist, her knees in the air, and her knickers (substantial old-fashioned type) firmly bound around them. Asked to demonstrate, she willingly obliged. She did not know that I had a right-angled view camera through which I took a series of pictures, finishing up with the one showing her trussed up in a position in which it would be absolutely impossible to have sexual connection, even with a contortionist.

The police did not proceed with the charge of rape (a young man identified by the girl having a complete alibi), but to serve her right for wasting our time, and as an example to any other possible wasters of our time, she was duly summoned to appear at West Kerrier Petty Sessions on a charge of causing a public nuisance; she was convicted. Whether or not the message was put out on the grapevine I do not know, but we had no recurrence of the nuisance for a long time.

Dealing with sexual antics in impossible positions, I once heard of an occasion where a man was accused of having unlawful sexual intercourse with a girl under the age of sixteen. There was no doubt about the sexual intercourse, but this particular offence was said to have taken place in the back of the first type of Mini motor car. The defence was that this would have been impossible, owing to the restriction of space. The case was tried by the late Mr Justice Croome-Johnson (a fellow Cornishman, with whom for too short a time I had a very congenial rapport). He sent for a Mini motor car, came down from the Bench, got into the back, squirmed about and then returned to announce that in his opinion, sexual intercourse in such circumstances was just possible, provided that there was co-operation.

It is not uncommon for a man accused of sexual assault to put up the defence that he is impotent. Many such have been sent to me. I have always replied that a much more accurate picture of the situation would be obtained if the examination was undertaken by a younger person of the opposite sex.

A case similar to the one just recorded, although it was not mine, is worthy of mention, as it was a Cornish case. I was in No.1 Court at the Assize Court in Bodmin, when loud laughter was heard coming from the adjacent waiting area. The Judge put down his pencil and ordered the Usher to remove the delinquents. Fortunately he did not order them to be brought before him — they were my wife and Dr Hunt, the Home Office Pathologist in Plymouth. It transpired that he was engaged in a case similar to the one that I have just related, when it was found at the very last minute that the accused had a wooden leg, which in the circumstances would have made intercourse impossible.

A case occurred at Grampound in which a schoolmaster was accused of having an affair with one of his senior girl pupils. The girl had become pregnant by him. I had to examine her, and then go all the way to Winchester Assizes just to say that in my opinion, she had had sexual intercourse; she was under the age of consent. There were two ladies on the jury. On the second day, a note was passed up to the Judge by the Foreman of the Jury to the effect that of the two lady jurors, one, an elderly spinster, was quite unable to follow the case and comprehend the nature of the evidence. What had the schoolmaster done to the girl, and what was wrong with it anyway? Fortunately, the other lady juror was a normal healthy matronly soul, and the Judge suggested that the Court adjourn whilst she took the elderly maiden lady aside and explain the facts of life to her. We anxiously waited for a long time for the return of the Jury; the case had nearly gone to its end, and we did not relish starting all over again. However, all was well; the Jury returned and the Foreman announced that everybody understood and appreciated the position. I tried to glean from the expression on the maiden lady's face whether or not she was pleased that so far she had missed out in life, but could not.

This case had a sequel that could have been uncomfortable for me. I had examined the girl, and found her pregnant. Not being a skilled obstetrician, and having something of a kindly feeling for her, my examination was probably a bit rough. About a week afterwards, she aborted. Somebody (unknown to me) complained and suggested that I should be prosecuted for procuring an illegal abortion! Nothing came of it.

Sexual crimes against children are an emotive subject. Children are usually considered to be the most innocent of victims, and yet it is estimated that two-thirds of child victims co-operate in one or more assaults, and indeed, on occasion, encourage them. There was a family of eight children at one time, in Kea, a hamlet near Truro, four boys and four girls, conveniently spaced as to age and sex, and they paired off together. The usual reward for the girls was two shillings to go to the pictures. The youngest little girl was aged five years, and we thought this was a pretty dreadful state of affairs, until her brother partner-in-crime said that this child used to parade up and down in front of her brothers and say, 'You don't want to look at dirty pictures, look at me!'

Sexual offences include happenings as the above, to the increasingly serious offences of indecent assault, incest, homosexuality, bestiality, sexual behaviour with children and rape; we have gone through the lot, and to the list can be added infanticide and abortion.

The Abortion Act has had a most profound effect on the number of unwanted newly-born infants that were found.

Previous to the passing of the Act, the bodies of newly-born babies were constantly turning up in all sorts of unlikely places. They have been found in parcels and boxes (usually shoeboxes) in railway carriages, in pails, usually upside down and drowned, and similarly in lavatory pans. Besides drowning, there have been suffocations, strangulations and physical injuries to the head and other parts of body. The majority appeared just to have been left to die of exposure, probably in the circumstances the most humane way of ending their lives. Only on very rare occasions have the mothers been traced, sometimes with surprising results. Such a mother put her recently-born baby on the top of the broad hedge in Love Lane, Penzance, in full view of the taller kind of passerby. She was traced, and charged with concealment of birth — a common form of charge in these cases. Her very able solicitor-advocate obtained her discharge on the grounds that not only had she not concealed the birth, but she had even exposed it to the view of all and sundry!

Since the passing of the Act, I have not had a single case of this kind.

Apart from rough handling, instrumental interference with pregnancy was at one time fairly common, in spite of its dangers. Mrs Juliffe, already referred to, was a queen of instrumental interferers. Catheters, knitting needles, bunches of tapers, syringes and what not were removed from abortionists. It is really remarkable that we had so few deaths.

A most curious piece of apparatus that I once encountered was an outfit called 'Selforda', used by a local hairdresser. These outfits, advertised in the press, were recommended for use in baldness and certain skin complaints. The apparatus consisted essentially of high-frequency neon light bulbs and tubes, which when switched on glowed dramatically and impressively. The effect generally was to heat the skin superficially, and also in some depth, and perhaps stimulate it to some good by high-frequency vibrations. The general effect would be to increase the blood flow and generally tone up the tissues — but only to a slight depth. No harm done, and possibly some good. A young woman however complained (?) that she had been aborted by having one of these appliances stroked across her obviously pregnant abdomen. Miraculously, the method worked in spite of all the odds against it.

There are, or perhaps I should say were, a number of sexual offences that were never understood as being crimes by some sections of the more primitive native population. It used to be said that nobody in Cornwall would ever be convicted of buggery, because half of the Jury practised it and the other half did not understand it. Even more, some became indignant when it was pointed out to them that certain practices, especially against animals, were against the law.

On 30 April, 1938, a farmer living out in the utter wilds of the Land's End peninsula complained to the police that he thought that one of his female goats had been 'interfered with'. Off we went in the dark, guided across muddy fields by a paraffin storm lantern, to a filthy stable yard. There we met the farmer with another storm lantern in one hand, and nanny in the other. My job was to examine the goat and take a swab from her. It soon became obvious that both the farmer and the police were looking forward to this performance with considerable enjoyable anticipation, knowing the habits of goats. Knowing them also, I approached from the side and made my examination. This showed two recent superficial abrasions on the right and upper sides of the vagina; bleeding would have been insignificant or nil, but I added to my report that the findings were consistent with an attempt to insert into the vagina an object larger than it was designed to accommodate.

Then there was the swab to be taken. I approached nanny carefully from the side, lifted her tail, and prepared to take the specimen. As soon as she felt what I was doing, she most obligingly and gently backed onto the swab and in a sense took her own specimen with evident enjoyment and to the great disappointment of the onlookers. The swab proved positive, and the suspect was apprehended. When examined, he presented a remarkable picture. He had obviously not had a bath for months, and grubbiness was deeply ingrained into his skin, excepting in one significant region. His pubic region was shining white — all but the tip of his penis which had obviously been held in one hand, and thereafter forgotten and neglected whilst the rest of his

231

suspicious area was polished. Goat hairs were later found around the fly opening of his trousers.

It used to be the custom at Madron Feast for the final event to be a chase after a goat in the fashion of primitive Grecian festivities. This happened more than once in my experience. Unfortunately, in the first instance we got hold of the wrong goat, but the mistake was subsequently rectified. So sure was the accused man of having the case against him dismissed by the Magistrates, that he took two half-bottles of champagne to the court with him, one for himself after acquittal, and one for the Chairman of the Magistrates. Unfortunately things did not go right for him, and he was found guilty. So, for consolation, he drank both half-bottles.

I have had many similar experiences with other animals, but I can now say that the habit appears to have died out completely, or almost completely, no case of this kind having been brought to my notice for over twenty years.

Sheep and goats now safely graze in West Penwith. I always thought it a pity that the witnesses and exhibits in these cases were not brought into court.

We lost one case because the Police confused Daisy with Buttercup.

20

Science

During the early autumn of 1936, strange happenings occurred at an extremely isolated farm on Bodmin Moor. A young farmer had recently married a young woman from a more civilised part of the county, and she was not happy in her new home.

One morning, early in the day he went to his yard, and noticed that all his piglets had lost their tails. This was more than a little surprising, but not altogether so, as young piglets are sometimes cannibalised. However, the matter took on a rather different aspect when he later found all the piglets' tails used as spigots in the latches of his farm buildings. He complained to the police, who promised to keep a lookout. For weeks, in all weathers, a poor unfortunate constable paraded the moors seeking a possible culprit who might strike again. Things settled down for a bit, and then one morning he discovered that a number of the farmer's calves had lost their tails. These duly turned up as some kind of door fastening.

Again the moors were watched over without result. A little later on, the farm jingle (small trap) was found to be missing; it was later recovered, turned over at the bottom of a nearby lane. Undoubtedly, said the poor wife, the place was haunted, and I am not staying here any longer.

The complete absence of any person found wandering the moors during these incidents soon made the police suspect that the strange happenings began at the home.

Det. Insp. Morcumb (as he then was) inspected the premises, and with his usual acumen suspected the truth — that the young wife, completely fed up with her unaccustomed islation, had conceived the idea of making the place appear to be haunted in order to pursuade her husband to move out. Mr Morcumb found and brought to me a hurricane lamp and a bone-handled domestic knife with a rather blunt and notched cutting edge. Examination of smears on the top of the lamp and stains on the knife where the blades joined the handle showed that they were due to blood, identified by precipitation tests as having come from members of the bovine (ox) and pig families.

A little discreet questioning by Mr Morcumb elicited confirmation of his suspicions. No further action was taken, and no further untoward events occurred at this isolated spot. The young couple continued to live there, I hope quite happily.

It is a curious and indeed a sad reflection that so little notice is taken by the public of the tremendous value of pure scientific investigation in the detection of crime. The medical investigation of horrible injuries, with lots of blood about, is what attracts the headlines. Poisonings attract some interest, but give the public a few splashes of blood and there is no holding them. Give them a bucketful and the salacious information that the body has been cut up into little pieces, and there is jubilation. Can anything be worse than the disgusting pictures paraded on the front pages of some of our newspapers, depicting women weeping over the bloodstained corpses of close relatives? Who on earth wants to see these? In my opinion, only the depraved.

The immensely valuable contributions of the pure sciences to crime detection rarely get more than a cursory mention in the press, yet it is on these that in numbers, more crimes are solved than by any other means. For those who are interested, and everybody should be, may I recommend that they read the book *Science against Crime*, Stuart Kind and Michael Overton, which gives a fascinating account of what can be accomplished. I hope that this book will do something to right the disparity between the public thirst for blood and its lack of appreciation of the efforts of the scientific back-room boys.

When I did my analytical chemistry, we were all quite pleased to obtain results within a few milligrammes, using sizeable amounts of material — whole bottles of medicine, for example, and whole pills. Microchemistry did not begin until 1923, with the first publication of *Microchemie*. My earlier scientific investigations were almost totally based on classical methods; these worked, but within wide limits. Later of course, these cumbersome methods were superceded by the new micro methods.

Although not strictly applicable to the object of this book, which is essentially to record my personal involvement in the detection of crime, mainly in Cornwall during my years of tenure of office, it should be of interest to the general public just to realise what can be done by the pure scientist. The chemist can estimate the blood alcohol content in a drop of blood the size of a pinhead. The physicist can date the Turin Shroud, and the biologist can identify an individual from his blood as accurately as the fingerprint expert. Traces of drugs, undetectable by chemical means, can be indentifed by mass spectroscopy. Atomic absorption spectroscopy can detect minute traces of the metals lead, antimony and barium on the hands of a person suspected of having fired a gun. Traces of the explosive can also be found.

Gas chromatography is probably the most versatile technique now employed in forensic laboratories, analysing with unbelievable and extreme accuracy pinpoint amounts of anything that can be volatilised, with an accuracy of one part in several millions. We thought we were very clever when we were able to estimate as little as a one-thousandth of a milligramme of arsenic in tissues by the Marsh test. Now, one thousandth of this amount can be estimated by neutron activation analysis.

I have a tremendous regard and respect for my forensic science colleagues. Generally, when both sides are investigating a case, and we are on opposite sides, we agree; when we do not, the case is fought out in the courts with the uttermost friendliness and courtesy between us. We may differ in our convictions, but there is never any aggro.

Dozens of books have been written by pathologists, doctors, coroners and ex-high-ranking police officers on the subjects of the crimes they have investigated. This is another personal record. To my knowledge, only the book that I have already mentioned has given an account of the triumphs of scientific investigation, along with two other publications, *The Scientific Investigation of Crime*, by Dr L. C. Nickolls, late Director of the Metropolitan Police Laboratory, New Scotland Yard, and *Forensic Science* by Dr H. J. Walls. They are all well worth reading, and I hope more will come.

But all these marvellous scientific aids to the detection of crime were in the future as far as I was concerned, and my own scientific investigations were limited to the knowledge available at that time.

Sheep stealing was, and still is, a profitable and not uncommon pastime.

On 14 October, 1935, Mr William Samuel Hosken of St Cleer purchased six Devon long wool sheep which he took back to his farm, and marked them across the shoulders and loins with a mixture of redding and water. Two months later, one of these was found to be missing, and one identical with it turned up on an adjacent farm, but it was covered with green paint. When examined, it was found that underneath the green paint there were red markings. The new 'owner' explaind that he had first marked the sheep with redding mixed with linseed oil, and subsequently covered the marks with green paint. A pretty feeble and unconvincing story, proved on analysis to be untrue. The underlying redding was the usual crude (impure) iron oxide used commonly for sheep marking, and it contained no linseed oil. This was undoubtedly the lost sheep, and the thieving farmer received his just reward at the next Assizes.

Many are the chemical analyses that I have performed to identify objects or relate one object with another or part of another. Recording most of these would be a rather boring exercise, so I have selected only a very few.

One ingenious mechanic thought up the idea of sawing a length of solid copper piping of suitable diameter into 'sixpences', with which he obtained an unknown number of packets of cigarettes from vending machines — 'those were the days'. He even went to the trouble of roughly 'milling' the edges. He obviously got the thickness and weight perfectly adjusted, because they worked — I tried them! My obvious job was to match the chemical composition of copper filings, solid copper rods and the 'sixpences'. This I duly did by old-fashioned laborious chemical processes. Today, the whole thing would be done much more accurately in minutes in a spectrograph.

Another simple scientific exercise involves the restoration of letters or figures that have been rubbed out or removed by filing. Such a case occurred on 29 January, 1938. It was at a time when there was an epidemic of bag snatching in Falmouth. On this day, a lady lost her handbag in this way. As would not be unusual, the key to her front door was one of the articles inside, as well as letters giving her address. At once the locks on the doors of the home were changed so that there were no distressful sequels.

Some months later, a man was apprehended for house-breaking in Newquay. Amongst his possessions there was found a 'Yale' type key, the serial number of which had been completely filed away. Etching with acid brought this number back again. The mechanism is easily understood. Brass, of which these keys are made, is not an homogeneous metal, but crystalline in structure. Numbers are stamped in by a heavy press or blow, and this results in fractures between those crystals that are immediately below, separating them slightly. Even if the superficial layers are filed out, the deeper ones still retain these fractures. If the metal is now treated with acid, the acid will permeate between the fractured crystals and eat away the edges, thus restoring the original number or letter. When this was done with this recovered key, the number 5390 came up. We were not quite sure if it was 5390 or 5396, the last number being rather indefinite. Fortunately for us, this lady's husband had kept his old keys, and one of them proved to be identical with the one recovered from the housebreaker, even to the defective 0 or 6.

I don't think I have ever seen a man in the witness box so surprised as was this one when he was shown the key, the number of which had been restored.

Sacrilege, whatever one's belief, is a nasty offence and universally condemned. Alas, and alas, it is becoming more frequent. Our churches were always open to every comer for reflection and/or admiration, for peace and quiet. Now almost all are shut up on account of vandalism. What a reflection on the times. Only once have I had to deal with a case, and that a rather pathetic one.

What does one do with a case like this?

'18 September, 1946. I respectfully report that at 11 a.m. on Tuesday, 17 September, 1946, Frank Fry, of no fixed abode, was arrested for sacrilege, viz. between p.m. Sunday, 15th and 11 a.m., Tuesday, 17 September, 1946, did break and enter Tretoli Methodist Church, Lanivet, and steal therefrom goods to the value of 3d., the property of the Trustees of the Chapel. Frank Fry has not yet admitted the offence. On his arrest it was found that his overcoat and coat were marked with colouring, and I am instructed to send to you for examination these articles together with a sample of colouring obtained from the wall of the Chapel. . . .' I found them identical, and Frank was duly convicted.

21

Exhumations

I have been involved in four exhumations.

The first was that of Mrs Lydia Curnow of St Ives. She lived with her husband, and to say that their relationships were strained would be putting the position more than mildly. They loathed each other, so much so that Mrs Curnow had to be prescribed sleeping tablets (Soneryl) by her doctor, Dr Barwell. Soneryl is an 'intermediate acting' barbiturate, producing sleep in about one half hour. The ordinary dose is up to 200 milligrammes at a time.

One morning in the middle of May 1949, Mr Curnow entered his wife's bedroom, and, according to him, found her dead. He at once sent for Dr Barwell, who confirmed the death, and gave it as his opinion that it had only just occurred. Mr Curnow mentioned that a large number of tablets of Soneryl were missing. In the circumstances, it appeared that Mrs Curnow had taken a poisonous dose of Soneryl with suicidal intent. A post-mortem examination was ordered. As I was away on holiday, this was done by my assistant, Dr Wood, who came to the conclusion that death was due to heart failure, due to myocardial degeneration accelerated by ingestion of a barbiturate. She took samples for analysis by our biochemist, Dr Eason, who found as follows:

Cerebro-spinal fluid: 1.7 milligrammes per 100 millilitres
Urine: 4.6 milligrammes per 100 millilitres
Brain: 3.2 per 100 milligrammes

Kidney: 2.5 per 100 milligrammes

In all, he estimated that the body of Mrs Curnow contained 1.7 grammes of Soneryl. This is not a fatal dose, especially in one probably addicted to the drug. The minimal fatal dose is two grammes or 6 milligrammes per 100 millilitres of blood or cerebro-spinal fluid. Less than half of this was found. The cause of death seemed to be open to question.

In addition, Dr Wood had overlooked a bruise on Mrs Curnow's chin. Det. Supt Julian was not happy. After a lot of consideration, an exhumation was ordered, and carried out on the night of 20 May, 1949; the same night I made a second post-mortem examination.

The bruise noted on the chin by Mr Julian was confirmed. I also found on the left arm a one-and-a-half inch bruise six inches below the shoulder in front, and at the back, an inch higher, a three-quarter inch bruise. On the right arm there was a three-quarter inch bruise just below the shoulder. Both suggested gripping of the arms. More significantly, I found quite a lot of bruising deep in the neck, and later on, microscopic examination of sections of the skin of the neck showed some light bruising. Deep in the neck there was bruising in the muscles on both sides of the spine, the bruises being two inches long on the right side and slightly less on the left side. In my opinion, these bruises indicated pressure on the neck, but not violent pressure. I must point out that no blame could attach to Dr Wood for missing these bruises. Light bruising is often not apparent immediately after death, but only becomes obvious after some twenty-four to forty-eight hours. What was invisible to her, was visible to me later. I found further light bruising in the muscle connecting the top of the sternum to the skull below the ear, on a level with the voice box.

My further findings were that the lungs showed no obvious congestion such as would be associated with chronic heart failure, especially if there had been added congestion due to respiratory failure due to soporific poisoning. In my opinion, the heart was in good condition, not enlarged, with normal musculature. The coronary arteries and vascular system generally were in good condition; I could see no sign of any heart failure, but there was some evidence of early liver congestion.

I gave it as my opinion that death was due to compression of the neck whilst unconscious due to an overdose of Soneryl.

The trial took place at Winchester. Were we flattened! The Prosecution was led by Fox Andrews KC. Just before the court sat, Mr Andrews asked me how I thought it had been done. I said I thought that Curnow had found his wife moribund, but not dead, and had polished her off by lightly squeezing her neck. I said that I thought only two fingers had been applied, and not the whole hand. Mr Fox Andrews asked me if I had seen Curnow's right hand. I said that I had not. He replied that Curnow had only a thumb and one finger on his right hand.

The Judge threw the case out, and ordered costs against the police! He said obviously quite rightly, that the two pathologists for the Prosecution could not agree on the cause of death. One said natural causes accelerated by an overdose (but not lethal overdose) of Soneryl, the other homicidal pressure on the neck whilst unconscious due to the again not fatal overdose of Soneryl. The accused was obviously entitled to be acquitted when there was so much doubt. To add insult to injury, the Defence brought in a young recently-qualified pathologist to say that the bruising in the neck was due to the neck being overstretched on the postmortem table!

On the way home to Cornwall, Curnow, Drs Wood and Eason travelled back in the same railway carriage. Dr Eason asked Curnow how he had done it. Curnow replied that he had not. He was a staunch Christian, and knew that God would look after him and assure his acquittal.

I must say that I was never altogether happy about the case, and was glad at the outcome.

Charles Treby Barratt died at his home in Bude on 22 November, 1972. There was nothing remarkable about this. He was duly buried in Bude churchyard, right at the top and close to a Cornish hedge forming the boundary of the churchyard. Beyond the hedge there was a footpath and small copse of trees.

Barratt's wife, Mrs Muriel Jean Barratt, died on 26 July, 1977. Because she had a history of chronic alcoholism, I was asked to do a post-mortem examination. As alcoholism came into my report as a contributory cause of death, HM Coroner for North Cornwall, Mr G. H. St L. Northey MBE, TD, decided that he must hold an inquest. This delayed her burial for a day or so. The family grave had meanwhile been opened up for her reception. When the burial was about to take place, it was noticed that there had been some strange happenings in the vicinity. The vicar, the Rev. David Wills, had discovered that two leaded windows in his church had been broken, a candle holder was missing, and it also appeared that somebody had spent a night on the altar. Bloodstains were found on the altar cloth.

Then the undertaker noticed some of the workmens' tools lying alongside the grave, and on looking into the grave he saw that considerable damage had been done to the lid of Mr Barratt's coffin. Only later were the police told about the undertaker's suspicions. Meanwhile, it was noticed that other gravestones had been disturbed; some had been turned around to face north and south, and some had even been broken off. The burial of Mrs Barratt duly took place.

A few days later, a young couple walking along the footpath bordering the graveyard came across what appeared to be a human lower leg thrown into the adjacent copse immediately behind the Barratt grave.

This limb was brought to me and identified undoubtedly as that of the lower leg and main bones of the ankle of a male human being. Very little flesh remained. Assuming that the limb had been buried, I estimated that it had been in the earth for some four to five years, corresponding to the time of Mr Barratt's burial.

In these circumstances, it was decided to exhume the body of Mr Barratt; a Home Office Order was duly applied for, and duly granted.

At 7.15 a.m. on the morning of 25 October, 1977, I went with numerous police officers to the Barratt grave. I expected to find the coffin of Mr Barratt lifted up alongside the grave, ready for me to examine it and its contents in some comfort. Not a bit of it. Mrs Barratt's coffin had been lifted out without difficulty, but Mr Barratt's coffin was firmly wedged down and packed down with heavily trampelled earth. The coffin lid had been broken into a number of pieces and thrown roughly in.

Enquiring gazes and hints produced no response from the officers of the Law. I was expected to go down and do the excavation myself — they said in case they disturbed anything. So, for the second time in my life I took my little trowel to excavate a body.

Commencing at the leg end, I shortly uncovered a right lower leg and foot lying in the line of the main direction of the coffin. This leg I found to be in exactly the same state of decomposition as the leg found in the copse, and to measure up exactly with that leg. There was no left leg in the coffin. A further finding was that this right leg had been severed from the body at the knee and had been thrown across the bottom of the coffin. Continuing the excavation, I uncovered the remainder of the lower part of Mr Barratt's body, including the upper legs. It was then noted with surpise that the body had been pulled down in the coffin towards the foot, to such an extent that the lower parts of legs, if still attached to the body, could not have been accommodated in the space available. Either the legs would have had to be turned upwards, or the knees bent upwards. In either case, the legs or knees would have projected above the level of the coffin and would be immediately noticeable when Mrs Barratt came to be buried. So the lower legs, from the knees, had to be disposed of, and so were cut off at the knees. There were definite signs of cutting, indicating that these lower limbs had not been separated by rotting. After this dismemberment, one lower leg was replaced between the thighs, riding some six inches above them. The other leg, for some reason that we found it impossible to fathom, was jettisoned over the wall. Had this not been done, it is unlikely that the affair would have ever come to light.

My excavation went on. Next to be discovered was the deceased's scalp, planted over his abdomen. Further rummaging about discovered a sheath knife with a blade about four inches long, lying to the left-hand side of the body.

Further sifting of earth in the region of the head was difficult because of the confined space, so the body had to be lifted up. This was found very difficult to do because it had been so far pulled down towards the foot end of the coffin, that it had jammed in the narrowing sides. This of course had presented whoever was desecrating the grave with a serious problem. The body had been so far pulled down, and would not go back, so that, as already related, the legs stuck up and had to be dealt with. However, by the sexton pulling on one arm, and I on the other, we managed to get the corpse upright. It had no head, and there was no head in the coffin. Later recovered was the candle holder from the Church altar.

This was obviously a case of desecration of a grave, and the police made their enquiries. These centred on the local library, from which a number of books on black magic had been borrowed, and not all returned. The borrower was Trevelyan Frederick Bolitho, aged eighteen years, unemployed, who was duly brought before the Magistrates. He pleaded guilty to unlawfully removing parts of the body. After removing the head, he had taken it down to the beach, scraped all the flesh off it with stones, and washed the brains out. He had then polished it with sandpaper. It was recovered from a wardrobe in his bedroom.

My friend, Mrs Sheila Corser, was the Chairman of the Magistrates who dealt with the case. They fined him £10, I think and Mrs Corser said that unfortunately this was the maximum penalty under the Burial Act. However, the desecrator of the tomb was also sent to the Crown Court for sentence on three burglary charges, with the recommendation that he received Borstal training.

Some fifty books on magic were found in his possession.

Black magic practices are by no means unusual in Cornwall. I hope I am not being libellous when I add that they appear to be concentrated in the sparsely-populated and isolated parts of the north of the county.

22

The Last Murders

It is now time to return to some more murder stories. The Michaelmas Assizes at Bodmin in 1963 were remarkable, in that for the first time we had three cases of murder running simultaneously, and I was kept running from one court to the other to keep up with things.

The first was a simple affair from the pathologist's point of view, with nothing remarkable about it. The facts were that a middle-aged woman, Mrs Capewell by name, was living with her children and a friend, Alfred Frank Collins, at Sand Hill House, Gunnislake. This is a large and beautiful house, set in its own grounds, and with its own private church. In August 1963 it was almost completely filled with household goods of almost every description, all destined for a perfectly legitimate sale. It however also contained a large selection of toilet rolls labelled Taunton UDC.

During the evening of 4 August, 1963, Mrs Capewell and her children were in the television room, watching television, when the door was flung open, revealing the presence of Mr Capewell. He had a loaded shotgun in his hands, with which he started blazing at all and sundry, including the ceiling, walls and everywhere. He shot at his wife. In her account of the incident at the trial, she said that she heard a loud bang and felt an acute pain in her side. When the same incident was repeated by Mrs Capewell's teenage son, he said that he saw the door open, saw his father appear in the doorway, heard a loud bang and saw that he (the father) had 'shot mother up the arse'. The boy's account was the more correct one. After this, Mr Capewell got hold of a bottle of wine with which he beat his wife across the head, smashing the bottle. She was severely injured, but mercifully not killed. Her clothing became saturated with her blood (group A), and her subsequent movements could be traced by following the blood spots of this group about the house. A sliver of bottle glass, clear and slightly curved, was found embedded in a heavy blood clot in the right armpit of her dress. Following the group A blood marks, they led all over the room, down a passage to the telephone room, and were found on the telephone itself and on a telephone directory. It was evident that Mrs Capewell, severely injured and bleeding profusely from her head had run to the telephone to raise the alarm, which in fact she did.

Whilst this was going on, Mr Collins appeared and met Mr Capewell at the bottom of the stairs. Here, Collins was shot in the chest at almost point-blank range. He did not die instantly, but lay for some time at the bottom of the stairs in the middle of large pool of blood before finally crawling along the passageway to the front door, where he finally collapsed and was found dead. His blood group was group B so that his movements could be easily followed, independent of those of Mrs Capewell.

The post-mortem examination showed a ragged perforating wound, one and one-half inches in diameter, in the middle of the upper chest. The edges were blackened and scorched. The shot just missed the heart, but damaged the aorta end of the windpipe and the blood vessels going to the lungs. Death was inevitable, but surprisingly not immediate, as shown by the ability of the stricken man to crawl from the bottom of the stairs to the front door.

The other remarkable thing about this trial was that Collins, Capewell and many of the witnesses came from Birmingham. When one of the latter started giving his evidence, the shorthand writer paused, looked blank and kept his pencil suspended. The Judge looked blank and put his pencil down. Counsel looked blank and repeated his question. No good. Not a person in the court could understand the native dialect. A previous witness had to be recalled and sworn in as an interpreter!

This was of course a plain straightforward case of murder by shooting, witnessed and confirmed by post-mortem examination.

The second victim was eighteen-year-old Judith Ann Enwright, already described. Both killers received comparatively light sentences.

The third victim was William Garfield Rowe.

In this third case, two men tried together for the murder of William Garfield Rowe were not so lucky, nor did they deserve to be. They were convicted of murder, sentenced to death and executed. It has often been said that these two were the last to be executed in this country for murder, but this is not correct. They were indeed the last pair, but shortly afterwards there was one other single execution for the same offence.

The two convicted men were Russell Pascoe, aged twenty-three years, and Dennis John Whitty, aged twenty-two years. Both had criminal records.

Pascoe at the time was a married man. He had been brought up by his parents at their cottage about one and a half miles from Nanjarrow Farm, where the murdered man lived. About four weeks prior to the murder, Pascoe left his wife and went to live with Whitty and three nineteen-year-old girls in a caravan in the Kenwyn Caravan Park at Truro; the five of them shared two beds.

When Pascoe was sixteen or seventeen years of age, he assisted from time to time at Nanjarrow Farm. During this time, the farmhouse was entered on an occasion when Mr Rowe was absent, and cash and small items of jewellery to the value of £264 were stolen. The cash, some £250, had been in tins and jam jars secreted in various rooms. No-one was apprehended for this theft, but after he was charged with murder of the farmer, Pascoe admitted being one of two thieves who had entered the farmhouse in 1960 and stolen the money etc. Whitty was not his companion then, and this person was never traced. Of importance of course was the fact that Pascoe knew that Mr Rowe was in the habit of hiding money about the place, having no trust in banks — and probably not in Income Tax Inspectors either. What Pascoe did not know at the time of the murder was that Rowe had invented a much safer method to hide his wealth, about which more later.

The other partner in crime was Dennis John Whitty, a labourer at the Truro gasworks. A small man, with fair, fine and slightly wavy hair, he wore plan gold earrings and had a passion for eating snails; these were provided in abundance whilst he was awaiting execution. Almost a little weasel of a man, it became apparent at his trial that he was the dominant personality in this tragic affair, Pascoe being a simple lad, easily led.

William Garfield Rowe himself was an oddity. A single man aged sixty-four years, he had lived alone at Nanjarrow Farm, Constantine, since his mother died in 1956. The farm is a very isolated one, one-and-a-half miles from Constantine, reached by about half a mile of very rough cart track.

William was born in Porthleven, and originally lived with his parents there. He was a man of peace, disliking all forms of violence. Conscripted into the Army in 1917, he survived the ordeal for not more than a week, deserting and returning home. He was traced and returned to the Army, and sent to a detention centre. From this he escaped , and again returned home. Curiously enough, he then appears to have been written off by the Army authorities, as they made no further attempt to get at him again. But he did not know this, and he went into complete hiding, becoming in fact an 'invisible man'. Any neighbour asking about him was told that he was just another soldier who had failed to return from the war, although curiously his name did not appear on the local war memorial.

William helped the family out by working in the dark of the evenings, and it must have been with some surprise that neighbours noticed farm carts, empty in the early part of the evenings, loaded up for market on the following morning. Whether or not they suspected, the truth was never revealed — probably a true case of Cornish clanniness and mutual help.

For more than thirty years, William lived the life of a complete recluse. The death of the father in 1949, however, made a move necessary, and he and the rest of the family moved to Nanjarrow Farm, Constantine. To escape detection, William lay at the bottom of the cart with sacks and household goods piled over him.

The family at this time consisted of mother, William and brother Stanley, another brother Joel, having married and left home. In 1954, Stanley, still a single man, died, leaving only William and his mother at the farm. She died two years later, leaving a problem for William. However, this was miraculously solved for him on the occasion of the accession of Queen Elizabeth II to the throne, when a total amnesty for all deserters of both World Wars was declared. But the habits of a lifetime could not be changed overnight. He remained an almost complete recluse, occasionally employed on local casual labour. Even after his reprieve, William's contact with the outside world up to the time of his death was scanty. He was extremely shy and reserved, and known locally as a hermit. Very occasionally he would visit cattle markets, travelling on foot and by bus to buy and sell cattle, sheep and pigs. Because of his frugal habits, it was rumoured that he was well-off financially; in this case, rumour was found to be correct; when his will was provisionally published on 13 December, 1963, it referred to a sum of £8,082 — quite a large amount in those days. There were no visitors to the farmhouse, not even his own only surviving near relation, his brother Joel, with whom he was not on good terms. If a cattle dealer called, the conversation would be held in one of the farm's yards or outbuildings. It was during this time he met Russell Pascoe, then a youth of sixteen or seventeen years of age.

Nanjarrow Farm is a sizeable Cornish farmhouse with five bedrooms, half tiled, and situated in beautiful country a mile and a half down a rough track. William lived in only one downstairs room. All the others were stacked with furniture and the accumulation of ages. When I saw them, there were clear signs that the two ground floor front rooms and all five bedrooms on the first floor had been ransacked. Drawers had been pulled open, emptied on to the floor and thrown down; cupboards had been opened and the contents strewn about the floor. The bed was in disorder, as if the mattress had been turned over. Even before this, however, the premises could hardly have been called tidy, but they were not dirty or verminous.

On the evening of 14 August, 1963, Pascoe and Whitty left their caravan, Pascoe driving a motorcycle and Whitty riding pillion. Pascoe was armed with an iron bar (case opener or jemmy) whilst Whitty had a double-edged knife and a starting pistol, the latter not lethal.

Three girls shared the caravan with them. They were told that they were going to do a 'job' at a farmhouse at Constantine and had borrowed articles of clothing from them, stockings which they tried out by pulling them over their faces, gloves, a black jumper and, very importantly, a dark double-breasted blazer with silver buttons. This was worn by Whitty, and, as he admitted, it made him look like a naval service man.

All three girls had seen, and subsequently identified, the iron bar, the knife and the pistol, and had seen the two men leaving the caravan with these weapons as well as the diguising clothing. They left at about 10 p.m.

The two men drove to a point about one mile from Nanjarrow Farm and parked the motorcycle in a field behind a hedge. They walked about a mile along the cart track and footpath to the farm. When they arrived, they saw a light on in it.

According to their own statements, Pascoe and Whitty arrived at the farmhouse at about 11 p.m., armed as they had left the caravan. By then it was dark. They knocked on the door, and William came out with a lantern in his hand. Pascoe stood aside with his iron bar, and William was confronted by Whitty. In his statement, Whitty says:

'Last Wednesday (14 August, 1963) when it was dark, I don't know the time, Russell and me went to a farm Russell said he knew near Constantine, where he said, the old man living by himself had a lot of money. I didn't want to go but he made me. We walked past a house in the lane and saw a light on, then we went to a door round the back. I knocked and an old man came to the door with a lantern. I told him I had trouble with a helicopter and asked for a phone.' In his borrowed double-breasted blazer, with silver buttons, it would be easy for him to appear to an old, not very worldly man, to be just what he described himself to be, and obviously what he intended to look like when he left his caravan. To continue with his statement: 'The old man came out to tell me where one was, and Russell (Pascoe) hit him. He then said to me, "Go on, stick him." I didn't want to and I started crying. He told me he would use the bar on me if I didn't do it, so I stuck me knife into the old man's chest three or four times and in his throat, I think. Russell was standing over me with the bar and told me he would hit me with it if I didn't "stick" the old man. I was crying all the time. Then he made me drag the old man to a corner of the yard and take some keys from his pocket. We went in the house and all we took was two packets of matches and an old watch. We left. I don't know what Russell did with the keys, but I threw the dagger away and he threw the bar in the dam. The next day I saw blood on my trousers so I threw them in the River Truro . . .'

Russell Pascoe also made a statement. It ran: 'I'll tell you the truth, definitely will. Last Wednesday night (14 August, 1963) with my mate Dennis Whitty I went to Mr Rowe's farm at Nanjarrow Farm, Constantine. We went on my motorbike.

'We were going to see if he had any money.

'Dennis knocked at the back door. Dennis was standing in front of the door. He asked Dennis what he wanted, and he said he was a helicopter pilot and had crashed in a field. I then hit the old man on the back of the head with a small iron bar. I meant just to knock him out, that's all. The old man fell down, and I said to Dennis, "Let it go at that". He took the iron bar from me and went mad. I knew he had a knife and I knew he was thumping the old man just outside the back door. I had to walk away, honest I did. He dragged him into the corner and then went into the house.

'I found four pounds under the piano, in a panel like, and Dennis took a watch and two big boxes of matches. I think there were a dozen in the packet. He also took some keys from the old man's pocket. He did say the old man was dead now as he had struck him in the throat with the knife. We then went home to the caravan. On the way, we threw the bar and the knife in the Argel Dam reservoir. I"ll show you where it is.'

These weapons were subsequently recovered. One was an iron jemmy or packing-case opener. It was square in section, fourteen-and-a-half inches long, and weighed two pounds five ounces. The other was a sheath knife, strongly constructed, six inches in length and sharpened on both sides, tapering to a point. It was eleven-sixteenths of an inch wide.

I went with Mr Matthews, Chief Constable, Mr Julian, Assistant Chief Constable and other police officers to Nanjarrow Farm at 4 p.m. on Thursday, 15 August, 1963.

I there saw the body of an elderly man lying face downwards and with the arms partly outstretched in a corner of a yard some few yards from the back door of the farmhouse. His head was in a pool of blood; it had been battered by a blunt instrument, and he was dead. There was very heavy bloodstaining in the yard in front of the door, and a line of heavy bloodstaining partly washed by recent rain ran from the door to where the body was lying. There were drag marks in the mud between the door and the body and mud had been dragged and heaped up under the face of the dead man.

Examination of the doorway showed splashes of blood running in an upward-flung direction on the door, the right-hand door jamb, and on the ceiling of a short passage leading from the door into the house.

These findings all taken together suggested that the dead man had been violently attacked from outside whilst standing in his doorway, and had fallen forwards gravely injured. He had then been dragged in to the corner of the yard.

Temperature recordings showed that he had died between 10 p.m. and midnight of 14-15 August, 1963.

The post-mortem examination showed that very numerous injuries were present, some made by stabbing with a dagger-like weapon, others by blows with a blunt instrument.

There were five stab wounds in the chest just to the left of the mid line. They all ran in a parallel, vertical direction, three-quarters of an inch wide with both ends sharply pointed. There was no sign of any dragging such as would have occurred if the body had been slumping or falling away whilst the attack was going on, showing that these stab wounds had been inflicted very rapidly one after the other whilst the victim was standing upright. Three of the wounds penetrated deeply into the chest, some four to five inches. One went into the heart, and two into the upper surface of the liver.

There were two other stab wounds; one ran horizontally in the upper part of the neck on the right side, penetrating deeply as far back as the spine, severing the main blood vessels on this side of the neck. The second was a more superficial cut on the front of the neck.

The head had been battered by a number of blows with a blunt instrument. There were six ragged splits in the scalp, from two and a half inches to three inches in length. Four were roughly parallel, again suggesting a rapid series of blows. Both eyes were blackened.

In addition, there were numerous scrapes, abrasions and cuts on the front of the face, and a ragged cut two inches long along the line of the lower jaw, the bone of which was shattered. These injuries were probably made by the body falling forwards on to the hard courtyard, and then being dragged into the corner where it was found.

The skull, which was exceptionally hard, but not thickened, was shattered, and portions of bone depressed inwards. The brain was bruised and lacerated.

There was evidence that the dead man had tried to protect himself from the blows being rained upon him. The top of the third finger of the left hand was severed through the last joint, and was missing. A lot of discussion took place at the trial as to whether this bit of the finger had been severed by the knife or the iron bar — as if it mattered! Four heavy blows had fallen on the right arm, three around the elbow, one lower down, all roughly parallel, and in a position showing that the arm had been raised up to protect the head. Where the blows had fallen, the skin was deeply split. There was a large bruise over the whole of the back of the left hand, probably also raised to ward off the blows. These blows had been made with a blunt instrument, not a knife, and almost certainly the same instrument as caused the injuries to the head.

All these injuries were made at about the same time, but some of the splits in the scalp showed far less bruising than others from which it appeared that some at least had been inflicted after death. Any of the blows on the head would have made the man unconscious before death occurred from his multiple injuries.

I gave it as my opinion that death was due to a combined attack having been made simultaneously by two assailants, one striking with a knife, the other battering with a blunt instrument.

This was a point that raised so much argument at the trial. I was questioned repeatedly when giving my evidence and in cross-examination, and was brought back twice after that by the Judge, Mr Justice Thessinger, to make this point quite clear. I was given by him three alternatives to explain the injuries. One. Were the injuries consistent with the simultaneous attack by two people, one yielding a knife, the other an iron bar? Two. Were the injuries consistent with there having been two assailants, one having a knife, and the other a bar, one first using the knife, and then taking the bar from the other, and continuing the assault with the bar — or the other way round, bar first, and then knife? Three. One assailant only, using both the bar and the knife, one in each hand, and striking simultaneously or alternatively. The alternatives of course arose from the statements of the two accused, each essentially blaming the other. My choice was the first; this was accepted, and both men were found equally guilty.

It was only during the last few minutes of the trial that the reason for this senseless murder came to light. Almost at the end of his evidence, Pascoe said in effect that as the old man came out of the door, and had been answering Whitty's questions, he (Pascoe) hit him on the head, through his cloth cap, not very hard. The man fell to his knees, looked up and said, 'why did you do that?' Fearing that he had been recognised from past acquaintance, Pascoe then said they had to kill him to prevent any action being taken against them. Could anything be more callous?

On returning to the caravan, Whitty went to bed with one of the girls and told her how he and Pascoe had killed the farmer. Subsequently they admitted to all the girls, after being tackled by them as a result of reports in the next morning's papers, that they had done the murder, at the same time threatening them that if they opened their mouths, they would end up the same way as Mr Rowe.

The girls themselves were no paragons of virtue. All three heard the two men say they were going to go to a farm-house at Constantine to do a job. No protest was made, and they collaborated by lending clothing and the essential blazer to the two men. The men left at about 10 p.m., returning at 1 a.m. the following morning, both laughing. All the girls had seen the knife and bar in the caravan before the murder, and identified them subsequently when they were produced in court. Two of the girls had on occasion accompanied Whitty on shop and housebreaking expeditions, and when thus engaged, Whitty was usually armed with both these weapons. One one occasion, one of the girls carried the bar herself, intending to hit a night porter with it if they were disturbed when breaking into a public house.

The stolen matches were found in the caravan, and Mr Robert Mitchell Allison, a fellow worker with Whitty, found the Elgin pocket watch belonging to Mr Rowe in a pocket of a waterproof mackintosh which he knew belonged to Whitty. The mackintosh was the in the workmens' locker room at the Truro Gas Works. Mr Edgar Stanley Collins, also a workmate of Whitty, found the second missing Elgin pocket watch in the pocket of a coat which he alleged he saw Whitty wearing on 15 August, 1963, the day following the murder.

Pascoe's mental state was not brought into question, but Whitty's Counsel, Mr Norman Skelhorn QC, brought evidence that he (Whitty) suffered from an hysterical condition, had had at least six blackouts, and Whitty himself spoke of 'strange and unnatural things that happened to him'. Not very convincing, and the Judge stressed that mental responsibility depended upon whether or not a man knew that what he was doing was wrong, and that he was likely to be punished if he was caught. There was no evidence whatever of any mental abnormality immediately preceeding the events of that tragic evening.

Although nothing to do with the trial itself, there remained the mystery of the whereabouts of any money that William Rowe had possessed. All the murderers got in cash was £4.

£3000 overlooked by the intruders was subsequently found in the house, and there was more elsewhere.

During William's long lifetime in virtual incarceration, he had spent a lot of his daytime hours in self-education, including the learning of Esperanto. In his desk there was discovered a small pocketbook in which various sums of money were mentioned by descriptive notes in Esperanto. These were deciphered by a Helston solicitor, and the directions given led to fields and hedges on the farm, and to the floor of the pig house. In places there were found milk bottles stuffed with currency notes. The tops were sealed with tallow, and the bottles had then been inverted into a bucket, also having a tallow seal.

In the course of investigations, many samples and objects have to be taken away for examination. But are we not rather overdoing it now, not only in the investigation of crime, but also in the realm of medical practice? I know that we 'old ones' know much better than those who follow us; sometimes we are right, and sometimes we are wrong. In my days, what we regarded as a few useful pathological examinations and X-ray photographs sufficed to help with our diagnoses. Now dozens of pathological tests are demanded, and dozens of X-ray photographs taken, a large amount of them unnecessary, with corresponding waste of public money. I remember a very dear old friend of mine, Mr Gordon Paull, senior surgeon to the Bristol Royal Infirmary. He decided one day to operate on a patient, on purely clinical nous. His Registrar said that he couldn't possibly do that because some out-of-the-way tests had revealed something wrong. Mr Paull, a man of few but significant words, said just one, and proceeded to operate, successfully. I often wonder how much time, waste of time, waste of resources, waste of money now goes on. I am probably wrong, especially as we now live in such a litigious age. When I retired from the Hospital Service in 1964, my contribution to my Medical Defence Union was £2 a year. In 1987 it was in the region of £700 p.a. and is about to be doubled. Why? Because of vastly increasing claims against doctors for negligence or malpractice. Some are undoubtedly justified, but I suspect that many are just a means of getting money easily. Nobody therefore can blame the doctor for doing everything possible in the investigation line to protect himself, regardless of the waste. I know of doctors who are giving up the struggle because of the cost and risk involved in medical practice. There has been recent newspaper comment on this waste.

The same applies to criminal investigations. I used to take just a few, what I considered necessary, samples or objects for examination. Now dozens, or hundreds of specimens are taken. You can't blame the police. If they slip up on even a very minor incident of no real importance, Defence Counsel will be after them, suggesting that as they have done their work so slovenly, all their work is suspect. It all throws an enormous burden on the staffs of our forensic laboratories — doing a lot of unnecessary work.

Take the case of Cyrus Hoar. It was a perfectly simple one, no doubt about it from the word 'go', and yet dozens of exhibits were taken for examination.

Cyrus murdered his brother and sister-in-law on 19 April, 1977.

Cyrus lived at Herodsfoot in a Forestry Commission cottage. He had not worked for the past sixteen or seventeen years because he suffered from 'nerves', accepted by the local Social Security Authority as a sufficient reason for the payment of substantial weekly benefit, although a local doctor had refused him the required certificates. Out of this benefit he had accumulated a vast and expensive collection of books, models and bicycles, as well as an assortment of unlicensed firearms. He had been over-coddled by his parents, and when first his mother and then his father died, he was left without any prop in his life. The bulk of the family possessions had originally been left to him, both by mother and father, but in January 1976, father, in hospital, made a new will leaving everything to his daughter-in-law, Doris Hoar, who became both executrix and beneficiary. Cyrus was disinherited, and was naturally resentful, especially as there was some suggestion that undue influence had been brought to bear on father by Doris. Cyril and his wife Doris seem to have visited Cyrus on several occasions, to make enquiries about their inheritance and the condition of the furniture that had been left to them. Some of this furniture had definitely been left to

Doris by her mother-in-law, but never collected.

Things came to head on Saturday, 10 April, 1977. Brother Cyril and his wife called at the house to enquire about the furniture left to them. They came by car. When they arrived, Cyrus was sawing wood in an outhouse. Outside there was a long-handled axe, used for splitting logs. An altercation about the furniture became a very heated argument culminating, according to Cyrus, in his brother taking up the axe and shouting, 'You bugger off, I'll finish 'ee.' Doris said, 'Yes, finish the bugger.' This altercation had been overheard by a close neighbour. Cyril then chased Cyrus into the house, yielding the axe, followed by Doris. Cyrus, in fright, ran upstairs, grabbed a single-barrel shotgun from his collection in a cabinet in an adjoining bedroom, loaded it, and fired it into Cyril's face just as he was appearing at the top of the landing. Cyril went over backwards to the bottom of the stairs, landing up with the axe beside him. By this time, Doris had appeared. She then grabbed the axe and (according to Cyrus) said, 'You bugger, I'll finish 'ee.' Cyrus went back to the wardrobe in which the guns and cartridges were kept, reloaded his gun, and shot his sister-in-law full in the chest as she apparently also was ascending the stairs, with the axe raised over her head. There were minor blood splashes on the walls of the staircase.

Confronted by two bodies lying in a large pool of blood at the bottom of the stairs, Cyrus dragged them into an adjoining room. He appears then to have panicked entirely. In fear that if they survived there would be a next time, he made sure that they did not. Amongst his large selection of guns he had a .22 rifle, and cartridges. Loading this gun six times he shot both his relations, each three times through the head at very close range, in a neat triangular pattern. He made the comment that neither of them said anything afterwards.

He moved the bodies to the kitchen, cleaned up a bit, but very ineffectually, and finally placed them in a wheelbarrow and dumped them beside their car, at about 11 pm. The bloodstained wheelbarrow was subsequently recovered. To cover his possible involvement in this slaughter, he left a note fastened to the back of the car, saying that the IRA had done it.

The guns Cyrus used were never found. He refused to say where they had been hidden.

Dr Hunt performed the first post-mortem examinations on the two dead victims, and as he has always most kindly done, he provided me with a complete account of his findings, which much lessened the amount of work that I had to do. I had been called in by the Defence to see if there was anything that could be said in favour of Cyrus. Obviously there was, if he had been in fear of his life and the pattern of the first shots into his relations was consistent with this. He appears, however, to have taken rather excessive measures.

The disturbing feature was that the vital axe did not appear to have been disturbed, and there were no fingerprints of Cyril on the handle. It was in exactly the same place as it had obviously been for a very long time. Cyrus's explanation was that he had picked up the axe after the affair was over, cleaned off the handle, dusted it and put it away in the exact place where it had always been. If only Cyril's or Doris's fingerprints had been on the axe, his story would have been completely vindicated. There seemed to be no reason why they should be wiped off, and this fact caused us some concern.

Cyrus's statement was never challenged — perhaps just as well. However, all the findings, apart from the problem of the axe, were completely consistent with his story. There was no trial. He pleaded guilty with diminished responsibility, and this was accepted by the Court. He had a relatively short sentence.

This appeared to me to be a pretty straightforward case, nevertheless no less than dozens of specimens or objects were taken for forensic examination.

More recently, some thirty articles and specimens were taken, in one of the simplest cases of killing.

On 28 December, 1977, Mr and Mrs Miller had a row, heard and practically witnessed by a babysitter. Mr Miller was serving in *HMS Ark Royal*, due shortly for a voyage overseas. Long periods of separation had strained the marital relationship, the wife wishing to settle down. On the fatal night, husband returned home at about 3 am, a little the worse for drink (blood alcohol 183 mg./100ml.) and, according to his wife, a bit 'stroppy'. An argument developed over the children, separation and general matrimonial difficulties. Mrs Miller went into the kitchen to prepare cups of cocoa. Her husband had already slapped her heavily across the face, and appeared to resent the fact that she had turned her back upon him in order to make the drinks. He caught hold of her left shoulder, whilst standing behind her, and swung her around towards him. She had a long, sharply-pointed kitchen knife in her right hand, and as she swung around, the knife entered the left side of her husband's chest, he having his arm up on her shoulder. It went right through to the base of his heart. He died within a few minutes. It is extraordinary how easily a pointed knife will cut through clothing and through the body; no great force is required. A turning action, to which an extra spin was given by a pull on the shoulder, would be all that was required to drive the knife into the body. This naturally was the basis of the Defence, for which I appeared, after the original examination had been made by Dr Hunt. Of course, she should not have had the knife in her hand in the first place, but she had an unfortunate background of violence having being offered to her, and her reaction to the blow and grip on her shoulder could have been defensive. The theory was never tested in court, as she pleaded guilty to manslaughter, and was appropriately dealt with leniently.

There is no doubt that, human nature being what it is, things sometimes get beyond control and the ability of people to deal with the situation. A quick flash of temper with a knife in the hand, even a blow to the face or putting a hand across a neck, can lead to dire results.

Before I left London, I was involved in an odd case. A young man and woman, after walking the streets for a while, finished up in the proverbial dark doorway of a shop. After the usual preliminaries, the girl took fright and said 'No.' The young man, now in a temper, told her that he would strangle her if she didn't and then said that he just put his hand on her neck, when she dropped down and he saw that she was dead. He at once went to the police station and told them what had happened. When examined, there was not a mark on or in the girl's neck. Her death was what we call vagal shock — stimulation of the vagal nerve which runs down the neck and slows the heart.

Relations with 'in-laws' are a fruitful cause of matrimonial trouble. I remember a middle-aged man in Falmouth living with his wife and mother-in-law who continually and increasingly interfered with the household. On one occasion, there was a hell of a row, and unfortunately his wife took her mother's part. A lot of unrepeatable name-calling went on, and on the following day he was in the doghouse. Tempers flared again at tea-time, when he asked his mother-in-law for the return of a loan. Her reply apparently was unprintable. In the succeeding row, plates and dishes were thrown about, and his face was cut in five places. He seized his mother-in-law by the neck, attempting to strangle her, but she got away and fled down the passage towards the toilet. Following, he caught up with her, pushed her head down the toilet and pulled the flush on her. Fortunately, she did not come to any great harm

How often do we hear of cases of death resulting quite unexpectedly after a punch-up, when even grievous bodily harm was not intended. The sort of thing that occurs after a drunken quarrel, ending in tragedy, and in this case a charge of murder.

Leslie Hubert Pendall went with others to a party in Plymouth held on 25 August, 1979. It was a quite well-conducted party, with only two guests who had had too much to drink, Pendall and a man, Gibbons. Both had been drinking before they went to the party, Pendall heavily, Gibbons probably less so, as there were witnesses who unanimously said that there were no signs that he had had too much to drink. However, blood taken from both men later that night showed that Pendall had a blood alcohol content of 193 mg./100 ml. and Gibbons 208 mg./100 ml. late that evening. In ordinary parlance, both men could have been aggressively drunk. Both would have shown some mental confusion, loss of inhibitions, impairment of judgment and impairment of restraint. They would have been inclined to be excitable, aggressive, and liable to take offence over relatively small matters. Two such minor events occurred. Pendall made an offensive remark about a half-caste brother-in-law of Gibbons, and later stubbed out a cigarette end on the carpet. These two events, and particularly the latter one, obviously irritated Gibbons, and led to a punch-up, considerably embroidered by sympathisers on both sides. One suggestion was that Pendall was not only knocked down, but kicked in the head and chest afterwards. Of this there was no evidence whatever. On admission to hospital, there were no signs of chest injury. All that was seen was a small laceration to the left corner of the mouth, and small grazes over the left eyebrown. Gibbons admitted two light blows to the head only, and the hospital findings confirmed this. This was not a vicious onslaught. Unfortunately, Pendall slipped and went over backwards; he might have contributed to his own fall by being drunk and unstable on his feet. There was indeed no evidence that the blows delivered by themselves knocked him down. The pavement outside the house was a narrow one, and it might easily have been that Pendall slipped backwards over the edge of the pavement, attempting to avoid further blows on his face. In the event, he went over backwards, knocking the back of his head on the road, rendering himself immediately unconscious. Fortunately, a passer-by saw what had happened, and immediately took Pendall to hospital, sitting upright in his car, although unconscious. He was unconscious and pulseless on arrival at the hospital. Cardiac arrest lasted for some fifteen minutes — during which irreparable damage had been done to the brain. The brain can withstand loss of circulation for only about five minutes without fatal damage. He was kept alive on supportive machinery until the fifth of the following September, when it was considered that his brain had been so severely damaged that recovery was impossible.

Dr Hunt performed a post-mortem examination and I followed up by doing one for the Defence on the following day. Later, after fixation, we examined the brain together. We both came to the same conclusion that 'death was due ultimately to damage to the brain by a combination of injury and lack of oxygen. The stoppage of the heart could have been due to the injury alone or could have been contributed to by obstruction to the airway after the head injury. If the deceased had been drunk at the time of the head injury, this could have contributed to the respiratory obstruction.'

Gibbons was charged with murder; he pleaded guilty to manslaughter, and this plea was accepted.

Which all goes to show what trivial causes can sometimes have devastating results, and what might have been possibly a trivial accident resulted in a charge of murder.

Some people 'get religion' in a peculiar way; such a one was Thomas Henry Trebilcock. He 'got religion', and decided in his disordered mind that most people were wicked and did not deserve to live. His unfortunate first victims resided in a bungalow, 'The Nock', at Colan, Newquay. They were Miss Mabel Tonkin, aged fifty-seven years, Miss Edith Emma Legg, aged fifty-four years, and Kathleen Mary Owen, aged two years.

Miss Tonkin was found in the kitchen, with her head and face completely battered in, and lying in a pool of blood surrounded by fragments of skull bone and brain. Heavy bruises on the arms suggested that she had held these up in an attempt to ward off blows aimed at her head. Near to her was the heavy wheeled section of a vacuum cleaner that had been broken from its handle; it was heavily stained with blood, and was obviously the 'instrument' that had been used to batter the old lady, as strands of her hair were found adhering with blood to the appliance. Splashes of her blood (Group A) were found all along the passage from the back door to the kitchen, so that it appeared that she had been attacked first of all whilst standing in the back doorway. The attack had been initially with the 'business end' of the vacuum cleaner; when this broke off, the attack was continued with the handle, as blood and hair were found on it, and then completed by kicking — blood and hair later being found on the shoes of the accused.

The other elderly woman, Mrs Legg, was found in the front room of the bungalow, but she had not been killed there. Smeared streaks of blood led from the body along the passage to the front door, down concrete steps to a patch of grass some four paces from the bottom of the steps. This grass was not only bloodstained, but portions of skull bones and brain were found in it. Her head had been completely battered in. Again, she had made an attempt to ward off blows aimed at her head, as her arms were heavily bruised and abraded. The instrument? — a billet of wood fifty inches long, four inches wide and two inches deep, found beside the body. It was heavily blood stained with Group O blood, that of Mrs Legg, which group enabled us to conclude that she had been killed outside the bungalow and then dragged indoors. On the billet of wood there were found six partially-crushed blades of grass, smears of brain, and hair similar to that of Mrs Legg.

There was more to come. In the front room with Mrs Legg there was the body of a small girl, later identified as Kathleen Mary Owen. Her head had also been completely bashed in whilst she was on an adjacent settee. Her hair was also found on the billet of wood that had been used to kill Mrs Legg.

The child had been killed after Mrs Legg, as hair from her head overlaid that of the dead woman. A broken and bloodstained worm-eaten broom head and handle were also found, and this apppeared to have been used after the initial vicious onslaught.

The reason for all this? As already said, Trebilcock had 'got religion'. He went up to these people, and in his own words asked them if they were, or had been wicked. The reply (we do not know for certain) was likely to have been that they supposed that they were, or had been. In that case, they were not fit to live, so, out they went. Others had been questioned, but fortunately survived.

What does one make of a case like this, reminiscent of the attack by Sheila Ferguson on her mistress?

For its size, the Bude area has produced more murders per head of the population than any other district in Cornwall. It is of course in the 'spooky' area of the county.

On 4 September, 1964, I was sent for to go to a house in Stratton. I found the upstairs in a bloodstained shambles. The blood had come from the daughter of the house, a girl aged sixteen years of age. I found her on the bathroom floor with a plastic bag tied around her head. She wore only pyjama trousers, and everything was heavily bloodstained.

Going into her bedroom, it was seen that her bed, which was against a wall, was heavily bloodstained, especially towards the top and around the pillow. On the wall above the bed, there were large numbers of heavy upward and downward splashes of blood, suggesting that the girl had been heavily beaten about in her upper parts whilst lying in bed. On the bed there was a bloodstained axe, the head of which had separated from the handle. The handle was heavily bloodstained, but there were only splashes on one side of the head. Obviously the girl had been attacked with this weapon whilst lying in bed, but before the first blow had been struck, the head had parted from the shaft. The attack had been made by the handle. Apparently it was found that this was not heavy enough to do the job thoroughly, because in the bed there was also found a whetsone, some fifteen inches in length, broken into four pieces, all of which were heavily bloodstained. This stone had obviously been used to continue the attack until it also came apart into unusable pieces.

From her bed, the girl, now dead or at least unconscious, was then dragged along the upstairs passage into the bathroom. On the way, however, she had been further assaulted, this time with a rolling pin, found heavily bloodstained half-way along the passage. Here were found bits of scalp and skull bones. Even this onslaught does not seem to have been enough. She had been dragged into the bathroom, a tap turned on, and an ineffectual attempt made to lift her into the bath, presumably to finish the job off by drowning. There were splashes of blood on the wall opposite the bath, and a wisp of hair on the cold tap. However, the assailant apparently had been unable to lift the weight of the girl into the bath, so finished off by tying a plastic bag over her head.

Smears of drips of blood along the staircase, steps and downstairs floors showed that the assailant had gone from place to place, gathering other weapons when those that had already been used failed by breaking.

Who had done this? Fairly obviously the mother, who was found in the same home deeply unconscious, her clothing heavily bloodstained and with a bottle of barbiturate tablets close beside her. She was rushed by ambulance to Exeter, but (fortunately) died on the way. There was a tragic background to this onslaught. It was a hard-working, but poor family; the girl had done brilliantly at school, and had won a scholarship for further and university education. This had required fitting her out suitably with prescribed clothing — which the family just could not afford. Rather than see her daughter suffer some possible social disgrace because she could not be suitably outfitted, the devoted mother decided to put an end to the matter.

There used to be a time when there were Knights of the Road who rescued young women in distress. Until recently, the more modern Knight often performed a similar service to young women stranded without transport to their homes. This was done willingly, courteously, a gladly offered and accepted service, with not the least thought of danger. Much of this still exists but alas, many of the Knights have been replaced by sexual highwaymen whose one object in life is to take advantage of women in distress, go to their aid and then sexually assault them, even going to the despicable stage of rape. What a comment on present-day ethics. Time and again women are warned of this danger, and time and time again the warning goes unheeded. What a relief and pleasure it would be to return to the old days of chivalry, mutual trust and respect. But some young girls do seem to ask for it, in spite of the warnings. In spite of the outcry that it caused, there is some sense in the remark of a Judge who said that in his opinion, some young women contribute to the offence by accepting lifts in dubious circumstances. They should know better. I have a sneaking regard for his pronouncement.

The murder of 'Virginia' should serve as a warning to young girls who 'thumb' lifts, especially at night time.

She was aged twenty years, living with her parents in Tiverton. She spent the week-end of 30 January, 1981, with a friend in Cardiff, and was expected home during the evening of 1 February that year. She did not arrive. Kevin James Bealey had seen to that.

She had been seen off at Cardiff Central Station at 6.45 pm on 1 February, 1981, wearing a blue-grey duffle coat, brown cord trousers, a loose-fitting pullover with a 'floppy' roll neck, and carrying two bags, one a blue cloth holdall.

She was said to have been very much in love, engaged to be married; there were numerous testimonies to her sterling

266

character, and not a breath of suspicion of her being in any way promiscuous. Far from that, she had no interest whatever in any man other than her intended husband. This was important in view of allegations subsequently made against her.

'Gini's' train arrived five minutes late at St David's Station, Exeter, at 9.10 pm. By that time the last bus had left for her home in Tiverton. She was seen by numerous people 'thumbing a lift', but nobody appeared to be going in her direction. One witness however, a Mr Harris, actually saw a girl of Gini's description, carrying two handbags, enter a car. He saw her facing the on-coming traffic when suddenly a car came up very fast, pulled into the nearside and stopped exactly where the girl stood and took her in. The natural impression was that she had been picked up by somebody who was looking for her.

A little later, ex-Police Sergeant Moore (accompanied by his wife) was driving along the Exeter-Tiverton road when he was followed by a speeding, overtaking car that bothered him because it had not dipped its headlights. He pulled into his nearside to allow the car to pass, and noted that it contained a man driver, and a woman sitting alongside him in the passenger seat. Being an observant ex-policeman, he partially noted the number of the vehicle, RWS with an 'S' suffix, and with a 9, a 4 and a 3 in the numbers — but he couldn't say in what exact numbers. This was the last that was seen of Virginia alive.

She did not arrive home as expected. By 10.30 pm her father was becoming increasingly worried and, after a phone call to Cardiff, he informed the police that she was missing.

Extensive enquiries and searches failed to find any trace of the girl.

Meanwhile, another drama was unfolding in a village nearby Exeter. A lady had become friendly with Ian Kevin James Bealey, who had been having a bit of wife trouble. He was the owner of a Citroen car RWS 493S — the car noted by Sergeant Moore on the night of Gini's disappearance. The lady had two children, aged ten and twelve years. On 2 February, following some telephone calls, they went to Bealey's house, where they found him eating a packet of chips. He seemed to be a bit 'edgy'. After having tea, they decided to make a social call and went in the lady's car along the road leading to Sidmouth. Bealey was driving; he stopped 'somewhere along the road' in a lane. They got out accompanied by their dog, who went sniffing around inside the hedge. The lady looked down to her left and saw something white in the field just off the hedge. Bealey went through a gap in the hedge whilst the lady and children stayed in the lane. He returned shortly afterwards and said, 'Don't say anything to the girls. There's a girl in the field.' If ever a murderer returned to the scene of his crime, this was one of them. Together they went to the nearest telephone, in a garage, and phoned the police; they remained at the site until the police arrived. Bealey appeared to be badly shaken, trembling so much that he had difficulty in getting a lead on the dog's collar.

At 7.14 pm on 2 February, 1981, a message was received as a result of a '999' emergency call to the Police Headquarters at Exeter, to the effect that the girl they had been looking for had been found behind a hedge. The informer was a Mr Bealey of 127 Oakhampton Road, Exeter. The message was relayed to PC Kerslake, who was on mobile patrol duty. He went at once to the Exeter Service Station from which the message had been received, and there met Bealey, who indicated that he would show the police officer where he had found the body, and proceeded to do so.

PC Kerslake records finding the body wearing brown cord trousers and a grey duffle coat which was drawn over her shoulders and head, exposing her chest. Touching the body, he found that it was cold and stiff. A scarf had been knotted around the neck.

After a restless evening, Bealey arrived by taxi at the home of the lady. They were both very upset by their recent experiences, and then Ian said, 'I did it', and told her a story that he stuck to right through all the subsequent interviews and proceedings without being shaken.

He said that he noticed the girl making unsuccessful attempts to get a lift, and that although he was going in the opposite direction, he took pity on her, turned around, and picked her up. It was a shocking night, dark, and foggy.

His story was that she was so grateful to him for the lift that she offered sex as a reward. He appears to have always had some difficulty in these matters, and said that he did not come up to her expectations. She taunted him with this, and as a result 'something snapped' and he strangled her. In more detailed statements later, and in his statement to the police, he expanded his version of what took place.

At one time he denied ever having picked up Virginia. Later, in making a statement to Detective Superintendent Reay at Police Headquarters, Exeter, he gave his version of a full account of what had happened that night. He said that he had watched a girl (on the night of February 1, 1981, at about 9.30 pm) attempting to get a lift — to somewhere. He asked her if she was having difficulty in getting a lift, and on being told that she had, and wanted to go to Tiverton, he offered to take her. She was carrying two bags, both of which were subsequently recovered, one from his car, the other from over a hedge where he showed them that he had thrown it.

Shortly after driving off, the girl said she was extremely grateful for the lift. The conversation then led to an increasingly sexual level, terminating in a suggestion that she would like to express her gratitude by having intercourse, and suggested stopping somewhere to indulge her whim. He asked if she was offering sex, and she replied, 'If that is what you would like, yes.' He stopped in a gateway, switching off the car engine and lights. She started to remove her coat, and they had some sexual play whilst he adjusted the passenger's seat to the reclining position. After more play, he opened and pulled her trousers and pants down to her knees in which position he had some kind of ineffectual intercourse, finally ejaculating between her thighs. After this escapade, they both dressed. Then she began to upbraid him for being ineffectual. They got out of the car and she said, 'Tell me how it feels to be a failure.' This rang a bell in his memory regarding a similar taunt by his late wife, and he replied 'Yes'. There was steady laughter from the girl, she repeating that he was a failure and more of a boy than a man. He then became frightened and told her that he was going to blindfold her to prevent her from taking the number of his car and complaining that she had been assaulted. First of all he grabbed her by the throat, and they fell to the ground, with him on top. He then started to manually strangle her. He ripped off her scarf and wound it twice around her neck. The first round he pulled tight with his fingers, then finding his thumbs getting stiff, he wound it again around her neck, and, putting a foot on one end and pulling with all his might on the other, he strangled her. Could there ever have been a more horrible assault?

He admitted that he had totally lost control. She kept on taunting him, and he just snapped. Afterwards he dragged the body along the ground to the top of a bank and through the hedge where she rolled over into a field. There was some suggestion that before the murderous assault was made, that the girl agreed to be blindfolded and have her hands tied so that she could not move very much, or read the number of the car when later she would have got out. When found, her hands were indeed lightly tied.

Let it be said here and now that any such behaviour on the part of 'Gini' would have been utterly and completely out of keeping with her well-known character and previous behaviour.

When interviewed by the Superintendent, the latter said, 'You cold-bloodedly and callously killed her? You murdered a defenceless girl? Ian Bealey replied 'Yes'.

Bealey said that he took the two bags the girl was carrying into his house. One was recovered from his car subsequently. The other, thrown over a hedge, was subsequently recovered by the police, led there by Bealey.

He denied that there was any sinister thought in his mind when he picked up the girl, thinking only to do her a good turn.

But now to return to the lady.

After Bealey's confession to her, she suggested that he give himself up to the police. Bealey said 'I can't do that, they won't believe me, they'll think I raped her.' To the end, he denied rape.

In well-understood mental anxiety, the lady suggested that Bealey phoned his friend Mike Bastin. This he did, only again confessing that he had killed the girl. Mike also counselled that Bealey give himself up, and this was reiterated by Mike's wife. He left. After a long conversation with Mike's wife, Julia, both women went to the police station.

Meanwhile, Bealey had gone to friends in London after telephoning his sister, confessing that he had 'choked a girl'. To her he also said that he had done it after being taunted that he had made a very ineffectual attempt at sexual intercourse. He said that they had had sex of sorts, but that he was as soft as a Chivers jelly and could not make it. He added that he was going to try and get out of the country, and again reiterated that the Police might think it was rape, and it was nothing like that. To his friends in London, he also confessed to 'choking' the girl, largely figured in newspaper headlines.

As a result of information received, Bealey was arrested in London, taken to Exeter, and charged with the murder of Virginia.

The post-mortem examination carried out on behalf of the police was conducted by Dr Bill Hunt on 3 February, 1981, and I followed with another examination on behalf of the Defence on the following 19 February.

We both agreed the findings.

These were that there were remarkably few injuries to the girl.

There was no sign whatever that any struggle had taken place.

There were no signs of any manual strangulation, in spite of the fact that the accused had said that he had at first tried manual strangulation. In the neck, however, there was a broad line of abrasion consistent with a scarf, still in situ, having been drawn tightly around the neck. There was no deep bruising, and no fractures of any of the bones comprising the windpipe — so often seen in manual strangulation, but not always present in the young. The face above the line of abrasion however was congested, and there were fine pinpoint (petechial) bleeding spots in the skin, particularly in the loose parts surrounding the eyes, and in the whites of the eyes themselves — typical signs of death by strangulation. The tongue was protruding through the teeth, again a sign of strangulation, and later examination of the lungs showed a few blood spots on the surfaces.

Similar blood spots were seen on the surface of the heart —
in both cases consistent with strangulation. All the organs
were otherwise normal. Death was due to strangulation by
ligature, and with this I completely agreed.

On these grounds there was no possible defence to a
charge of murder.

The question of rape caused some concern.

One of the most remarkable features of the case was that
the clothing of the dead girl was completely undisturbed,
apart from the probable final pulling up of the chest
clothing.

The trousers were so tightly fastened that it was only with
difficulty that they could be undone. The pants were in
position, and completely undisturbed. Both Dr Hunt and I
thought that after a vicious rape, it would have been almost
impossible for the assailant to have replaced the clothing so
neatly but of course the impossible is always on occasion
possible.

Examination of the contents of the vagina showed the
presence of spermatozoa of the accused's group, group 'O'.
From this it would appear that Bealey had had full
intercourse with the girl, in spite of his denial. Several
suggestions arose from this finding. In the first place it could
have confirmed that the girl had had willing sexual
intercourse with Bealey, as he said, dressing herself with all
its difficulties afterwards. The only rebuttal of this possibility
was the universally repeated belief that the girl would never
have consented. But she did not put up any fight. There
were a few minor bruises on her body that we classified as
of domestic origin. No claw marks on the neck, so often seen
when an assailed person tries to relieve the pressure of
strangulation, no bruises, no abrasions, no skin under the
fingernails due to clawing at an assailant, no fibres
underneath the nails. No resistance whatever. Did the girl
accept sexual intercourse and then regret it and threaten
revenge? It seems unlikely, and Bealey did not suggest it.

Whatever happened took place in the car. The only mud
on the girl's body, on the front, could be accounted for by
her having been dragged and thrown on to the ground
where she was found. There was no mud along her back or
on the back of her clothing that would suggest that inter-

course had occurred in the field in which she was found.

A woman who is threatened with rape is expected to put up some sort of physical resistance. Here we have none. But there is an exception. A woman can be so terrified of physical injury, even death, that all power of resistance is lost.

Dr Hunt suggested this in his report. With this I completely agreed, and had independently suggested it to the Defence.

Ian Kevin James Bealey was duly convicted of murder at Exeter Crown Court on Wednesday, 8 July, after a trial lasting eight days.

I felt that there was nothing to be said for him and was not called upon to give evidence. He was sentenced to life imprisonment. Some aspects of this case still worry me a little.

☆   ☆   ☆

The murder of Anita Kathleen Quaile on 15 June, 1979, at her home in Plymouth raised a national outcry. Ronald Sailes, the murderer, was a twice-convicted rapist who killed this sixteen-year-old girl within seven months of being let out of Broadmoor. The outcry was the greater because Sailes was the fifth ex-patient freed on the recommendation of one of the Hospital's senior consultant psychiatrists to commit murder after his release.

The first woman to be raped by Sailes was a Borstal Officer's wife, whom he attacked whilst making an escape attempt in 1955; she was forced to strip and submit after deep wounds with a carving knife were inflicted. For this attack, Sailes was jailed for four years.

In 1962 Sailes, on the excuse that his wife was ill, lured a neighbour and her six-year-old daughter into his bedroom. He tied the child's hands with one of her mother's stockings, and then forced the mother to cover her daughter's mouth with sticking plaster. The child was then locked in another room whilst her mother was raped. For this, Sailes was sent to Broadmoor and a fifteen-year Restriction Order was imposed on him. At the end of this time, the Broadmoor Consultants decided to continue his treatment, and in

November 1978 he was given a month's rehabilitation leave, during which he went to a Plymouth hostel with a probation officer assigned to him. Reports were encouraging, and further leave was approved, the last towards the end of May 1979, about two weeks before the murder of Anita Quaile. Too late, a spokesman said, 'The Section 60 order would have expired on 20 June. Broadmoor were considering extending it because they still felt he needed supervision. Unfortunately, before the date in question he committed the offence.' There had been previous outcries about the early release of inmates of Broadmoor, notable the release of Graham Young the poisoner, Bryan Knight the murderer, and others. An enquiry headed by Lord Butler in 1972 called for major changes in the law and practice relating to prosecution, detention, treatment and after care of mentally abnormal offenders. The Committee made in all 140 recommendations; these were adopted, but still the processes were unsatisfactory. Naturally, in this case, the doctor concerned in Sailes's release came under considerable criticism. A Senior Consultant at Broadmoor (not personally responsible for Sailes's release) said that about twenty people had been killed by discharged Broadmoor patients since 1960, but added that there would be 2,000 people locked up in perpetuity, as opposed to twenty people who have lost their lives. This, however, is poor comfort for the victims and their families.

Of course the problem is infinitely difficult. As Mr Justice Melford Stevenson once said on one of these occasions, 'Broadmoor is the largest single source of "repeater" offences in the country's penal system,' and added, 'Nobody is better at producing the appearance of a reformed character than someone who is desperate to get out of confinement.'

Devon's Assistant Chief Probation Officer said that Sailes had been sent from Broadmoor on leave to the Friary Hostel and was 'supervised' in the circumstances as well as was allowed. 'He was released into the community by the hospital and put in an open residence, where he was free to go out and come in at certain times in the day.' Although he did not spend the night of 12 June at the hostel there appears to have been no attempt to trace his whereabouts, and he was obviously breaking the conditions of his parole.

The Plymouth police were not informed of Sailes's release on licence. They knew nothing about him or his record, the machinery in being at the moment not catering for information about releases of this sort reaching them. They regarded him as a man of mystery, with no clear picture of his life; even his acquaintances at the hostel did not know much about him, and he was pretty well free to go where he chose. That freedom led him to dance halls, and he became a regular at 'over twenty-fives' nights.

He had had a hard upbringing. Evacuated from Poplar during the last war, he had a succession of foster parents and early brushes with the law. He went through a hostel for maladjusted children, approved school, Borstal and finally prison, before he finally ended up in Broadmoor.

It was during his time at the Plymouth hostel that he became friendly with the Quaile family, Mrs Quaile and her daughter and Mr Hewins, who lived with them. The friendship was about a fortnight old when the tragic event occurred. Sailes came to the house and seemed very generous, taking them out for drinks and food, and giving them numerous gifts.

Mrs Quaile and Mr Hewins were both in work, but the daughter Anita, aged sixteen years, had not found work since leaving school, so she stayed in, looking after the home and doing some of the housework. At the time she was suffering from a mild attack of chicken pox, and on occasion Sailes had taken her to the hospital where she was receiving treatment.

On Wednesday, 13 June, 1979, Mrs Quaile and Mr Hewins left for work at about 6.35 am. They heard Anita coughing in her room as they left.

Mr Hewins returned home from work at about 4.30 pm. He knocked on the door of the flat (having no keys available), but received no reply. Thinking that Anita was out, he hung about for a while, but there was no sign of her returning. He rang the flat bell in case the girl had been asleep, but again there was no answer, so he went upstairs again (it was an upstairs flat) and gave the door a kick; rather surprisingly, it opened. On entering, there was no sign of the girl, so he went into her room. Looking

275

towards the bed, he saw a blanket that she had been making herself, and a pair of feet sticking out at the bottom. Thinking that she was asleep, he pulled the blanket back at the top, and saw a pillow over her face. Lifting it up, he thought she was making a funny face, and then realised that her tongue was sticking out and her eyes were horrible. Pulling the blanket back a bit, he saw a cut right across her throat.

He rushed out of the house, and immediately called the police and the ambulance. By luck, a police car was passing at the time, and they took immediate action.

Detective Superintendent Leonard immediately took charge, and sent for Dr Kennard, Home Office Pathologist at Salisbury, to do a post-mortem examination.

Dr Kennard arrived at 9 pm and made his examinations. He was accompanied by Mr Northcott of the South-West Forensic Laboratory.

They reported that they found the body of Anita lying transversely across the bed, the feet towards the head of the bed, the head towards the tailboard. The upper half was covered with a pillow and an old knitted woollen shawl, and a bedspread pulled over the body, with the exception of the feet.

She was wearing a plum-coloured cardigan, a brown striped 'T' shirt, a white brassiere (properly secured), jeans, pants and shoes. The upper clothing had been pulled up, the trousers unzipped and torn downwards at the crotch, and the pants split. A green belt had been tied around the ankles. We were never able to find a satisfactory explanation for this unusual finding. A slightly soiled sanitary pad was in situ.

A piece of red material (later identified as a pair of pants) had been jammed deeply into the mouth, pushed far back, bruising the mouth and completely obstructing air entry.

Temperature recordings suggested that death had occurred shortly before mid-day. The post-mortem showed that the body was that of a physically normal teenage girl. She was rather blue in the face, and there were cardinal signs of suffocation present, notably pinhead bleeding spots in the cheeks, whites of the eyes and in the loose skin around the eyes.

There was an extensive bruise over the left cheek, and later there appeared a small bruise under the left jaw, and one below the left ear.

The cause of the suffocation was a pair of ladies' red cellular pants rammed so deeply into the mouth and down the throat that they were barely visible from the outside.

There was a long (five inch) superficial gaping cut running horizontally across the front of the neck; no deep or major blood vessels had been cut.

More important, there were seven stab wounds in the chest and abdomen, five of which penetrated deeply; three had penetrated the heart, and one the lung. Each cut was $7/10''$ wide. They were all approximately right angles to the body. All the cuts had the appearance of have been caused by blows with a knife some $4/5''$ wide, sharp on one side only, and about three and a half inches long, probably by an assailant kneeling beside the body, raining the blows upon it.

At the request of the Defence Solicitors, I made a further post-mortem examination on 26 June; this completely confirmed Dr Kennard's findings, and there was no dispute over them.

Asked at this stage what my opinion would have been relative to these findings, I should (and did) say: A person, probably known to the girl, visited her on the morning of her death. They apparently spent quite a bit of time, probably some hours, together in acceptable conversation. This is suggested by the finding of cigarette stubs in two astrays that had been emptied the night before and were empty when Mrs Quaile and Mr Hewins left in the morning. One ashtray held four cigarette ends, and the other thirteen — some of 'Dunhill King Size', known to be smoked by Sailes. Thirteen cigarettes, even amongst two people, take quite a lot of time to get through, so that it can be supposed that agreeable conversation had been going on for quite a long time, probably some hours. It would then appear that an improper suggestion was made to the girl. Trying to make her escape through the door, she was struck very heavily on her left cheek, and probably stunned. She was thrown on to the bed, and, to complete the silencing, a handy pair of pants were jammed viciously into her mouth and down her throat. This did not kill her, although she was most likely unconscious by this time. The next move was then probably to pull up her upper clothing and tear her jeans down to expose her private parts. Finding that she was menstruating, in frustrated rage he made the final attack with a knife in his possession. This was my first, and final impression, *but* one had to take regard of his own version of the affair and consider if it was reasonable.

Immediately after the murder had been reported, Sailes was suspected. Enquiries revealed that he had not been at his hostel for twenty-four hours, and the police, on the direction of the Director of Public Prosecutions, took the unusual step of naming Sailes as the man they wanted to question. Forces throughout the country were circulated with a photofit picture. Police discovered that Sailes had hitched a lift to Exeter; he was finally tracked down in Glasgow, where he was arrested — still carrying the knife with which Anita Quaile had been murdered. He was flown back to Plymouth, and interviewed by Detective Superintendent Leonard.

Sailes freely admitted his friendship with the Quaile family, and added that he had spent the night previous to the murder at the home of a friend. She gave him a lift in her car the following morning to a point close to the Quaile flat, where he arrived at about a quarter to nine. Anita let him in — there was no reason why she should not, he being a friend of the family — and they had tea and a smoke together.

Later, the conversation took a sexual turn. He said that she had no objection to intercourse, but that when he found she was menstruating he became very annoyed and stopped. He said that they had previously undressed, but redressed after the abortive attempt at intercourse. Afterwards they had another cup of coffee, smoked and talked, until about 11.30, when he said that he heard someone coming up the stairs. He thought she was going to scream, so he hit her heavily in the face, and then jammed the pants into her mouth to stifle her cries. He said, 'I tried to strangle her first. Then took out my knife and stabbed her a number of times.' He admitted that he must have been in a frenzy. He denied having intercourse with the girl at any time, before or after her death, and this was confirmed by subsequent forensic examination of exhibits, no spermatozoa being found anywhere. He admitted tearing the jeans, and cutting the pants. In essence, he made a complete confession, confirming all the findings in the case. He even admitted the theft of a Giro Order made out to Mr Hewins. Sailes however refused to sign the notes of the conversation he had had with Superintendent Leonard.

This would appear to be the end of the matter, but Sailes asked to see a solicitor, and to him he told a very different tale.

He confirmed that he went to the Quailes' flat on the morning of the murder, finding the girl alone, dressed only in a kind of wrap. When he remonstrated, she dressed properly.

After about half an hour they became more closely friendly, and after some sexual play and conversation they undressed and got into bed. It was after some more sexual play that he discovered that she was commencing her period, and angrily withdrew. They made up the quarrel, and then engaged in some form of abnormal sexual practice. After this, they both redressed, but again indulged in sexual exercises. At all times the girl was said to be willing, if not the instigator of what was happening. By then they were smoking again, and Sailes said he would go out and get some more cigarettes. He thought that she was doubtful about his returning, so he left his car coat as a sort of hostage. He bought some 'fags' and returned about twenty minutes later, leaving the door on the latch. He noted that his coat which he had left behind had been moved from the chair just inside the door to the chair opposite.

When he came back he saw her on the bed, dead. 'Like a fool I picked up the bloody knife. She'd been killed while I was away. Somehow the knife I had was by the side of her. I'd not taken it out myself, and I realised what I had done by picking it up.' He noted the injuries, threw a blanket over her and 'scarpered', taking all his stuff and a Giro cheque that did not belong to him.

He panicked. He had been wearing a neck collar as he was suffering from arthritis of the neck; this he took off and left in a nearby toilet as it was an easily recognisable feature — it was later recovered by the police. After a series of hitch-hikes, he finally arrived in Glasgow where he was arrested.

What did I think about his version of the killing? I thought it improbable, very improbable indeed. However, my function was not that of the jury. They would have to decide between the two accounts given by Sailes. My function was only to see if Sailes's account to his solicitor reasonably fitted the findings.

My opinion as to the cause of death of the girl was due to haemorrhage from multiple stab wounds which could not have been self-inflicted.

The cause of death, and the manner in which the injuries had been inflicted, was not in dispute. The friendship was generally acknowledged, and the fact that he had spent three hours with the girl before her murder I considered reasonable. There was nothing sinister in this. He had purchased the knife with which the murder was committed somewhere in the Barbican, but not on the day of the murder. Murder therefore does not appear to have been in his mind when he called on the girl. Masses of exhibits were taken from the scene by Mr Northcott, and after he had examined them, I examined them myself. Or the great number, only a very few I thought were of importance. Firstly, the suit Sailes had been wearing. He admitted that the one he was wearing when arrested was the one he wore on the day of the murder. It was a nice suit, clean and fresh, and not greatly worn. I thought it impossible that he could have had it cleaned whilst on the run. There was only one very small spot of blood on it, in the middle of the front of the right thigh. It was about an eighth of an inch in diameter. There was just enough to determine that it was blood of human origin, but not sufficient to group. No blood on the jacket. None on the shirt. None on the pants or on a white vest.

A single stab wound with a sharp knife into the chest would probably result in very little bleeding externally, because such wounds tend to close as soon as the knife is withdrawn. With multiple stabs however, the risk of external bleeding increases, especially if there is great internal bleeding, as there would have been as the heart had been punctured. Successive blows on a resilient chest would be expected to pump some blood out of previous wounds, and yet in this case we have virtually none on the clothing of the suspect. The stabbing had not been done through the ample clothing Anita was wearing; this might have prevented blood splashing, but the stabbing had been done through the bare skin. The original police request for help in tracing the murderer stated that he was most likely to be heavily bloodstained — and yet there was nothing. This seemed to support Sailes's second version of what had happened, that somebody else did the murder.

The other possibility of course is that Sailes (if he was the assailant) was naked when he made the attack. In both statements he mentioned undressing. This would account for the absence of blood on his clothing, and also for two other findings. One was a white brassiere, the property of the mother, not of the girl, found heavily smeared with blood of the girl's group. Was the brassiere picked up by the assailant after the onslaught, to wipe his bloodstained hands with? A further exhibit was some lightly bloodstained water from the foot of a shower. Had the assailant either had a shower or at least washed his bloodstained hands in the shower?

There were one or two other important forensic findings. There was no blood on the jeans where they would have been gripped to open and tear them, and none on the pants which had been cut. Further, there was no blood on the pants rammed into the girl's mouth. Handling of these articles therefore must have been done before the onslaught with the knife.

I came to two alternative conclusions. One was that, however unlikely, Sailes's account that he gave to his Solicitor could have been right, and that murder had been done by someone else who escaped, probably heavily bloodstained. Sailes's subsequent actions in running away are of course suspicious, but as he himself said at one time, with his background he would be an obvious suspect, however innocent.

The second alternative was that Sailes was the murderer. That after a fairly long friendly association on the morning, he made an improper suggestion to Anita. She rebuffed him and attempted to escape, the escape being foiled by a heavy blow on the face which would have considerably dazed her, if not completely knocking her out. Possibly she made an attempt to scream, and this was blocked by the forcing of the pants into her mouth after she had been flung on to the bed. This would have rendered her almost immediately unconscious. In this state, he tore open her trousers and cut her pants, only to find that she was having a period. Intercourse would have messed up his clothes. There was no evidence (no spermatozoa) that he had had intercourse with the girl. The knifing took place after all this. Only he knows, and probably he does not remember the sequence of events.

I made a careful search of the nearby streets, to see if there was a tobacconist's shop within ten minutes walking distance of the flat. I did not find one, even in a more extended locality. A tobacconist within the area, who could have recognised a customer wearing a surgical collar, would have almost certainly have corroborated Sailes's story — but there was not one.

On balance, I came to the conclusion that only Sailes himself could have been responsible for the murder, and that his story to his solicitor and his alibi were not consistent with the facts.

In sentencing him to life imprisonment for murder, the Judge described Sailes as 'a brutal, cunning, compassionless and evil man.'

23

An Unresolved Murder and Some Reflections

Apart from Mrs Russell, we had only one unsolved case of murder. This was Harold Hand, aged sixty-five years, a visitor to Newquay, with his family in July 1958. On the twelfth of that month, a busy Friday when a rapid weekend change-over of visitors was as usual taking place, a visitor wanting to use the public convenience on the headland was just about to enter when a young man dashed out and past him, saying that there was an old man inside who had fallen down and injured himself; this young man said he was going to phone for an ambulance, which he was seen to do, and actually did, and within minutes the ambulance arrived.

Meanwhile the other young man had gone into the lavatory, and found there lying on the floor an elderly man severly wounded in the head, but still alive. He was taken by the ambulance to the Royal Cornwall Infirmary, where he survived for several days, but died ultimately of head injuries due to multiple fractures of the skull, due to blows on the head with a heavy 'instrument'.

Looking around the lavatory after the ambulance had gone, the witness suddenly spotted what at first appeared to be a screwed-up bundle of newspaper, heavily bloodstained, in a corner. Picking it up, to his surprise it was not a bundle of newspaper, but a heavy stone wrapped in newspaper. The position was now very different. The witness immediately phoned the police, and they took over, discovering almost at once that the old gentleman had had (and fortunately still had) around his neck a wallet containing some £70.

Unfortunately, the only description of the young man seen running from the toilet to the telephone box was a very hazy one; in fact, the only really important feature was that he was wearing a green shirt. With the massive turnover of visitors on a holiday weekend, the police faced an impossible task, and the murderer was never discovered.

Every man obviously wearing a green shirt that could be spotted in Newquay after this happening was closely questioned. All but one had a supported alibi. One young man that we were deeply suspicious of was taken in for investigation. He was wearing a green shirt, and there were spots of blood on it. These were blood grouped, but were found to be of a group different from that of the victim. The victims blood group was group O; that of the spots was group A.

It seems right that I should end these reminiscences with my personal views on Judges, juries and punishment.

For H.M. Judges, I have nothing but the utmost regard — even if very occasionally they have not agreed with me! I forget whom it was who said it, and I forget the exact words, but they were to the effect that if ever Justice was heard to be done, it came from the mouths of our presiding Judges. I could not agree more.

With regard to juries, I used always to follow the dictum of the late Mr Justice Humphries, who said, 'The correctness of a jury's verdict has almost become an axiom with me,' and on another occasion, 'It is my opinion that the verdict of a jury is almost always right.' However, there have been occasions when the jury has brought in a perverse verdict, to the chagrin and wrath of the presiding Judge. One must also remember that a Judge's opinion is not always right, as shown by the numerous instances of a verdict being upset by the Court of Appeal on the grounds of misdirection. On the whole, and especially now that majority verdicts are acceptable, I am of the opinion that the system works more satisfactorily than any other system that could be devised. I am, however, getting a little worried about jury verdicts and actions lately.

Extraordinary anomalies have occurred. I can remember two almost identical cases of persons charged under the old offence of driving a motor vehicle under the influence of alcohol. They were tried at the same time in adjacent courts at Bodmin Quarter Sessions. Their blood alcohol levels were almost identical, and the circumstances of their arrests were similar. One court was presided over by a teetotal Chairman, and the other by a friend of mine reasonably addicted to alcohol. The defendant in the first court 'went down', whilst the one presided over by my friend was acquitted. But the verdicts were those of the juries, not the Chairman.

The days of the old Assizes and Quarter Sessions were days of great happiness to me. On numerous occasions I had the honour of being invited out to lunch with Counsel and Court Officials. When this happened during Quarter Sessions, there used to be considerable (amiable) jockeying for positions, one court being presided over by a teetotaller, the other by one of more liberal taste.

Obviously I have often been asked my views on punishment. They are basically crude and Mosaic — 'An eye for an eye and a tooth for a tooth.' I believe in capital punishment for premeditated murder of policemen and in some (but not all) cases of murder committed during the furtherence of a crime. On this basis I have always considered that Miles Giffard was justly hanged, because if there was ever a premeditated murder for purely selfish ends, this was one. Pascoe and Whitty were justly hanged. They may not have contemplated murder when they set out to rob William Garfield Rowe, but they deliberately killed the old man after he had recognised them, just to escape retribution for the furtherance of a petty crime. Trenoweth, who killed tobacconist Bateman, had no intention of committing murder, although he was committing a crime, should not, I think, have been hanged, but in those days, a death resulting from the commission of a crime was punishable in this way.

In this connection I recall the words of an IRA bomber whose devices had killed a number of innocent people, saying that the only thing he was really afraid of was of being hanged. Had this punishment still been available, many lives would have been spared.

The *Daily Telegraph*, 2 March, 1985, reporting the possible early release of the notorious Moors murderers, Ian Brady and Myra Hindley commented that Brady had said in the past that he never wants to be released because of his fear of reprisals if he were ever returned to the outside world. The installation of such fear into the minds of many potential murderers might have saved the lives of many innocent victims.

In a quite different category are the unpremeditated and often sudden passionate lashings-out that lead to death. These include the suddenly picked-up knife that is plunged into the body of a person causing annoyance, possibly unbearable annoyance. No-one should hang for that kind of crime — as they sometimes did in my early lifetime.

A thing that annoys me intensely is that more often than not little sympathy is extended to the victims of crime and their relations, unless they commit the unforgivable sin of selling their story to the cheque-book reporters of our more sensational newspapers. Sometimes it almost seems to have been the fault of the victims themselves for being in the wrong place at the wrong time. I hope that some of my descriptions of injuries inflicted often on perfectly innocent victims will do something to shift the sympathy so lavishly bestowed on the perpetrators of these acts, to the victim. My reaction to the present vogue of soft treatment, so much advocated by the wrong brand of do-gooders, to thugs and hooligans has received a great boost from no less a person than Dr Mervyn Stockwood, Bishop of Southwark. In his August, 1978, diocesan newsletter, he calls for all political parties to end the 'appalling violence and evil' in society. Dealing with a blind old age pensioner, beaten up and mugged, he adds, 'I wish a little of the sympathy which is showered so lavishly upon our thugs and hooligans could be transferred to him.'

I think the ultimate in sloppiness occurred a good many years ago in Falmouth. I was present at a Juvenile Court when the Chairman suggested to a little late-teenage hooligan who had been before the court time and time again, and time and time again put on probation, that it would be a good thing if he were to go to Sunday School. This, however, was not made a condition of his yet another period of time on probation! If this Chairman had seen the smirk on the face of this useless youngster as he left the court, he might have revised his sentence. Unfortunately he did not, but I did.

Is a tough line really justified in dealing with these utterly selfish and irresponsible thugs? I think it is, and in support often quote from certain happenings that occurred in Liverpool some good many years ago now. At that time there had been an outbreak of mugging and bag-snatching. The late Mr Justice Oliver was sent up to deal with it. He sentenced every convicted hooligan to so many strokes of the 'cat' — I do not recall how many. He then announced that he was coming back at the next Assizes, and if there were any more of these cases he would double the number of strokes. He duly arrived, but there were no more cases.

I have been asked on numerous occasions what would I do with these delinquents. I have gone on record as saying that I would bring back the stocks, the pillory and 'cat' for them. Nothing is so much anathema to these little cowards as being ridiculed; they would soon learn, and society would be that much safer.

I would bring back the cane to schools, and use it as frequently as it was used in my time. It never did my generation any harm, but the present lot seems to be so soft that, according to some child psychiatrists even a harsh word is going to ruin the whole of their future lives. Do we really believe that? Spare the rod and spoil the child has been the wisdom of the ages, overthrown in a few years, and now we are suffering from it. We are manufacturing unrestrained the hooligans of the future at an ever-increasing rate, as crime statistics show, by our sloppiness in our homes and in our schools and in our unwillingness to discipline our children. A few years ago, my wife and I were staying at the President Hotel in London. One evening, a woman arrived with two youngsters, a girl of about twelve years and a boy about ten. The boy went up to the hall porter and began kicking and pummelling him. The girl went to the reception counter, put her arm across it at one end and swept it along, throwing everything on to the floor. The mother's reaction? — 'Ain't they cute!'

On several occasions I have broadcast these opinions on television and on the radio. Following them I have had numerous letters and phone calls expressing agreement. I have never had an adverse comment.

I have been told, 'You cannot put the clock back'. Of course you can. Why not? If the clock goes too fast, you put it back.

Obviously over the years the subject of punishment, and particularly capital punishment, crops up at our dinner parties. It engenders so much heat, controversy and downright bad temper, and is so disruptive, that the subject is now strictly taboo. A reflection on the attitudes of our guests is however rather surprising and greatly illuminating. Almost without exception, our male guests are against capital punishment, whilst almost all their lady companions are in favour of it. Another example I suppose of the axiom that the female of the species is more deadly than the male. I can see their point of view, however — far more women are the victims of violence than men.

It is interesting that over the past few years, a significant number of men friends who originally were totally opposed to capital punishment have seen the light, and now agree that in the worst instances, capital punishment is justified.

On second thoughts I would bring back transportation. It would save a lot of money and the delinquents would have a happy time amongst themselves. The muggers could mug the hooligans, and the hooligans could run amock amongst the muggers. They will require feeding so I would send all those greedy farmers who have so largely dispoiled our countryside. For housing they could have our monstrous developers, and for entertainment all those composers of the everlasting raucous distracting musical background that ruins almost every broadcast.

Inevitably my various appointments had their associated obligations.

I have lectured to all sorts of lay and professional organisations. I have opened fairs and fetes, judged ambulance competitions, judged Christmas puddings, mince pies, cakes, jam and Cornish pasties.

On occasion, I have judged baby shows. On the last

occasion I gave the first prize to the smallest, a little skinny but beautifully-brought-up little boy after I had been informed that the young mother had practically devoted her life to bringing him up from a wizened premature wreck. It is usual on these occasions to 'say a few words' after the judging, saying how difficult it was to pick out a winner from so many lovely babies. On this occasion I was rapidly escorted from the platform to the howls of all the mothers of fat babies that I had ignored. I was never asked again.

Before World War Two, we had what were called 'Hospital Sundays'. That meant that the individual members of the hospital medical (and surgical staff) stood at the back of a horse-drawn cart positioned in the village square or local 'Big House', flanked by the Vicar. After the Vicar had said a word or two, and we had sung a hymn, it was the duty of the medicine-man to address the assembled multitude (mostly inquisitive children) on the virtues of the voluntary hospital system, and the evils of a state-run hospital service. It was of course a waste of time. The inevitable NHS had to come, but we have lost something. Who in those days had heard of hours of work, or waiting lists for hospital admissions? But I must not be so destructively critical. I recognise that enormous advances have been made, and that many worthwhile modern procedures save lives that it would have previously impossible to do and some of them take a long time.

The collection of Hospital Sunday was lucky to reach £10.

EPILOGUE

In conclusion, I hereby record my gratitude for having had such an interesting, varied and happy life, one that I hope has been a little useful. With the passing of time, the usefulness has now mostly departed with my virtual retirement, but the happiness associated with my work remains. These happy memories are inseparately associated with the long list of friends and helpers so closely connected with my work. None of my work would have been possible without the unselfish and unstinting help given to me by all my associates — members of my laboratory staff, the police, members of the legal profession and HM Coroners. Their names are recorded in my memory with grateful thanks. I recall the days when hours spent at work did not matter. If the bench work had not been completed by five o'clock, it did not matter. My helpers all stayed until it was completed — seven, eight or even nine o'clock sometimes, with no mention of overtime or any grumbling. We were a happy bunch.

My greatest tribute goes without stint to my wife. Even before we were married, she was my right hand, and later became half my left hand as well. I believe I am right in saying that we were the only husband and wife cutters-up of bodies in the whole country. On occasion, she has pointed out to me things that might have escaped my notice. She has corrected my reports, arithmetic and conclusions, and thus saved me from some disastrous cross-examination, all in addition to being a loving wife. I appear to have been lucky in all ways.

Friday, 26 August, 1988, was a sad day for me. It was the

day on which the last case was being heard at the old Bodmin Assize (Crown) Court. I remember the old place with affection; I had appeared there in the witness box on innumerable occasions for nearly fifty-four years, which I believe makes me the oldest inhabitant.

My last appearance was on 5 August, 1988. The case concerned a young lady accused of shop-lifting. During the three and three-quarter hours previous to her offence, she had consumed four tots of whisky, two pints of high alcohol Merrydown cider and two pints of Hofmeister lager. Her blood alcohol level would have been in the region of 347 milligrammes per 100 millilitres of blood, less a little due to the passage of time. This is almost a lethal level, but perhaps fortunately for her, she was a chronic alcoholic and so could 'carry her drink' to some purpose. She was convicted, as voluntary alcoholic intoxication is no excuse for crime.

As a final thought, I would like to apologise to all present forensic pathologists and scientists for my earlier apparent denigration of them. This is not so. I hold them in great regard, and acknowledge that they do far more to help in the detection of crime than I ever did. In my time, crime was relatively simple, and simple means detected it. Now, crime is sophisticated, and complicated means must be employed to combat it. Nobody now can cover all the mass of accumulated knowledge that can be employed to combat crime. Each facet must have its specialists. I pay tribute to them all. But they will never have the fun that I had as Pooh-Bah, 'Lord High everything'.

A personal touch.

Some years ago my wife's niece, Dierdre McCauley who lives with her mother in the States, came over with school friends on holiday. One of her first requests was to see an autopsy. I agreed, and gave out scalpels and forceps to help. On returning to school, they had to write the inevitable essay on what they had done during the holidays. They wrote that they had been cutting up dead bodies. Immediate summons to the headmistress's room indicated immediate dismissal. However, all was satisfactorily resolved.

The same body of urchins, now somewhat augmented, wait patiently outside the Inquest rooms anticipating further free entertainment. It comes in the form of the hapless Coroner's Officer who intones 'Oyez, Oyez, Oyez. All manner of persons who have had anything to do before Her Majesty The Queen's Coroner for this county, touching the death of . . . may now depart and take your ease. God Save The Queen.' This generally meant that we adjourned to the local pub, the time of the Inquest having been selected to coincide with opening hours.